THE NEW BASIC READERS

CURRICULUM FOUNDATION SERIES

REG. U.S. PAT. OFF.

CAVALCADES

BOOK 6

Helen M. Robinson
Marion Monroe
A. Sterl Artley
Charlotte S. Huck
William A. Jenkins

Linguistic Advisor, W. Cabell Greet

Scott, Foresman and Company
Chicago Atlanta Dallas Palo Alto Fair Lawn, N.J.

Contents

This World of Men

Dream of Freedom

Round Earth and Open Sky

Dreamers and Doers

Legends, Myths, and Other Tales

Then As Now
by WALTER DE LA MARE

Then as Now; and Now as Then,
Spins on this World of Men.
White—Black—Yellow—Red:
They wake, work, eat, play, go to bed.
Black—Yellow—Red—White:
They talk, laugh, weep, dance, morn to night.
Yellow—Red—White—Black:
Sun shines, moon rides, clouds come back.
Red—White—Black—Yellow:
Count your hardest, who could tell o'
The myriads that have come and gone,
Stayed their stay this earth upon,
And vanished then, their labour done?
Sands of the wilderness, stars in heaven,
Solomon could not sum them even:
Then as Now; Now as Then,
Still spins on this World of Men.

THIS WORLD OF MEN

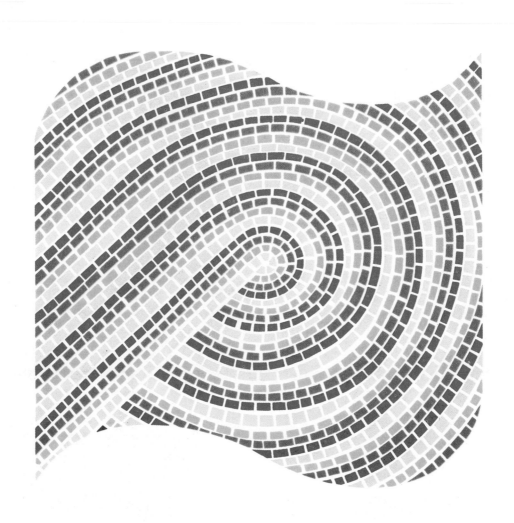

8

Henry Has an Idea

by KEITH ROBERTSON

Henry Reed is traveling by car across the United States with Midge Glass and her family. Henry is keeping a journal about his trip. Here is a selection from it.

Saturday, July 3rd—Hansonville, Kansas

We are in a little town in Kansas called Hansonville. It's located on the southern border near Oklahoma. It's dry, dusty, and hot. No one driving through the town would ever notice it. The only reason anyone would ever stop would be to buy gas or to spend the night at the motel. The people of Hansonville are very friendly, which

From *Henry Reed's Journey* by Keith Robertson. Copyright © 1963 by Keith Robertson. Reprinted by permission of The Viking Press, Inc.

is good, because we are going to be here several days. Mr. Glass went to school here when he was a boy. This is the first time he has been back since his family moved away, about the time he finished the eighth grade.

It has really been hot driving today. All day long we sweltered, and the only thing that kept Midge and me from melting away to grease spots was the hope of finding a swimming pool at the motel tonight. About ten miles out of Hansonville we saw a sign which said, *Stay at the Motel Sunflower in Hansonville—Air-conditioned Rooms—Air-conditioned Lounge and Dining Room—New Swimming Pool.*

"Is that where we're staying?" Midge asked.

"It is," Mr. Glass said. "When I lived here, there was an old ramshackle hotel called the Grand Hotel. It was about to fall down then, and I imagine it has since. I hope the Motel Sunflower will be slightly more modern, but I have no faith whatever in signs."

The sign told the truth, and the Motel Sunflower is a very attractive brick motel on the edge of town. The rooms are air-conditioned and so is the dining room. There is a swimming pool, but there is one hitch. There isn't any water in it. It's so new it isn't finished.

The swimming pool is made of steel. I thought that pools were always made of concrete, but on this trip we've been swimming in several made of steel. Right now this one looks like an enormous tank sitting up above a big hole in the ground. When Midge saw that it wasn't finished, she gave a yowl that must have been heard in Oklahoma. I felt just as disappointed, but I didn't yowl.

We all went into the office while Mr. Glass registered. Mr. Glass looked at the man behind the desk several times and then said, "Aren't you Jim Murray?"

"That's right."

"I went to school with you through the eighth grade."

Mr. Murray looked at the register and said, "Fuzzy-top Glass! It's been a long time, hasn't it? Good to see you!"

Midge started to giggle at the idea of her father having the nickname Fuzzy-top. He's two-thirds bald now. It's hard to imagine your parents or the parents of your friends as kids with silly nicknames, but they were once human, too.

Mr. Glass and Mr. Murray spent some minutes talking about what had become of this or that classmate, and how they had fooled Miss Somebody-or-other, who was once their teacher. From the conversation, I'm surprised they didn't get kicked out of school every week. They'd never get away with that much today. I guess they were more lenient with kids then. Sometime or other Mr. Glass must have done some studying, because he is considered to be a brilliant research chemist now.

By the time we were settled in our rooms, it was time for dinner, so we went to the dining room. About halfway through the meal, Mr. Murray joined us.

"You are in the doghouse with the younger element," Mr. Glass said. "They were looking forward to a swim."

"I'm in the doghouse with everyone over that pool," Mr. Murray said sadly. He looked like my beagle Agony when he has lost a rabbit trail. "I doubt if anyone in the county will speak to me after Monday."

"Why?"

"I promised it would be ready for the Fourth of July. You may have noticed that the American Legion and the Volunteer Fire Company are setting up that field across the way for a big celebration. Tomorrow is Sunday, so the celebration will be Monday, the fifth. Several months ago I promised that the pool would be ready and that all children could swim free. There isn't any place to swim within fifteen miles, and I think the children were looking forward to swimming more than they were to anything else in the celebration—even the fireworks display. You know, it gets hot here in Kansas—much hotter than it did when we were young, in my opinion. I'd like to take a swim myself."

"Why isn't it finished?" Mr. Glass asked. "What's holding it up?"

"Remember our old friend Bud Turney? He has a welding engineering company over in Coffeyville now. He builds a lot of oil-storage tanks. Things were slow for him this spring, and when he heard that I planned to build a pool, he wanted to build it out of steel. He gave me a good price—he's my brother-in-law—so I told him to go ahead. I bulldozed the hole, laid the pipe that goes under the pool to the center drain, and got everything set. He laid those beams across the hole, brought the steel in, and fabricated the tank."

"It looks practically completed," Mr. Glass said. "What's the snag?"

"There were two cranes working on the bridge over Gannet's Creek. Bud arranged for them to lower the tank into place after he was finished. Then all he would have to do was weld in the bottom connection and hook up a few pipes. But he had to pull two men off to work on a rush oil-tank job, and my work was delayed for a week. The two cranes had to move over to the other end of the county, and we can't get them back for at least three weeks. I'm what you might call 'high and dry.' "

"Do you mean the only thing that keeps that pool from being finished is getting it down into that hole?"

"Looks simple, doesn't it?" Mr. Murray asked bitterly. "I thought so, too, for a while. Believe me, that is no simple operation. That is a big tank—fifty-two feet long and twenty-eight feet wide. It weighs tons!"

"Can't you just yank those beams out and let it drop?" Mr. Glass asked. "It's sitting directly over where you want it, isn't it?"

"It is," Mr. Murray agreed, "but it's not that easy. In the first place, nothing can yank those beams out while the weight of the tank is on them. Secondly, if it isn't lowered gently and evenly, the tank will twist and break the welds."

"Lower it on the beams and remove them later."

"That sounds possible, but it isn't. I have the ground all smoothed out underneath the tank, ready for it. I would have to dig trenches across to allow for the beams. Then the beams would be down in the ground, and I'd either have to leave them there and pay for them or do a major excavating job to get them out."

Mr. Murray got up to go over to speak to some other diners. He certainly was sad about his pool, but he wasn't any sadder than I was. I wanted to swim. I was still thinking about it when our dessert came. I had ice cream. I was watching it melt slowly when I happened to think of the Hopi Indian fire dance Midge and I had seen and how the melting ice had made the fire disappear.

"I know how to lower the tank into the hole," I said to Midge.

Midge thinks I can do anything. Of course, she's usually right, but sometimes she has so much confidence in what I say that it puts me on the spot. This was one of those times.

"Henry can get the tank lowered," she announced to her father, not even bothering to ask how I would do it.

"That so?" Mr. Glass asked between bites of pie. I could see he wasn't taking her too seriously.

"Mr. Murray!" Midge called. "Henry's got a plan!"

Mr. Murray had left the other table and was walking toward the cashier's counter. He didn't hear her, and I was just as glad.

"Don't be in such a hurry," I told Midge. "We ought to talk this idea over first."

"Do you really have an idea that will work?"

"I think so."

"Then what is there to talk over? Time's a-wastin'."

"Well, it's really an old Hopi tribal secret," I said. "Do you remember that disappearing-fire trick? It's based on that. Maybe we shouldn't say anything."

"I don't see why not," Midge said. "Just don't mention the Hopi trick, and no one will ever connect Hopi fire dances with a swimming pool in Kansas. Besides, it can't be such an old secret. The Hopis never saw any ice until the white man invented refrigeration."

I learned how to make fire disappear into the ground when Midge and I became friends of an Indian chief in Arizona. To do the trick, the Hopis put blocks of ice in a hole. Then they stuff newspapers around the ice, and on top they put a flat pan upside down. The pan is just the right size for the hole. When a fire is lighted on the top of the pan, the ice melts. The fire sinks slowly into the earth and disappears.

"What are you two muttering about?" Mrs. Glass asked while Midge and I were talking.

"Henry's plan to lower the tank," Midge said. "It's wonderful, and I think we ought to tell Mr. Murray."

"What is it?" Mr. Glass asked.

"I don't understand it exactly," Midge said, "but it's got something to do with ice."

"Why couldn't you raise the tank a little, build some piers of ice under it, pull the beams out, and let the tank melt down into the hole?" I asked.

Mr. Glass paused with his coffee cup halfway to his mouth. He froze that way for a minute and then he said, "Henry, give up the idea of being a naturalist and chasing bugs. The country needs engineers like you. Hey, Jim! Come over here! Henry's solved the problem!"

Mr. Murray came over, and Mr. Glass explained my idea. As Mr. Murray listened he got more and more excited.

"I'll probably need about two truckloads of ice. I can get Bert Simpson to go over to the ice plant in Coffeyville.

Maybe they'll have another truck. If not, I'll dig up one some place."

In an hour there were about fifty people working around the pool. I think the entire Volunteer Fire Company turned out to help. They got a number of heavy construction jacks and timbers and built cribs under the beams to support the jacks. Then they jacked up the beams. Everything was ready by the time the trucks arrived with the ice. By nine o'clock they had built eight square piles out of ice blocks. The real excitement came when they slowly let the tank down on the columns of ice. I don't know what people thought would happen. Maybe they thought the ice would be crushed, but nothing happened. The tank simply sat on the ice. Everyone stood looking at it until suddenly Mr. Murray came to life.

"Don't let down now. We've got to yank those beams out of there fast before the ice melts and lets the tank back down on them."

They put chains around the beams, hooked them to a tractor, and in a few minutes had dragged them clear. This left nothing but the ice between the tank and the hole. Mr. Murray looked worried. I know what he was thinking. He was wondering what would happen if the ice slipped at one end and not at the other, and the tank got twisted and ruined. Nothing happened, however. Mr. Glass was the most confident one there. He said the heavy weight of the tank had pressed the big ice cakes into one solid mass, and there was little danger of the piers collapsing. He was right, I'm glad to say. By eleven o'clock the large tank had dropped noticeably.

Mr. Murray had men inside the tank, walking around. They kept checking on how it settled. If it didn't go down evenly, they planned to put tubs of hot water over the piers that were melting too slowly. I don't think they will have to do it.

"It'll be hours before all that ice melts," Mr. Glass said to Midge and me. "There's nothing to watch, so you two might just as well go to bed."

Mr. Murray came over to shake hands with me. "Henry, you're the hero of Hansonville," he said. "You've saved the day. By tomorrow afternoon I expect to have the pool ready for swimming. At the celebration Monday I am supposed to make a little speech. I'd like you to be up on the stand with me, so I can tell the town who deserves the credit for having the pool ready on time."

It feels good to be called the hero of Hansonville, but it's a big responsibility. I can't get to sleep thinking about it, which is the reason I am bringing my journal up to date. It's now after twelve. I just peeked out the window, and the tank seems to be settling all right. I'd certainly feel terrible if something went wrong and I woke up in the morning to find the pool was wrecked.

It isn't just the pool that worries me. If I get up on the stand with Mr. Murray, I might have to make a speech. I've never made a speech to a big crowd before, but I rather like the idea. The trouble is I don't know whether I should admit that the idea wasn't really mine but belongs to the Hopi Indians, or whether I should keep quiet, as Midge says, and protect the secret of their disappearing fire. Making important decisions is a tough job.

The Singing Cave

by EILÍS DILLON

The night before I discovered the Singing Cave brought the worst storm I have ever seen in our part of Connemara. I buried my ears in my featherbed and drifted into a heavy sleep. When I awoke, I was mighty relieved to find pale daylight at the window. The sky was as white as milk; the wind shrieked even louder than it had during the night. I thought of a contrary bullock we had and wondered if he had strayed from the others. Once I had thought of him, I could sleep no more.

The cold flagstones of the floor stung my feet so that I hopped from foot to foot while I was dressing. My door creaked as I opened it gently, but I knew that my grandfather could not have heard it above the bellowing of the wind. I paused in the kitchen to lay a few sods of turf on the ashes of the fire. Then I slipped out through the back door and around the corner of the house.

Immediately I felt as if I were gripped in a pair of giant arms that were trying to lift me off the ground. The air was full of strange, wild scents from faraway places that mixed delightfully with our own homely smells of salt and seaweed, turf smoke and spring grass. Down below me, the thundering sea was a greenish-gray edged with white. Farther west, where the cliffs were, the spray from the tall waves moved in a cloud over the land.

Then I saw our bullock. He was standing on a rocky spur of a cliff that overhung the sea. He was stock-still, with his head down and his legs splayed out as if

From *The Singing Cave* by Eilís Dillon. Copyright 1959 by Eilís Dillon. Adapted by permission of Funk & Wagnalls Company, New York, and Faber & Faber, London.

to steady himself against the force of the wind, which every moment struggled to send him plunging down between the spur and the face of the cliff.

To get to the cliff top I had to cross three walled fields and climb a long, unsheltered slope covered with short grass. The wind beat around my ears. Walking against it was like trying to get through a wall of glass. As I climbed higher, every step became harder, and I was soon drenched and blinded by spray. Long before I reached the bullock, I was down on my hands and knees. With my heart in my mouth, I crawled out onto the spur of rock. A moment later I had him by the tail.

It was while I was hauling at him that the earth below us began to sing. It was a long, deep, ringing sound, as I have often imagined the bells of drowned ships must ring under a swelling sea. It filled me with instant terror, for all in a flash I imagined that the spur of rock had broken off under the combined weight of myself and the bullock and that the sound I heard was the hungry song of the triumphant sea.

Even when this fancy had left me, I was still shaken with strange fears. The sound ebbed and flowed with every gust of wind.

Then I remembered that there was a cave just under this part of the cliff and that it was always called the Singing Cave. It was just a niche, hardly worth visiting, though I had been there once or twice in my currach. It could be approached only from the sea. Usually the waves moved in and out of it with a sluggish, dead sound. It was dry at low water, but when the tide was full, the sea just covered its floor.

There were many stories about the reason for its name. Some people said that the seals always swam in there and sang before a storm so that the fishermen out in their boats would hear them and come home to safety. There was sense in this story if you believed, as most of my neighbors did, that seals are inhabited by the souls of drowned sailors. Certainly their round, melancholy eyes and drooping mustaches have a very human look. Another story was that a local man, on the run with his wife from the soldiers, had hidden her in the cave for safety. But he was killed, and the tide had come up and drowned her, though she sang and sang in the hope that someone would hear and come to her rescue. They say she still sings at every spring tide, but I have never met anyone who himself heard singing in this place.

Though my head was full of these stories, I did not lose my hold on the bullock's tail. I heaved as if I were hoisting a sail. Presently he took a step backwards, and little by little I backed him down off the cliff. As I went, the singing grew fainter with every step.

I knew that if one of the neighbors happened to have a reason for walking out toward the cliff, the strange, wild sound would become the talk of our island. The boats would be out, clustered like puffins around the mouth of the cave. I might even be left behind if my grandfather's currach filled up too quickly with boatless neighbors. By now my curiosity about the Singing Cave was so strong that I would almost have put out in a currach there and then on that terrible sea.

Of course this was impossible. I knew that I could not crest even the first wave. I brought the bullock back to the field where he belonged and gave him a lecture about his sins. He seemed to have learned a lesson at last, for he joined the herd meekly enough.

Back in the kitchen, my grandfather had the kettle on. I told him how I had rescued the bullock. He laughed. "The sooner that bullock goes to market, the better for us, Pat, my boy," he said.

We made our breakfast of strong red tea and soda bread and eggs. While we ate, I told my grandfather about the strange sound that I had heard on the cliff.

"It's the Singing Cave for sure," I said. "Something has happened there. We must go and see it the first minute that the wind drops."

My grandfather agreed to this at once.

Twenty times during the day he went to the door to see if the wind was slackening in force. When the neighbors came in at the fall of night, he questioned them until he discovered where each man had spent the day. When he found that they had all stayed near home, he was satisfied.

The men were full of talk about the destruction done by the storm, but not one of them spoke of the Singing Cave. Like us, they had been busy mending nets and harness and tools, and making furniture or painting. These things were always left for stormy days when it was impossible to work outside.

For two days we were kept in by the rain, and then on a fine morning we found that the wind had moved a point to the south. The sea was shining under a sweet, gentle breeze, and I was reminded of the peaceful innocence of a cross baby who has at last fallen asleep.

We launched the currach, with a sharp eye out lest one of our neighbors think we were going fishing and offer to come along with us. We each took a pair of oars for speed. Soon we were shooting out between the long fingers of rock that formed our little harbor.

We kept as close under the cliffs as we dared so as not to be seen. At this early hour they cast a broad shadow, cold and mysterious. The tide was falling, but there was still enough water within the cave to float the currach. We shipped the oars a little distance out from the cliff and glided silently into the darkness, holding the cold cave walls with our hands so as not to be washed out.

"The candle," said my grandfather. "It will stay alight in here out of the breeze."

I fumbled about until I found it and a box of matches. The little flame laid a long streak of yellow on the dead black water. Then my grandfather said very quietly, "Look at the back wall, Pat. There is the cause of the song you heard."

I turned to look.

It seemed as if a great organ had been erected in the cave. When I had been here before, I had noticed that the back wall was ridged vertically from floor to ceiling and that each ridge was polished smooth by the continual stroking of the waves. Now every other ridge had fallen out,

leaving long, empty gaps through which light air moved
even now with a delicate humming sound. It was like an
echo of the majestic, full-throated song that I had heard
during the storm. And it was quite plain that beyond these
stone organ pipes there was another, deeper cave. One
of the gaps between the ridges was wider than the rest.

"I could fit through there," I said to my grandfather.

"You could, faith," said he.

We were silent while we thought about it. The candle
flame flickered. I did not want to creep through that narrow space. I think I had some faint notion that it might
close up as mysteriously as it had opened and prison me
within. Still, I knew that I could not turn my back on it
and suffer my curiosity for the rest of my life.

"It's likely enough to be dry in there," I said at last,
"unless there's a big drop inside."

I shivered at the thought of the big drop, possibly with
a fat monster lying in wait below to bite the legs off me.

"If there was a drop, we'd hear the water sucking in
and out of it," said the old man. "Go on, boy. Take the
candle with you." He put his hand on my shoulder and
gave me a little push.

"Here goes!" I said loudly to frighten the monster.

We edged the boat over to the stone organ pipes. It
grounded gently on the rocky floor of the cave. Even
since we had come in, the tide had dropped a little more,
as we could see by the glistening walls.

I got an arm around one of the ridges to steady myself.
Then I poked my head through the biggest space and
my other arm, which held the candle, through the next.

I saw a fine, high, vaulted cave with a floor of rock lightly sprinkled with silver sand and strange flat shells.

"It's as dry as a threshing floor," I said with a sudden burst of courage. "I'm going in."

And without further delay I climbed through the space and dropped onto the floor.

"Watch your step!"

My grandfather's voice came to me in a half whisper. When I answered him, I found that my own voice was the same, through some curious trick of the formation of the roof. As I walked a few steps forward, I found that I could no longer hear the friendly beating of the sea nor the seagulls' sharp cries. But the hum of the breeze through the stone pipes sounded louder than it had from outside.

I lifted my candle and looked all around me. I was astonished at the smoothness of the floor with its neat carpet of sand. The walls showed no drip or trickle of water. I supposed that the sea must have dropped since the days when it carved out this great hole in the cliff.

Toward the back the cave took a turn and narrowed, and its roof sloped a little downward. I walked on, somewhat disappointed now that there was no more mystery. Then all at once I stopped. For several minutes I stood quite still, until the hot grease of the candle spilled over onto my hand and brought me to my senses again. Then I took one more step and gazed down at my find.

It was the long, narrow hull of a wooden boat. It had not rotted but had shriveled up and fallen apart. Only its prow, carved with a dragon's head, still stood, propped between two big stones. And leaning back against it, as if tired, were the bones of a huge man. He wore a bronze helmet, decorated with short, straight horns. The bony fingers lay listlessly on the hilt of a long sword. Thus he had sat, I supposed, for a thousand years.

After my first surprise I could see that this was the tomb of a Viking. There was no mistaking that horned helmet. When I was a small boy, our teacher had described so vividly the raids of the Norsemen on the Irish coast that for many months my dreams were alive with narrow, black-beaked galleys full of helmeted warriors, darting up our rivers, pillaging our monasteries and towns, and bearing our people away to slavery. I had never thought that I would see a Viking face to face.

I went a little closer, and then I saw the gaming board. It may have been placed on the Viking's knees once, so that he could amuse himself during his long waiting time. It had fallen down long since, and now it lay on the ground between the shriveled limbs of the boat.

I had never seen a board like it before. It was square and rather like a board for playing draughts, which is a favorite game with us. It was made of a thick block of wood, carved all around the edges with an intricate pattern of snakes nibbling at each other's tails.

I stooped down and lifted the board very carefully, and I saw at once that it was tough and strong. Only a tiny crack at one side showed how the moisture had dried out of it. It had warped very little. I held the candle close and examined it.

At either side a carved head projected like a handle. One was the head of a man with a longish, surprised face.

He had a flat nose and a pointed beard. The other was the head of a wolf, with pointed ears and snarling lips and little round, terrible eyes. But the thing that charmed me most was that all over the board, arranged in even rows, were tiny carved bone figures. Each piece was finished with a short peg that fitted into a corresponding hole in the board. All the pieces were little wolves' heads except one, which was the head of a man. This was placed in the exact middle of the board, and the wolves filled the remainder in rows of seven by seven. There was an extra hole in each corner, but each of these was marked off with a segment of a circle, so that I guessed there were no pieces missing.

With a gentle finger I stroked the little wolf's head that I was holding. It was a satin-smooth, close-textured bone, so clean that it reflected little points of light from the candle. For a little while I forgot that I was in an uncharted cave half under the sea. The children in my part of the world do not have many toys—most of our games are played with stones and sticks that can be picked up anywhere on a day's walk. This meant that I could see the possibilities of the Viking's game all the more clearly. One could invent a dozen ways to play it. The man, of course, was trying to escape from the wolves into one of the four corners. So the wolves must make the first move, or else the man must sometimes be allowed to jump over them.

As I was settling down to play the game, I remembered my grandfather. He would be frightened for my safety. He might even have started back to Barrinish to rouse the neighbors to dig me out. Carrying the board carefully, I hurried back to the mouth of the cave.

My grandfather was still there. He was calling me, sure enough, peering anxiously through the stone pipes. I tumbled out the story of my finds.

"And whoever arranged the cave did a tasty job," I said. "Beautiful clean sand sprinkled everywhere, and shells of some strange fish that I never saw the like of before. I wish you could come in and see the boat and the old soldier sitting back in it."

"God rest his bones!" said my grandfather. "What have you there in your hand?"

I showed him the board. Like me, he was delighted beyond measure at the neat, smooth little figures.

"We'll have many a game with those on the long winter nights," I said eagerly. "We'll make our own rules, but once they're made, we must keep to them."

He was silent for a moment. Uneasily I asked, "Won't we be able to have it for ourselves? Who has a better right to it? What is it, anyway, but a game?"

Even while I made one excuse after another, I began to realize a little of the excitement that would be caused by the discovery of the Viking and his game board. We were not so ignorant as to imagine that people all over the world would not hear about him in time, and that historians and archaeologists would not be ready to tear out each other's hair because of him. We knew of such things, because our friend Mr. Allen often spoke of them.

Mr. Allen lived alone in a little cottage at the far end of Barrinish Island from us. Whenever he visited our house, his talk opened up great new roads for me so that I was never the same again after he had gone away. I had a great respect for his learning, and it was natural that I should suggest now that we ask him for advice.

"Yes," said my grandfather. "Mr. Allen will know what is to be done. He's a fine man of knowledge. Now just put the board back where you found it, and we'll be going home."

We argued for a long time about this. Of course I wanted to take the board home with me and show it to my great friend, Tom Joyce. Already I was glorying in the prospect of being a great hero, the owner of this wonderful treasure and the one person who would decide who was to play with it next. Patiently my grandfather pointed out that if we took it home and showed it to the people, we would have to say where we had found it. Even if we managed to keep the existence of the inner cave a secret, the board itself was such a curiosity that it would almost certainly bring crowds of strangers nosing about, asking questions and even foraging for themselves.

"There's no end to what they might find," said the old man. "It wouldn't be hard for them to find the Clooney Cave. If they did, the people of this parish wouldn't be a bit thankful to us, you may go bail."

That settled the question for me. The Clooney Cave was at the outermost part of the island. It served us all as a warehouse in which to hide the wrack that we rescued from the sea, which, by a stupid old law, we were supposed to hand over to the Guards. We had no qualms about keeping the wrack. If we did not bring in the timber and bales of cloth and barrels of oil and meal that were sent to us by the sea, they would be destroyed by the waves among the rocks, and then no one would have the benefit of them. What man would risk his neck and his good boat to bring in wrack for the Guards, who never got their feet wet if they could help it? So we put the stuff in Clooney Cave until we could use it a little at a time.

I agreed with my grandfather reluctantly. Then I felt my heart squeeze as a new thought occurred to me. "What will we do if the tide comes up and fills the cave and washes away the boat and the board and the old Viking? How do we know that won't happen?"

"When it didn't happen in the storm, it won't happen on the tide," said my grandfather. "When you were inside the cave, I wasn't idle. You left the matches behind you, and I used them to find out something that was puzzling me. Tell me, now, did you wonder how they got the boat and the man into that cave that day long ago?"

My astonished face told him plainly that I had not thought of this at all. He chuckled at my expression.

"Hold that candle high," he said, "and I'll show you. This whole gateway, as you might say, closing up the cave, is not natural at all. There's marks of a chisel here at the sides where the stone was chipped off so that the stone grid would fit. And the grid is made in several pieces. Look at the joints. I'd swear there's a tongue and groove holding them together."

I peered at them and saw that this was so.

"First they brought the boat and the Viking and fixed him up inside," my grandfather went on. "Then they put up the grid, and last of all they filled in the spaces with stone. And I wish I knew why they went to all that bother when they could have buried him decent, like a Christian, above in Cluan na Marbh."

"They weren't Christians," I said. "They believed in Valhalla and gods of thunder and storm. Maybe that's why they made the pipes, so the wind could sing through them."

"Back with the board, then, and we'll be going home."

I turned without a word and went back into the depths of the cave. Very softly I replaced the precious board in the exact position in which I had found it. I stood for a moment looking down at it and wondering if I should slip a few of the little wolves' heads into my pocket. But though I would cheerfully have taken the whole board, it seemed wrong to break up the perfection of the game.

I did not run on the way out. It was a friendly place though it was so strange. I climbed out through the stone grid and into the currach. A moment later we were out in the sweet blue air again and heading for home.

High Tide

by JEAN STARR UNTERMEYER

I edged back against the night.
The sea growled assault on the wave-bitten shore.
And the breakers,
Like young and impatient hounds,
Sprang, with rough joy on the shrinking sand.
Sprang—but were drawn back slowly,
With a long, relentless pull,
Whimpering, into the dark.

Then I saw who held them captive;
And I saw how they were bound
With a broad and quivering leash of light,
Held by the moon,
As, calm and unsmiling,
She walked the deep fields of the sky.

 From the collected poems *Love and Need* by Jean Starr Untermeyer. Published by The Viking Press, Inc., New York, 1940. Used by permission of Jean Starr Untermeyer.

A Thread of Understanding

by PHYLLIS A. WHITNEY

A beautiful Japanese maple tree flung its shade across one end of a bench, and Celia decided that this would be a perfect place to sit and sketch. Now that she had reached the top of the small hill she had been climbing, she could see mountains rising still higher behind and stretching away on both sides. Within their many extended arms lay the city of Kyoto, its sounds dissolved to no more than a hum in the distance. Only the booming of some great temple bell reached her, and its deep-throated sound seemed in keeping with this place and did not break the spell.

From *Secret of the Samurai Sword* by Phyllis A. Whitney. Copyright © 1958 by Phyllis A. Whitney. Published by The Westminster Press.

After days of mist and rain, the sun felt warm and relaxing. Celia stood for a moment letting it bathe her lifted face with warmth. The peace of the mountains, the quiet of this lovely place, seemed to flow through her. From somewhere in the soft-wooded greenery of the mountainside came the liquid sound of bird notes.

If only she could capture some of this wonderful feeling in a drawing! A picture wasn't just something you saw—it was your feeling about it, too. Perhaps that was the most important part of a picture—the feeling it brought to the one who beheld it, all because the artist had felt it first.

She sat down on the bench and looked about for the picture she would choose. Not a whole scene, but something simple and beautiful in itself—like that twisted pine tree on the hillside below. She took out her pencil and began to block in the shape of the pine, with its curved trunk and graceful, outflung branches, the clustered needles that rounded the tree in graceful green layers.

No wonder Japanese prints always had a special look about them! They were just like the countryside they depicted. You would know the look of a Japanese pine tree anywhere, she thought.

How long she worked on, absorbed, with the little shrine behind her and the city below, she didn't know. Her drawing was taking shape now, and she was trying to get in something of the detail.

In her concentration she heard no step on the pine needles that covered the earth of the little clearing. She did not know anyone was near until she looked up, startled, to find that a man in a long gray kimono had come to stand beside her.

His bald head was well shaped, his face noble and keenly intelligent. Even as she gave a little start of astonishment, she realized that this was the grandfather of Sumiko, her Japanese friend. Though Sumiko lived near Celia, the girls saw each other only occasionally and always by accident. Sumiko's grandfather did not approve of friendship between Japanese and American girls. He did not like Americans.

Celia remembered at once that he was a great artist, and she did not want him to see her poor little drawing. Quickly she flipped over the cover of her sketchbook, but he reached out and took it calmly from her hands. With the quiet, courteous manner of one who had the authority to do as he chose, he turned the pages.

Celia could feel the warmth rise in her cheeks as he studied a drawing of Japanese children sitting on the ground, a sketch of a stone lantern, and one of a great camphor tree with huge uncovered roots. Then he turned back to the pine tree and studied it for a moment. With a gesture, as if he asked her permission, he sat beside her and held out his hand for her pencil.

She gave it to him wordlessly and watched while he pointed to her drawing, then to the pine tree, and made several swift strokes here and there on the paper. At once the pictured tree seemed to take on something of the beauty and life of the original, and Celia could see where lines had been wrong, where she had missed the grace that was there in the original.

Gratefully she took the book from the long-fingered hands of the artist when he returned it to her. "It's beautiful now," she said softly of the drawing.

If he did not understand these words, he at least understood her tone, for he smiled again and nodded. Then he gestured toward the pine tree on the hillside below and spoke one of his few phrases of English.

"My teacher," he said.

She knew what he meant, and it was a wonderful thought—that the pine tree itself had taught him out of its own beauty. Celia forgot that he was Sumiko's stern grandfather. She forgot everything except that this fine-looking man was a great and distinguished artist. She would have given anything to thank him, to ask him questions, to gain advice from him. But his language was not hers, and a wall stood between them. Nevertheless, it was a wall that reached only as high as their hearts, and over it the old man and the young girl could look at each other in appreciation and understanding. It did not seem to matter in the least that he was Japanese and she American, for they had reached each other on common ground.

When he rose, he made her a low, very polite bow, and then turned his attention to the nearby shrine. He picked up a dipper from a stone trough and spilled water over his hands. Then he stepped before the shrine, clapped his palms three times to attract the god's attention, and bent his head over his hands in prayer.

He didn't seem to mind that she watched him, and when he turned away, he smiled at her gravely again, made her another courteous bow, and went down the hill.

When he had gone, she sat on in a dream, thinking about what had happened and about this man, Gentaro Sato, who was famous all over Japan. She would not work again on the sketch in her book because his pencil had touched it, and she would treasure it always.

A few days later Sumiko came over and asked Celia if she would come to see her grandfather.

Celia was both pleased and a little dismayed. She was not at all sure she could recapture the way she had felt about Gentaro Sato that day on the hilltop. She had dropped back again to feeling a little awed and frightened, as she had felt before she met him. She remembered how sternly he had opposed her friendship with Sumiko. Still, she wouldn't miss going, and

Sumiko would be right there to translate, so that it might be possible this time to talk to him a little.

They ran across the alley together, and Sumiko's mother met them at the gate of the house. The Sato house was small, and it held many people. Sumiko's mother, two aunts, several cousins, and Sumiko herself all lived in the downstairs rooms. Fortunately, in a Japanese house the beds are folded away in cupboards in the daytime, and there is very little furniture.

Only a section of the house had an upstairs, and this part was reserved for Gentaro Sato. Sumiko's mother had work to do in the kitchen, so one of the aunts went upstairs with the girls. She smiled delightedly at Celia and murmured a welcome in Japanese. But she was clearly in awe of her father-in-law, for her smiles vanished when she ran ahead of them to see if Mr. Sato was ready to receive company.

The usual slippers had been provided at the doorstep, so that Celia could take off her shoes and walk on the polished floors of the entryway and stairs. In the short time she had lived in Japan with her grandmother she had learned caution in climbing the steep, narrow steps that were best suited to small Japanese feet. She and Sumiko padded up, left their slippers at the head of the stairs, and stepped onto the *tatami*.

The sliding *fusuma* in this upstairs section had all been opened to make one large, airy room, open on three sides, looking out on hillside and city. This was the artist's studio. Gentaro Sato came to greet them, and Celia saw that he wore a fine silk kimono of charcoal

gray with a small crest in white on each sleeve. He bowed courteously low, and Celia found herself bowing, too, and murmuring *"O-hayo gozaimasu"*—the polite "good morning" her grandmother had taught her.

Mr. Sato gestured with a paper fan toward some cushions of purple silk that had been set out for the girls. Sumiko and Celia curled up on two of the cushions. The artist knelt on a cushion before a large black lacquer tray on which stood painting things.

Among them were a lovely blue jar containing many brushes with bamboo handles, some dishes of water, and tubes and saucers of paint. Beside him rose a tiered set of many drawers with small brass handles.

Here he probably kept sheets of paper and other kinds of equipment connected with his work.

It was odd, Celia thought, but Mr. Sato's finely shaped bald head did not make him look at all strange. In fact, it gave him a noble appearance and one of great intelligence. While his face looked as though it might grow stern on occasion, his expression was most benevolent this morning, his smile kindly.

He opened a drawer beside him and took out two small fans, which he presented with ceremonious gestures to Celia and Sumiko. Sumiko looked impressed and pleased and said quickly that her grandfather had painted these fans and did not give them to everyone.

Celia opened hers and admired the branch of plum blossom that had been painted across it. Sumiko's fan showed a wisteria spray.

"Thank him for me," Celia said. "Tell him I think it's beautiful, and I will keep it always."

Sumiko translated, and Mr. Sato nodded pleasantly. He fanned himself with the somewhat larger-sized fan that gentlemen use and beamed at his granddaughter and his visitor. Then he spoke to Sumiko in Japanese.

"He says you show talent in your drawing," Sumiko said. "My grandfather wants to know if you are planning to become an artist."

"I—I don't really know," Celia faltered. "I love to draw, and I'd like to do something with drawing when I grow up, if I can. But it's too early to tell."

There was a lengthy translation into Japanese. Then Mr. Sato spoke, and again Sumiko translated for Celia.

"Grandfather says it isn't too early to tell—that you have natural talent. If you want to work hard and give your life to it, you can become an artist."

Not being sure what she wanted to give her life to, Celia smiled and was silent, and Mr. Sato spoke again. This time Sumiko looked at her curiously as she repeated his words in English.

"He has hit on something I've felt about you—only I never knew how to say it. I can see what he means in Japanese, but it's hard to change it into English. He thinks you are—well—tuned to the people and the world around you."

"Tuned?" Celia repeated, puzzled.

"He means that you truly see what you look at. He thinks most people don't. He says that you sense what people are like, back of their words, behind their faces. He says there was a thread of deep understanding and appreciation between you and him that day he met you on the hilltop near the shrine. This does not happen to him with very many people. Because you have it, you should try to paint pictures so that others will experience what you feel."

Celia grew pink with pleasure, though she wasn't altogether sure she understood what Gentaro Sato meant. Anyway, it was wonderful to know that this important and obviously noble person liked her.

Now Mr. Sato turned to the tier of drawers beside him and took from one of them an almost square piece of stiff cardboard. A hair-thin band of gilt paper bound the edges all the way around. One side of the board was smooth and sprinkled with silver speckles. The other side was a white surface made for painting.

"He's going to paint a picture for you," Sumiko whispered in a tone of excitement. "This is an honor."

Celia held her breath as the artist selected a brush, moistened it, and dipped it in water-color paint. He held the piece of cardboard at an angle against his knees as he knelt on the cushion and touched the brush to the white surface. Watching, Celia could see the purple blossom of an iris come to life in only a few strokes of his brush.

Gentaro Sato glanced at her rapt face and then nodded toward the *tokonoma*—the alcove of honor. A blue vase held a single iris flower and a few green leaves.

Celia remembered and knew what he meant. "Your teacher," she said softly.

He laughed with pleasure and made a gesture for her to watch. Carefully he dipped a fresh brush into green paint on one side, turned it, and dipped a touch of yellow on the other side of the brush. Then he made a single swift stroke down the paper, from the sharp point of the leaf at the top to the broad base at the bottom—and a marvelous thing had happened. The leaf began in dark green and then shaded off into yellow along one side, green on the other. He had shaded it and painted two colors into it, all in one stroke.

He performed the same thing with several other leaves and the stalk of the flower, and the picture was done. As lovely a painting of iris as Celia had ever seen.

Finally he took a brush and black ink and stroked in the characters of his name. From a small black box he took a tiny seal, pressed it into the red paste the box contained, and stamped a seal below his name.

"What's that?" Celia asked.

"It's the personal seal an artist uses," Sumiko said.

With a low bow he presented the painting to Celia.

This time Celia didn't bother about translations. She spoke directly to the artist and she put her heart into her words.

"Thank you so very much! I'll put this up in my room when I go home, and I'll be proud of it and remember you always."

If he did not understand all the words, he understood what her eyes were saying and her tone, and his smile was warm and friendly. Again he spoke in Japanese, and this time Sumiko looked a little uncomfortable as she translated.

"He says he does not like all Americans. He says they are sometimes noisy and impolite and have no respect for his gods. But you have made him stop and think that perhaps he has judged without knowing very many. He is glad that you are my friend. He thinks you may be good for me."

"I wish I could talk to him," Celia said regretfully. "I wish I could tell him what a good friend you are, Sumiko, and how much I like you."

Sumiko shrugged. "I can't tell him that. And he probably wouldn't believe you, anyway."

The old man spoke again, gently, and as she listened, Sumiko's expression softened.

"He says that the beauties of nature have grown more dear to him than ever, for they contrast with the suffering Japan has known. He hopes that one day all people will

live at peace with the beauty about them and not try to destroy it."

Celia nodded solemnly. He was a wonderful old man. Sumiko was lucky to be his granddaughter. But now, she knew, they ought to go. She had been here long enough.

Japanese Haiku
translated by HARRY BEHN

Listen! What stillness!
Cicadas buzzing in sun,
drilling into rock.

BASHO

After the bells hummed
and were silent, flowers chimed
a peal of fragrance.

BASHO

O moon, why must you
inspire my neighbor to chirp
all night on a flute!

KOYO

Since my house burned down,
I now own a better view
of the rising moon.

MASAHIDE

From *Cricket Songs: Japanese Haiku*, translated and © 1964 by Harry Behn. Reprinted by permission of the author and Harcourt, Brace & World, Inc.

A Gift from Allah

by ROBERT DAVIS

Like a puff of smoke, a gray shadow passed behind a rock. Driss sat up with a jump, sucking in his breath. A shiver of excitement ran down his backbone. Leaning across from his donkey, he tugged at the sleeve of his grandfather's cloak.

"I have seen four jackals since we left the Singing Brook. Please will you stop and let me see whether there isn't something among those bushes?"

Driss and his grandfather were Berbers. They had sold their charcoal at Thursday Market and were hurrying home with their six donkeys, hoping to reach their village of High Pastures before nightfall.

"Those little jackals are cowards," said the old man, inside his hood. "They do not hunt until it is dark, and then they attack some person who is old or sick or some animal that is weak or injured. Night will be here soon, and the jackals are gathering for a feast. Look behind those rocks while I keep the donkeys here. But hurry. Soon it will be too black to see anything."

Driss slipped to the ground, raised the folds of his *jellaba* above his knees, and ran among the dwarf palms and jujube bushes. Presently his shrill voice shouted, "Come quick, Grandfather, quick! Four jackals are sitting around a baby donkey! They are showing their teeth, ready to jump. The donkey is only two or three days old. He is cold and lying down, but he is not dead. Bring one of the charcoal baskets. Oh, come quick! You never saw a donkey of this color before."

As Sidi Ahmed approached, he aimed well-directed stones, which sent the jackals scurrying to a safer distance. Driss was kneeling and holding in his arms an animal about as big as a setter dog, but all legs and floppy ears. The donkey opened his eyes sleepily when the man and the boy tumbled him into one of the charcoal baskets. Driss tucked his woolen cloak around the animal. The jackals, furious at seeing their supper disappear, were barking and snarling, but Driss threw some sharp flints, and they galloped off to find a meal elsewhere.

The six donkeys of the charcoal merchant were again climbing the steep path toward High Pastures. It was a good thing that old Fortunata, the leading donkey, knew every inch and pebble of the trail, for it was now dark. The others heard the clink of her iron shoes and followed obediently.

Driss had never felt so happy. Sitting upon his donkey, he reached into the charcoal basket and laid his hand upon the animal beneath his cloak. The little donkey was nothing but bones. In all the lands of the Berbers had there ever before been a baby donkey of this color?

He was the pale gray of the mourning pigeon when it builds its nest. His nose was white, and the inside of his ears was like cotton wool. His eyes were the color of the chief's saddle when it had been rubbed smooth with wax. His body was fuzzy like plush, like the back of a sheep that has just been clipped short.

With a sharp stick Driss prodded the donkey he was riding until it was side by side with Fortunata, on which Sidi Ahmed rode.

"Tell me, Grandfather," Driss asked, "do you think that I can keep him alive? He is a gift from Allah, isn't he? Did you ever before see an animal with that black cross upon his shoulders?"

"I am afraid that you are too late," said the old man. "He was left to die, I fear, by one of the big caravans that bring salt from the country of the striped tents. He is an Egyptian donkey, as you see from that black cross upon his shoulders. These Tuaregs of the great desert know animals well. Never would they have abandoned him unless they believed that he was about to die. If they think that an animal is not strong, they do not waste their time with him. Son of my son, I fear that your trouble will be for nothing."

But the boy had a reply ready. "There may be another reason why the donkey was left there. Perhaps someone stole him and hid him, intending to come back to get him before sundown. Only the thief was late, and we passed that way first. A few minutes more and the jackals would have eaten the donkey. I saved him from the jackals, didn't I, Grandfather?" The boy's voice was intense in its earnestness, and the old man nodded.

"If I can keep this donkey alive, will he be mine?" asked Driss. "Will you speak for me if any man comes to take him from me?"

The charcoal merchant, who was also the headman of the village, smiled and nodded. "Yes, he will be yours, and I will stand beside you in the court as your witness. But for you he would have been meat for the jackals."

Before the path reaches the village of High Pastures, it skirts the edge of a lower and poorer village, Low Pastures, where lived Driss' best friend, Amroo. Here in Low Pastures the houses were of straw, and the men owned less land than in the more prosperous tent settlement of High Pastures on the plateau above.

Driss was shouting at the top of his voice before the file of donkeys entered the cedar grove which surrounds Low Pastures. "Oh, Amroo, you sleepy-headed turtle, come and hear the news! In this charcoal basket I have something such as never before came to our tribe."

Out of the farthest straw hut rolled a dusty figure. It rose to its feet presently, waving both arms as it ran. "It's that nest of flying squirrels in the hollow tree," the figure cried.

"No. Guess again." In the dark, Driss, riding with his hand upon his new pet, smiled in a superior way.

"It is the cub of a spotted bear," said Amroo, out of breath, running alongside.

"No, it's a baby Egyptian donkey, with hoofs no bigger than the eye of a cow and the color of tortoise shell. Around his eyes and his nose are circles of white. Along his back and across his shoulders is a black cross." The boy's voice trailed off into a distressed silence. "Grandfather thinks he will die, but we've just got to keep him alive. Put your hand under my hand and feel him. He is cold, but he is still breathing."

Driss continued, "Sidi Ahmed says that we must give him goat's milk, the half of a bowl, all night, every time the rooster crows. Who in High Pastures or in Low Pastures has a goat with lots of milk?"

"Cousin You-Seff has a goat whose kid fell over the cliff. She has much milk," replied Amroo.

"Run and get her, Amroo. Tell Cousin You-Seff that I will work five days for him if he will rent her to me until this donkey is weaned. Bring her to our tent, and ask your family if you can spend the night with us."

In the tent of Sidi Ahmed the barley porridge was warm, and the fire was smoking in a hole beside the entrance. Fatma, the wizened cousin of the village headman, who kept house for him and his two grandchildren, had already gathered the young lambs and goats and chickens under shelter. On her side of the curtain that divided the tent into two rooms, she and Rabka, Driss' ten-year-old sister, and two little servants who helped with the animals and the cooking were asleep. Fatma had spread the matting and the rugs on which the man and the boy would sleep. As the night was dry, the sides of the tent were open to the air.

The Egyptian donkey opened his eyes, but he was too weak to stand when Driss carried him inside. His awkward legs folded up like broken sticks. Amroo could be heard coming up the hill, leading a bewildered goat that was bleating at the end of a rope.

Driss milked the goat into a bowl of baked clay, and dipping his fingers in the warm liquid, he wet the lips of the donkey. The donkey opened his eyes wide and flopped back his ears. But he would not drink when Driss pushed his nose into the bowl. He sneezed and drew his head away.

Around the end of the curtain partition, Rabka had been watching Amroo and her brother. Now she came forward and took the bowl. "Let me try," she said. "Sit down, Driss, and hold his head on your knees. Open his lips." The girl filled her mouth from the bowl, puckered her lips as though she were going to whistle, and blew a thin stream of milk down the donkey's throat. Within five minutes the bowl was empty, and the donkey was holding his mouth open of his own accord.

"Good, Rabka!" exclaimed Driss. "I didn't think a girl

could be so clever. You go back to bed, and Amroo will tie the goat under the tent. Just as soon as the moon rises and shines in the door, we'll give our boarder another meal.

"You lie on that side of him, Amroo, and I'll lie on this side. Snuggle up close, all of us under the one rug, so as to make him warm. Sidi Ahmed says that our only chance of saving him will be to keep him very warm and to feed him often."

The boys settled down for the night, with Driss putting his arms firmly about the neck of his new pet.

By the end of the third day it was no longer necessary to feed the baby donkey in Rabka's way. He would push his white muzzle into the bowl and drink without help. In fact, he pushed so greedily that he nearly broke the bowl. After the fourth day he was able to stand, even to walk a few unsteady steps.

To fill his stomach seven times a day required the milk of three goats. Several evenings were spent at the home of Cousin You-Seff at Low Pastures to decide how much the rent of the three goats should be. Finally it was settled that Driss, Amroo, and Rabka should each give the goatherd four days' work, their only reservation being that, whatever You-Seff made them do, all three should do it together.

As the boys were obliged to leave the village early each morning to pasture the cattle and sheep higher on the mountain and did not return until sunset, they could not feed the donkey during the day. That task was given to Rabka.

As the weeks grew into months and Cousin You-Seff never claimed his four days of work, the boys became worried. They knew that the goatherd had not forgotten, for when they spoke of it he would grin mysteriously and turn away.

But one morning in September, as he strolled up from Low Pastures behind his flock, You-Seff called to Driss, "Will you watch my goats tomorrow? I am going on a journey. When I get back, I'll tell you and Amroo the job I have in mind. Come to my house tomorrow after your evening meal."

The next evening You-Seff said, "I am going to build another house. My family needs more room. Today I have been to the marsh to see whether the tops of the rushes have turned yellow enough to cut them for thatch. I am going to build the finest house in this village, with a foundation of stone as high as your shoulder that rats and snakes cannot dig through, with a bamboo framework so strong that the winter wind will not blow it over, and a roof so thick that no rainy season will ever wet us.

"The rushes are perfect," continued You-Seff. "Tomorrow we will go with four donkeys and cut a big load. My two daughters, with Rabka to help them, will then cut the reeds into short lengths and tie them into bundles like brooms, while they are still soft. This is the work that I have been saving for you boys—to help build my new house. At my age I am a little stiff to climb ladders and fasten bamboos together."

The following morning, even before the mountain to the east was tipped with pink fire from the rising sun,

You-Seff and the two boys, each astride a donkey, were descending the zigzag path to the river. Once on the floor of the valley, they ascended the stream to the place where it broadened and flowed sluggishly, and the cattails along the bank grew as high as a man's turban. With their harvest sickles they slashed the green rushes, laying them in neat armfuls, tied at either end with palm cord, until the sun stood straight overhead. In the shade of a wild olive tree they ate their white cheese and crusty barley bread and drank from the waterskin that You-Seff had filled at the Sulphur Spring. Then the three stretched out for a good nap, each pulling the hood of his *jellaba* tight about his ears to keep out centipedes and spiders.

Going back to their work among the rushes, Driss was walking ahead. Suddenly he halted, signaling for the others to do the same. Finger on lips, he tiptoed back, pointing to a spot on the crest of the muddy bank. Where the sun beat hottest, curled up like a coil of thick rope and fast asleep, lay the largest snake that any of them had ever seen. Its skin was a shiny black, with yellow stripes round its body, like a giant hornet.

Driss was whispering excitedly, "The snake charmers at Thursday Market have nothing as big and fierce as that. Do you think that we might be able to capture him alive, Cousin You-Seff? The snake charmers will pay us four or even six pieces of silver for him."

The goatherd rubbed his ears as he tried to think of a good plan for capturing the snake. Then he replied, "The best way would be to use forked sticks. We must pin him down in the mud and hold him until I can get a grip just back of his head. Once I have him there, he cannot bite. After that we may be able to push him into our waterskin and knot it tight."

You-Seff went to cut some sticks. He soon returned with three willow branches, each about six feet long, split at the end, with the openings held apart by small wedges.

"Spread out, boys," he said. "Driss, go first, then myself, then Amroo. We will walk quietly along the water's edge until I am opposite him."

The snake had not stirred. When You-Seff and the two boys were in place, each holding his split branch before him like a spear, You-Seff tossed a pebble into the black-and-yellow coil. A wicked head lifted a few inches, the forked tongue flickering like a scarlet string. Slowly the head flowed forward, graceful and sleek, the body unwinding like a spring.

The snake made a direct course toward Amroo, who stood tense upon his toes. While its head was still three feet distant, the boy threw himself forward. The snake swerved sideways toward You-Seff, its jaws open, its orange throat visible. The boy missed the head by an inch, but it gave time for the man to catch the body near the middle. He pushed the wooden points of his stick into the soft earth with all his force. The snake's tail curled up around You-Seff's stick as high as his hand. The head lunged savagely to right and left, just out of reach of his bare legs. By working the crotch of his stick forward from the point of You-Seff's hold, Driss was finally able to pinion the jaws in the mud.

"Bear down hard on the head, Driss," cried You-Seff. "And you, Amroo, unwind his tail from my stick. It won't hurt you. Pull it out straight and stand on it. I am going to get my fingers around his neck. If I can get a good grip just back of his head with both hands, he will soon quit fighting. The second I have his throat, Driss can help Amroo hold his tail out straight."

You-Seff's turban had fallen off, and drops of perspiration came out on his shaven head as he squeezed. The two boys braced their heels and pulled. In a few seconds the struggles of the long black-and-yellow body became less violent.

"Now be careful, Driss," panted the goatherd. "Take the waterskin from my belt, open wide the neck, and work it over his head, very slowly."

Once the blunt nose and the unwinking eyes were inside the waterskin, the chief danger was over. Inch by inch You-Seff forced the body through the opening, with Driss holding the waterskin and Amroo keeping the tail from doubling up. Then with two deft knots the man fastened the neck of the bag with a leather thong that he was holding in his mouth and threw the skin into shallow water. It rolled and writhed and swelled like some horrible headless, legless creature. The bag was the skin of a full-sized goat, but the snake was so big that it filled it. The sides bulged out sharply as though punched by a fist on the inside. That was the head of the snake, trying to bite its way out.

Now that the battle was over, the boys sat on the bank, fascinated by the strength of their prisoner and terrified at the thought of their own recklessness in attacking him.

"Now let's hurry home," urged You-Seff, "before that monster rips a hole in the bag. I won't feel comfortable until we get him inside a solid wooden box."

The bundles of rushes were hurriedly loaded and roped upon the donkeys. The bag containing the snake was wrapped in You-Seff's cloak and placed in the middle of a saddle, with rushes wedged around to steady it. "I don't mind letting a snake have my seat for this once," grinned You-Seff.

As the trio climbed to the plateau, they made plans as to what they would do with their prize. The next day was Thursday Market, and it was agreed that Driss, who had discovered the snake, and whose idea it had been to capture it alive, should start early to market with the animal in a box covered with strong bamboo grating. He should show it to the three or four snake charmers who would be at the market and sell it for the best price offered. With the money he was to buy sugar, soap, and tea, which luxuries were to be divided into three equal parts. Meanwhile, Amroo and Rabka would help You-Seff cut and peel the bark from forty maple saplings, to form the framework of the new house, working extra hard and long to make up for Driss' absence.

As the sun was setting the next day, Driss' donkey trotted among the workers at Low Pastures. The boy was bursting with news. The snake had been the sensation of the market. After much bargaining it had been sold for six pieces of silver.

Driss went on to tell in detail about his adventures at the market. Then You-Seff, with his share of the sugar, soap, and tea in his arms, said that tomorrow Driss would begin with his work on the house. "Nothing," he said, "must prevent the house being finished at the end of the four days, which you boys owe me. Finding the snake will not replace the regular work that you three promised for the rent of the goats. It was a gift from Allah such as we do not receive every day."

Driss picked up his share of sugar, soap, and tea and galloped his donkey toward High Pastures. Those words, "a gift from Allah," reminded him of something. He had his own gift from Allah at home—a gift that would be waiting for its supper.

The Witch Doctor's Trial

by REBA PAEFF MIRSKY

Nomusa, daughter of the Zulu chief Zitu, has gone to live with the nurse Buselapi in a modern Zulu village in South Africa. Nomusa is studying to be a nurse.

Nomusa learns that the witch doctor in her kraal is accused of bewitching a villager's cattle. She and the nurse decide to attend the witch doctor's trial.

Although Nomusa and Buselapi had come to the kraal in great haste, it was considered good manners to enter in a dignified, unhurried walk. Their pace became slow and deliberate.

Among the large throng of people they saw before them, Nomusa quickly found her father. He was sitting on a chief's stool before his hut, his carved wooden staff of office in his raised hand. The Elders sat in a circle around him, the children and their mothers, neighbors and relatives squatting at a respectful distance.

In the center of the kraal yard sat the witch doctor, motionless, a wide, empty space on each side of her as if she were a source of evil. She looked proud, even scornful, her bony hands clasped in her oxhide skirt as she waited to be questioned. Her eyes darted about searchingly, then fixed themselves on Nomusa and Buselapi, who had found places beside Nomusa's mother.

The witch doctor raised her gnu-tail wand in recognition. Nomusa flushed under her piercing glance and was thankful for the diversion caused by her little sister.

Reprinted by permission of Follett Publishing Co., Chicago, from *Nomusa and the New Magic* (Chapter 7) by Reba Paeff Mirsky, copyright 1962.

Bala had jumped up from her grandmother's lap to wave at Nomusa. There was an ominous air about the trial, and when Zitu the Chief began recounting the accusations against the witch doctor, everyone listened and watched attentively.

"Umtakati, you say that the witch doctor has bewitched your cattle because you summoned the nurse Buselapi instead of her when your wife fell ill?" asked the Chief.

"That is so, Chief. Before, if there was sickness or bad luck in my kraal, I sent for the witch doctor, and nothing ever happened to my cattle. After we gave up the witch doctor, our troubles began. The cattle sickened. Many died. Ill fortune has clawed me like a leopard. There is no doubt that she is a sorceress and has put an evil spell on my cattle."

"What do you have to say to Umtakati's accusation?" Zitu politely asked the witch doctor, who did not look at all worried.

The witch doctor's eyes narrowed with scorn for her accuser as she answered proudly, "Chief, it is not what I have to say, but what our ancestral spirits decree. The troubles of Umtakati are not due to me but to his ancestral spirits. He has, no doubt, neglected to make sacrifices to them and remember them with good deeds. That is why they are punishing him. He has brought this powerful curse upon himself. I swear by the spirits of my ancestors that I have done nothing to add to his ill fortune."

The low whispering among the Elders and Zitu was like a winter wind blowing through a tiny crack. Zitu turned to the witch doctor again. "Is it true," he asked, "that you are angry when someone summons Buselapi the nurse instead of you?"

With a loud *Tsss-s-s,* the witch doctor drew in her breath. The small children, terrified by the threatening sound, clung to their mothers.

"People often have sickness and ill fortune because their neglected ancestral spirits are displeased," she explained. "Although our ancestral spirits no longer live in the flesh, we know that they are, nevertheless, all about us and in constant contact with the living."

"We hear you," said the Council of Elders.

She continued, "Doctors and nurses do not understand this. They know nothing about certain poisons nor how to protect people by mixing thunder with medicines made from herbs and plants. How, then, can they help a sick person or drive away bad luck if they cannot find out, and do not care to find out, who his enemies are so as to protect him? I am not angry with those who neglect their ancestral spirits to seek the help of doctors and nurses; I am sorry for them."

She spat on the ground scornfully and added, "Those pills and medicines Buselapi gets from the white doctors in the city are but foolish magic!"

The women looked at one another as if to say, "Is there going to be trouble over Buselapi now?" Some of them liked Buselapi's new ways of helping the sick.

Zitu called out, "Buselapi, come forward."

Buselapi rose and walked over to the witch doctor, bowing to her respectfully before sitting down next to her. Zitu asked, "What say you, Buselapi?"

"Chief, Council of Elders, my people: No medicine, neither the witch doctor's nor mine, can always be helpful. Some misfortunes cannot be avoided. Others will come only so long as we Zulus remain in ignorance and have diseases without knowing the true reasons for them. Without education, our people will always remain superstitious and fearful, needing the witch doctor's magic and reassurance more than my medicine and advice.

"Many witch doctors are clever, wise, and helpful in giving hope to those suffering from ill fortune; they have good ways of dealing with certain kinds of nervous sicknesses, with broken bones, and skin diseases. But I am sure they do not cast evil spells on anyone out of resentment of me."

There was an uneasy stir among the Elders. Buselapi continued, "Our Great Chief, if our people go on thinking they have to submit to anything that happens to them because it is their fate, if they believe all their suffering comes as a punishment from the ancestral spirits or from sorcerers, they will remain weak and afraid. It is only by accepting the new knowledge that they can again become the strong and powerful people they once were."

Angrily one of the Elders shouted, "Buselapi is disrespectful and insulting. She is an example of what the new knowledge does to our children. Oh, Noble Chief, consider whether it is wisdom to send your daughter Nomusa away to school. Do not let our ancient customs be broken like a calabash with a stone."

Nomusa's throat tightened, and she trembled at hearing this. Would her good friend Buselapi be punished?

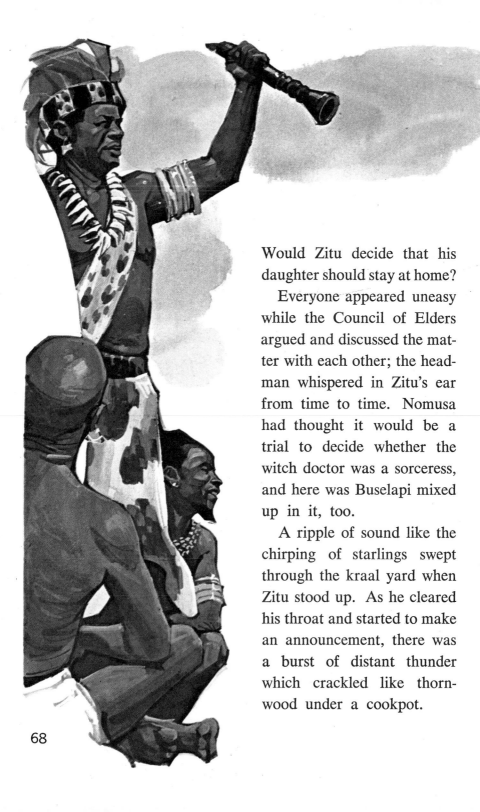

Would Zitu decide that his daughter should stay at home?

Everyone appeared uneasy while the Council of Elders argued and discussed the matter with each other; the headman whispered in Zitu's ear from time to time. Nomusa had thought it would be a trial to decide whether the witch doctor was a sorceress, and here was Buselapi mixed up in it, too.

A ripple of sound like the chirping of starlings swept through the kraal yard when Zitu stood up. As he cleared his throat and started to make an announcement, there was a burst of distant thunder which crackled like thornwood under a cookpot.

Worried, everyone looked up into the darkening sky to see massed clouds moving swiftly toward each other like threatening, dark-plumed warriors. Flashing spears of green-blue lightning flicked across the sky. Birds, with shrill cries of warning, flew to hide in trees and bushes, surprised by the change of weather.

The witch doctor looked up at the black, full-bellied clouds and clapped her bony hands in glee and triumph.

"Good! The ancestral spirits will soon make their wishes known; they are hurling their daggers of rain."

With the first raindrops, she declared, "I await now the decision of our wise Chief and Elders, unafraid. Although disasters fall on Umtakati's kraal like hailstones in a storm, I swear by the ancestral spirits that I am blameless. Do with me what you like."

There was a deep silence while Zitu consulted again with the Elders. He then held up his war shield and announced loudly, "The witch doctor has been wrongfully accused, so Umtakati must pay her for the injustice with three healthy goats. If his cattle are sickening or dying, he must look to himself or to those whose knowledge can help him."

"We agree!" said the Council of Elders.

"Serves you right!" said the witch doctor, hurling her words at Umtakati and waving her gnu-tail wand at him fiercely. She scoffed, "Like a hen, he has been talking with words that are all noise and no sense. Bah!"

Zitu raised his staff to end the torrent of words the witch doctor showered on her accuser. She stopped and turned to smile triumphantly at Buselapi.

Zitu began, "My people, I know that many of you are not pleased with the changes taking place in our great Zululand. Yet even when Chaka, our warrior king of long ago, lived, he understood that if we Zulus were to become a strong, united people, some things would have to change, new ideas would have to be adopted.

"It was due to him that we became famous. He himself said, 'Because things have been done the same way for hundreds of years is no reason for continuing so.' For a time the new ideas and methods he encouraged brought us prosperity, and we flourished. If we are to become once more a great people, we must not despise new knowledge nor scorn those who offer us fresh ideas. Let him who prefers to summon the witch doctor for sickness or ill fortune do so. Those who wish to have Buselapi may do so as well." Zitu looked around at the attentive throng like a firm and loving father and added, "There is help to be had from both these good women. Perhaps there is a still greater magic of which we are thus far ignorant."

"We hear you, Mighty Lion!" shouted the throng.

Continuing, he said, "I myself do not fear that the new knowledge will breed any disrespect for our customs and beliefs. We can all learn from those who know more than we do, keeping the best from our old way of life and adopting some of the new. I have finished."

Zitu turned toward his hut, followed by the Elders. The witch doctor jumped up and cried, "Wait! The ancestral spirits have sent a message."

"What is it?" asked Zitu and the Elders.

"They say Umtakati's cattle have been poisoned by the thornlike shoot of the umtente grass; if he takes them to graze in fields of white clover, they will get well."

Buselapi rose and laid her hand on the witch doctor's arm, saying, "I did not know about this remedy. There is much I can learn from you, and I hope you can learn from me."

The witch doctor gave Buselapi a friendly tap with the gnu-tail wand. "I think we can learn from each other," she replied. "Perhaps there *is* more powerful magic than mine coming into the land."

A Son of India

by JEAN BOTHWELL

Hari Singh, farmer, lives only a scant mile from a river that flows into the great Ganges. His village has been his family's home, his father's and his grandfather's, back through many generations. Hari Singh has never lived anywhere else, and no one in his family has known any life but farm life.

In India there are thousands of families like the Singhs, who work on the land but make their home in a small community of blacksmiths and barbers, merchants, dairymen, weavers, cobblers, and day laborers. In the beginning farmers settled near each other because they feared wild animals and roving bands of thieves. They felt safer

 From *Cobras, Cows and Courage: Farm Life in North India* by Jean Bothwell. Copyright © 1956 by Coward-McCann, Inc. Adapted by permission.

living near other people who could help them if they had trouble. They also believed that evil spirits roamed the earth to harm people. The farmers of North India still have these same fears. So they live in small villages for safety. They go out to their farms in the morning and return at night for food and sleep.

Most people of North India work at something that has to do with farming, and they all live in villages like Phulpur—the name means "place of flowers"—where Hari Singh has his home.

Hari Singh's body is thin, and he walks slowly, but he walks tall and proud coming from the fields at night with his plow across his shoulders. He has to carry it back and forth. No one leaves any farm tools out at night for fear they might be stolen.

The men sing together coming in. Singing makes the journey shorter, and they believe it helps drive away evil spirits lurking in the bushes. If a man must walk alone, he sings louder.

This farmer of India is not a solemn man, but there are fine lines at the corners of his eyes that seem to narrow them. Such lines appear in the face of any man who has a far view at his work, on land or sea.

Hari Singh's far view is the mountains. He would like to make a journey there to see what they look like up close. But except for the time of his wedding, he has never been farther than ten miles from Phulpur.

It is the custom to take a wife who belongs to another village. To find a girl of the Singhs' caste who was suitable also in other ways, Hari Singh's father took time and much thought. It came about that friends of friends knew the family of a girl named Shoba. And so the arrangement was made. Hari Singh, with his father and brothers, went to a village eighty miles distant to claim the bride he had never seen.

During that trip Hari Singh saw the Ganges, the mighty Mother River, for the first time. He was surprised to find that land so far from home looked much the same as his own land and that the farmers grew the same things he did—wheat and millet and barley—all of them good nourishing grains if the heads were filled out at harvest.

Since then Hari Singh's longing to see the mountains has grown stronger. In the cold weather when the air is clear, far to the north he can see a deep blue shadow thrust against the pure cloudless blue of the winter sky, and he knows that he is looking at the far Himalayas. It would be wonderful to walk and climb until he reached the famous ice cave in the hills, where the drip from a glacier is believed to be the source of the great Ganges. But this is only a cherished dream of Hari Singh. There are Shoba and the two little boys and the baby girl, and he must stay by the land and grow their food.

Hari Singh's father followed the old custom of dividing his land among his sons when he died. Each of his four sons received about three acres. The portion that fell to Hari was too small to raise the food he needs for his family, so he rents part of the ground he farms.

Since his fields are not close together, Hari has to go back and forth between them, getting each plot ready for seed and gathering the crop when the harvest comes.

The distant fields make Hari Singh's work hours longer. There is also the worry that while he is away from one part, crows or wild parrots will swoop down and eat the planted seed. When the seed comes up, he is afraid that someone's goat or a wandering cow will get into his unwatched field and harm the young plants. When his son Govind, who now herds cows, grows older, he can watch a field, and then Hari's troubles will be one less.

Meantime, the family lives as others do, from harvest to harvest, depending on weather for their living and going hungry if the crops fail in any season.

It takes courage to live this way, but the Singhs have it. Their name means "lion."

"The hour of cow dust" is an exciting time of day in any village of North India. The children drive the cows in from the day's foraging by the roadside or along the edges of the fields. The dust kicked up by the cows' hoofs looks golden in the sunset. After the children, come the fathers with their bullocks and gear.

The crows fly in from far fields to nest at dusk in their home tree. They caw loudly and take a long time to settle down for the night. Sometimes peacocks roost near a village, and their raucous cry adds to the homing din. The cows bawl, and the milking begins. The milk is thin, and there isn't much of it because the cows, like the farm people, do not get enough nourishing food.

At the close of day the village mothers usually begin coming to the well in the square to fill a last water jar and to hear the latest news. Each waits her turn and leaves slowly with the full earthen or brass jar balanced on her head.

Some of the women, like Hari Singh's wife, Shoba, are already at home, crouched on the floor before their low stoves, each of them coaxing a little supper fire to "burn, burn quickly for my husband's supper."

Shoba has dough ready, made from flour she ground between heavy stones, from the wheat Hari Singh grew the past year. In India the bread is made fresh for every meal. The dough would spoil if a housewife tried to keep some for the next day.

Little pinches of the gray-looking mass are rolled and slapped into large thin rounds like pancakes. When the coals glow in the tiny stove, the bread is baked on a

dome-shaped iron set above it. The flap of bread is baked on both sides. Next, Shoba slips it into the hot ashes, where it puffs into a big hollow ball because of the steam inside. Then it sinks like a pricked balloon, and Shoba keeps it hot in a basket with others already baked.

Outside, a village dog barks, and then another and another, and they are answered by the voices of the children. Shoba knows then that the cattle and the little cowherds are coming and that the men will not be far behind.

The houses in Phulpur are built close together, and the evening sounds run from one house to the next like the harmonies on an organ, up and down the narrow lanes. Neighbors know what the next family is doing, what its daily habits are, and what is being cooked for supper.

The Singhs' house, though small, has two rooms. Many people have only one room for all the purposes of living—eating and sleeping, and being born and dying.

There is a small courtyard in front of the little mud house. Mud is the only building material Hari Singh could afford. Wood and brick cost too much.

The entrance to the courtyard is the Singhs' front door. The bullocks enter there, too. The courtyard is the stable for them and for Hari Singh's one cow.

When Shoba hears the thump of the chain on the wooden front door, followed by the tramp of the heavy bullocks and the thud of their yoke on the ground, she knows that Hari Singh has come. Her eyes glow in the light of the fire, and she hurries the last of the bread while she feeds the baby.

Then Govind follows his father in, and little Jassy follows him. Jassy is crying. He is tired, he declares. He is only five, but he thinks he has done a man's work this day with Govind. So he wants a man's food—bread with a trickle of coarse brown sugar and two helpings of everything else Shoba has prepared.

Inside the Singhs' house there is warmth from the supper fire. The baby gurgles contentedly, and the children chatter about the day. As the members of the family talk, they deftly break off pieces of bread and roll up a bit of the cooked food with their fingers and pop it, bite-size, into their mouths. There is no problem of garbage disposal in the Singh household. Nothing is left.

Shoba knew, when little Jassy asked, that she had only one helping each of chopped vegetable and milk curd.

Because she serves everyone else first, no one notices that her portion is smaller tonight. She smiles to herself. Jassy will grow up fast and have real troubles. Let him have a little extra now. He will be thin soon enough.

Hari Singh thanks Shoba for his supper and steps out quietly. She knows without asking that he is going to talk with the men in the village square.

As soon as the fathers leave for the meeting, the mothers tuck the children and the babies away to sleep. Shoba covers the glowing coal left on her hearth with thick ashes. It will be there, red and warm, in the morning, so that she can start her fire quickly. If it should go out during the night, she must borrow a live coal from her neighbor. Shoba has no matches to kindle a new fire.

Tonight the stars come out, and the little new moon sinks in the west. The tender notes of an evening song played on a shepherd's flute fill the pauses in the talk of the men. All is well in Hari Singh's village. Tomorrow's work is several hours away. No one grumbles that it is hard work or that the wheat sowed today looked shriveled. The farmer accepts his lot and works with all his energy to grow a good crop.

A change that will make life very different for Hari Singh and Shoba and their children began one day when a stranger came to the village of Phulpur.

He wanted to talk to the farmers, he said. He was a quiet man, so he didn't wait to make a loud speech in the square after supper. He went out to the fields, where the men were preparing the land for another wheat crop. He had brought them a new kind of seed wheat.

American Foundation's News Service Photo

In field after field where the visitor went, the farmers shook their heads. There was something wrong, they felt. Why should anyone give away seed, even if the man was from the Government, as he said? How did they know the seed would do what he claimed? He said that crops grown from it would be double what they were now getting from their own seed.

And then the man came to the field of Hari Singh. Hari was working on the field he owned that day. He listened to the quiet man's words. He looked at the soil of his little acreage and back to the plump, fine-looking grains of wheat in the man's hand. He wanted to believe in the promise. If he got a good crop in the coming season—he didn't dare finish his hope, even in thought.

80

Often he and Shoba had planned what they would do with some extra grain. But no great yield had ever happened.

He could do what he pleased on this piece of ground, he argued to himself. It was his own. If the stranger was not telling the truth, the family would suffer because he had risked ground to sow the new seed, but no one else would be harmed. The landlord would get his rent from the other piece. He would have no complaint.

Hari Singh shifted his weight from one foot to the other. He stooped and picked up a clod of earth and stood there crumbling it in his fingers while he listened and thought.

"There is no magic in it," said the visitor urgently. "The Government wants to help farmers, and government scientists have now produced this good seed in the Pusa experiment station to show you what good crops you can grow. This is Pusa 14, the name they gave it in the laboratory."

Hari Singh held out his hand. "I will try. I will sow one half of one acre, and we shall see who speaks truth."

The government man returned the seed to his pocket. "I will come back when you are ready to sow your crop," he said. "This is only a sample. But I will bring enough when I come again to sow your half acre, and I will help to plant it. Let your neighbors be witnesses."

In good time all came about as the visitor had said. The Pusa 14 was sown carefully in the ground Hari Singh had prepared. The headman of the village and Hari Singh's closest friends were among the farmers who watched that day. The government agent himself dropped the first seeds into the ground and covered them with his hands.

Never was a piece of ground watched and cared for as that one was. Govind began his own lifelong toil on the land that season. Jassy was left with the other herdboys, and Govind undertook to watch the field so that the crows would not dig up the wonderful seeds before they rooted.

When the harvest time came, the government stranger appeared once more. He had Hari Singh's name in a little book. He wanted to put down beside it the yield of grain from the new seed. The same group that had been present at the planting went again to the plot where Pusa 14 was growing. The crop was tall and sturdy and heavy-headed, filled out to the tip with fine grain, and there was no rust.

In a field beyond Hari Singh's acre there grew an ordinary crop, which would thresh out only about half the amount Hari Singh would get from his risk.

While the farmers marveled, the owner of the village came hurrying to them along the paths between the fields.

He started to shout before he reached them. "What is this they tell me?" he yelled. "Have I dolts for tenants? A miracle in these fields, and I haven't been told about it until now! Where is this stupid Hari Singh who has planted only his own ground and not mine with the new wheat? Why was this Pusa 14 not planted in my fields?"

The farmers looked at each other. Each had refused to risk planting the new seed. What could they say? Their guilty feeling made them silent.

The agent said, "Sir, your tenants are cautious men. They could not believe that the new seed would do what I claimed. I do not blame them. If they had raised a poor crop, you would have been even more angry than you are now. Hari Singh was wise, but cautious as well. He risked only part of his own ground. Thus he protected you in case the seed I offered did not do all I promised for it."

"I see it is as you say." The landlord's voice was quieter. "These are not dolts, and Hari Singh's caution was wise. But next year you must all plant Pusa 14."

He was turning away when one of the men put his hands together in the ancient position of a pleader, fingers extended toward the landowner, and asked, "How shall we get the seed? Our crop this year is only ordinary. There will be nothing left over and above our poor needs. When has any of us ever bought seed wheat?"

Then the agent spoke. "There is no need to worry just yet about the seeding of a new crop. Harvest these fields, and I will come again. The Government will give you measure for measure in new seeds for your old supply."

When Hari Singh heard the agent's plan, he wanted to let out all his breath in an unseemly shout. Now Shoba would have the new red skirt she wanted so much. He had promised it if there should be an extra yield. There would be new shirts for his boys, too.

In his imagination Hari Singh was already at the cloth shop. He would take time for his bargaining. All the village would admire his prosperity. He would have hard silver rupees in exchange for his fine new wheat.

That was how it would be. The government agent might think there was no magic in the harvest. Let him think so. Hari Singh knew there was. The magic had come out of the ground. It was there, though hidden.

Dive into Danger

by LORENZ GRAHAM

It was a Friday afternoon in the middle of May. David was supposed to be studying the decline of the Roman Empire, but it was a hot day. The school windows were open, and noisy spring flies were going in and out. Across the highway David could see a pattern of brown rows curving with the hill. A mule-drawn wagon passed by on Route One. On the lowered tail gate of the wagon two boys sat with their feet swinging. They waved at the school, knowing some of the pupils would be watching.

David thought of the old mill beyond the hilltop. It would be cool out there. The water would be chilly at first, but it would feel good to have a swim.

He wrote on his tablet, "Swim tomorrow?" and held it up for Ben Crawford to see. Ben nodded.

The next morning David hustled through his work at home. He was sixteen years old and serious about his responsibilities. At noon Ben came by, and the two boys started out without telling anyone where they were going.

It was hot again. They walked along the highway and then followed a dirt road to the millpond.

"It's funny," Ben said, as they started taking off their clothes. "When you want to go swimming, it's so hot you think you can't stand it. Then when you get to the water, it seems right chilly."

David agreed.

"Did you ever go in the mill?" Ben asked. "Spooky old place! I bet gangsters hide out in there sometimes."

The boys looked at the abandoned mill for which the stream had been dammed. The great water wheel no longer turned. Moss and vines and saplings were holding it fast.

At the upper part of the pond, the end away from the dam, the water was not so deep as farther downstream. There was a stretch of clean gravel on the bank. The boys called it "the beach."

David put a foot into the water.

"Man, it's cold!" he said.

The boys debated the best way to go in. Farther downstream it was deep enough to dive from the bank, but the swiftness of the water as it poured over the dam made it too dangerous to go in there. In summer the water went over the dam in a thin sheet. Now, early in the season, the stream was swollen. There was a great rush. It seemed there must be three feet of water pouring over.

David and Ben got well back from the water, and, each holding tightly to the hand of the other, they came down running fast and on into the water until they fell. It was as they knew it would be. The water chilled their skins, but as they thrashed about they got used to it.

Both boys were strong swimmers. They swam across the stream and back without stopping. When they came out, they were several yards farther downstream than where they had gone in.

"That current was sure pulling us," David said. "We've got to be careful."

"We're far enough away from the dam," said Ben. "You just got to swim kind of upstream and you'll stay in line."

"I read about a guy going over Niagara Falls in a barrel." David went on to describe the attempt. Niagara, he said, was nearly a mile high. In the pool below the Falls, friends were waiting with motorboats. They got the barrel, but when they opened it, the man was dead.

"Smothered, he was. But no bones broken."

"He must have been crazy," Ben said.

"Not crazy. He just wanted to take a chance," David argued.

"Anybody that takes fools' chances must be crazy," said Ben. "What's the good of it? What does he get if he lives?"

While they lay in the warm sun, to get tanned, as they said, they argued on the merits of taking chances.

"Well, now, look." David sat up and pointed toward the lower end of the millpond. "Suppose somebody you knew had gone over the dam and lived to tell about it. Suppose he told you just what he did and how he managed to save himself. I guess that information might be a help to you."

"You're crazy!" Ben said. "A man wouldn't have any kind of chance at all going over the dam. You try it, and I'll be down below to haul out the remains—if any."

"But if you had to, what would you do?" David persisted. "Let's go look at it."

The two boys rose and walked down along the bank. Near the dam they had to talk loudly, and when they had worked their way down to stand at the pool below the waterfall, they had to shout to make themselves heard above the steady roar. They finally agreed that a person would probably be killed on a trip over the dam. Neither of them spoke again until they got back to their beach.

"Just one thing a person might do," David said. "If I got caught in it, I would head upstream so I would go over feet first. Just as I reached the dam, I'd take in all the air my lungs would hold. When I went down, I would relax—you know, just go limp. And I'd pray."

"Yes, you'd need to pray, I guess." Ben was solemn at the thought. "Let's cross over again, and this time we'll keep swimming upstream."

They were nearly halfway over when they heard someone call them from the bank. Looking back between strokes, they saw that a group of boys had come to swim. They were white boys.

Between the white and colored boys of South Town there was little conflict. Seldom was there even an argument. They just stayed away from each other. They attended separate schools. They seldom talked together.

If colored boys came to the millpond and white boys were swimming, the colored boys would take off their clothes and go in. Nobody objected, but the white boys would soon leave. If colored boys were in the water when the white boys came, they would start swimming and the colored boys would leave. There was no discussion.

But David thought that a few of the white boys were mean. Harold Boyd, who was in the group on the bank, was one whom David disliked most.

When David and Ben reached the far bank this time, they went ashore and sat down to rest. Among the boys across the stream they recognized Little Red, Harold's cousin.

Harold cupped his hands and hollered across the water, "You all come on out now! We want to swim!"

"Come on in, if you want to," Ben shouted back. "Nobody's stopping you!"

David and Ben had been almost ready to leave, but they did not like to be told that they had to go home, especially by Harold Boyd. The fact that there were five of the others did not bother them. They had no thought of a fight. It was clear that Harold was just trying to be bossy. The boys with him started undressing.

Again David and Ben headed upstream so they would come out at the beach. They swam with slow, very even strokes, keeping close together. When they came to shallow water and got their feet on the gravelly bottom, the others were still watching them. As they came out of the water, Harold asked, "You all through now?"

"Well, I can't say," Ben replied. "We've been having fun, and we might want to be going in again."

"Sure," David added, throwing himself down to lie in the sun.

"Well, go ahead then, and hurry up," Harold said.

David lifted himself to look at Ben. "You heard what the man said, Ben. He wants you to hurry up."

Ben put a surprised look on his face. "Yes, Dave," he said. "I'm hurrying. Just watch me." He lay on his back and put his hands under his head.

"Aw, come on, Harold," said one of his friends. "They're no trouble. Let's go in."

"I don't associate with——" Harold paused as David raised his head to look at him. "I don't socialize with field hands," he said.

The white boys walked a few paces along the bank going toward the dam. There was more talk, with Harold holding out and the others trying to make him see that no harm would be done even if all were swimming in the water at the same time.

"All right," the self-appointed leader said loudly, "but they'd better not come in while I'm in there."

The boys did not enter the water at the little strip called the beach. They went downstream. The bank was steeper there. It was also nearer the dam.

David did not like that. Maybe he shouldn't have bucked against Harold Boyd, he thought. He raised up and looked at the boys standing waist deep in the water. They had not swum out into the stream yet.

"Hey, fellows," David called, trying to keep his voice friendly, "the current's awful swift down there, and it's deep. Come up this way."

"You mind your own business," Harold called back.

Ben turned over and said, "Come on, let's go. We've had our fun."

David agreed. They had had their fun. They had stayed around long enough to show that they could not be chased. "Okay," he said, and they started for their clothes.

Ben was dressed and David was sitting on the ground putting on his shoes when the others started to swim across the stream. All of them seemed to be good swimmers. They were heading upstream to avoid the pull of the current. It was a long way down to the dam, but there was a strong current, and they had to deal with it.

"Look at that," Ben said. "They're taking an awful chance."

David got to his feet to see better.

"Yes," David said, "that's dangerous. Little Red is a good swimmer, but he's stroking too fast. He'll get tired."

Some of the swimmers were now turning back; others were going across to the other side of the stream. All were swimming hard.

Little Red was slowing down. He treaded water for a moment in midstream. It was plain that the current in midstream was pulling him.

Ben called, "Go on, Red! Keep on going! You can make it."

But Red looked back. He tried to measure the distance from shore to shore, and he turned and started back.

"The other way, Red," David called, motioning his arms. "You're closer to the other side. Go on!"

The boy was confused. He started pulling faster. For a while he made progress. David and Ben moved down along the bank.

"The current's carrying him too fast," David said. "He's getting panicky. Ben, the kid won't make it."

David shucked out of his clothes. Ben grabbed his arm.

"You can't do it, Dave," Ben shouted. "You can't help him. You'll both go over."

David kept his eyes on the redhead, who was less than half the stream's width away.

"I've got to try. I've got to."

David dived, getting all the gain he could from the plunge. Near the shore the current was not too strong. David figured that if he kept swimming straight from shore the current would carry him downstream just about as fast as it was taking Red. He would have to keep going to reach the kid before he was swept over. Maybe he could help the younger boy reach the shore, but more likely they would go over the dam together. Maybe the plan he and Ben had talked about would work.

As he raised his arm from the water, he looked back and saw Ben helping one of the other boys up the bank. Ben would know what to do. It was good they had talked about it. Ben would be at the foot of the dam. Now David could hear the roar of the water, and there was Red's face ahead of him.

"Hi, Red!" David smiled, but the younger boy was too exhausted to smile back; maybe he was scared, too. David turned beside Red. "Put your hand on my shoulder and rest yourself. That's it. I got you. Take it easy now. We'll be all right, Red."

David set himself a slow breast stroke. He found he was tired too, but he tried to make his voice sound easy.

"We can make it, Red. Ben and the others will be on the other side to help us. Take deep breaths now. Loosen up all you can. We're heading upstream so we'll go over feet first. You don't get hurt that way. Just before we go over, you take a deep breath and hold it, but let your body go loose. On the other side you can swim again. The fellows will be there. Get it?"

There was no spoken answer, but David felt Red's hand on his left shoulder tighten. It was like a handshake. He turned and looked into Little Red's eyes, and Red's face broke into a smile.

The last thing David remembered before he went over was Little Red's smile.

This was it!

He was falling, falling, falling.

There was a sudden shock to his whole body, and then everything was dark. He was still falling, and in the darkness there was light. Falling gently, and the lights were dimmer. Falling. Falling. Falling.

Sometime later it seemed that he was drifting. Just drifting in space, and then he seemed to be drifting upwards. Far away a familiar kindly voice said the same words over and over: "Place, pressure, release. . . . Place, pressure, release." If he could only move. If he could move only so much as a finger. He tried again, thinking hard about it. His finger twitched, and then he knew someone had spoken his name.

David smiled, and somehow he knew that everything was all right now. He could tell just by the sound of Ben's voice that Little Red was all right, too.

A Tapestry of Dreams

I have met people from many lands who became American citizens. As I learned to know them, I realized that the notion of a "melting pot" was an inaccurate figure of speech to use for our country. We are not a mess of people boiled down to the lowest common denominator. Our unique strength lies in our diversities. We are like a tapestry, made up of many threads, some sturdy, some gay, some long, some short, all woven into one fabric by our shared dream of freedom.

CLARA INGRAM JUDSON

   From *The Lost Violin* by Clara Ingram Judson. Copyright 1947 by Follett Publishing Company.

DREAM OF FREEDOM

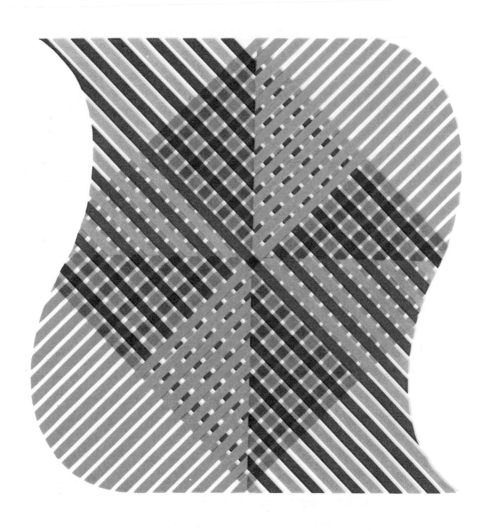

The Captive

by ELIZABETH YATES

The captives were led through the jungle from early dawn until noon, when they reached the bank of a wide river. There they were given water but no food. Under the ever pointed muskets of their captors, they were allowed a brief rest while canoes were readied for the journey downstream. Loud commands in a tongue meaningless to the black men filled the air. The At-mun-shi people, so tired and hungry that their fright was secondary, squatted on the ground with heads between their knees.

At-mun, young prince of the At-mun-shi, looked from one to another, signaling with his eyes. Through the weary group a quiver of hope ran, uniting them to him.

Adapted from the book *Amos Fortune: Free Man* by Elizabeth Yates. Copyright, 1950, by Elizabeth Yates McGreal. Adapted by permission of E. P. Dutton & Co., Inc.

Whatever they had left behind and whatever lay ahead, their chief's son was with them. They knew that he would care for them.

At-mun realized that he and his people were being enslaved by power and cunning and that they must bide their time. Slavery was a part of tribal war, as old as African life itself, but the At-mun-shi had always been a free people, putting no bonds on others and resisting any put on them. At-mun looked from one face to another. In his heart he was troubled about his people, for something had made them spiritless.

The slavers ate well and drank freely. Then, while the sun was at its highest, pouring fierce heat upon the land, they crept under crude shelters of wide palm leaves and slept. No one took any thought of the At-mun-shi. Under the rain of heat they waited patiently, each one knowing that a rain of fire would be his if he moved. When the sun was westering and a breeze had come up, the captives were loaded into long canoes. They were twenty to a canoe—with a native in the stern to direct the course downstream and a white man in the bow leveling a loaded musket on them.

Chained to each other, the At-mun-shi did little more than crouch in the boats. In the rear canoe At-mun still held his head unbowed. He was determined to watch the course so that if a time came when his people could assert their freedom, he would be able to lead them back to their own village.

The current was swift, and the long, narrow, heavily laden canoes moved down it easily. Now and again the boats passed small clearings where flocks of goats grazed and tribesmen watched their animals with more interest than they did the canoes going down the river.

The sun, though it had dropped far down the sky, still had the heat of the day, and the forest blazed and quivered with its beams. All along the way the land cried out the year's new growth. As the afternoon wore on, there were more and more places where the land had been subdued. Stone encampments instead of rude huts could be seen on the hilltops.

At-mun saw it all. It was to him as if he had reached the world's horizon and stepped across it, so different was it from the world he had known—one small village hemmed around by the dense growth of the jungle. Hunger gnawed at him, weariness weighted his limbs, and a seam made by a lash on his back ached in the blaze of the sun. But more than all that, he felt something expanding within him—a strange feeling that rose to meet the new world his eyes were absorbing. He who had known nothing but the jungle for the fifteen years of his life now found wonder that there was a world beyond.

Night came, and the captives slept. The white man in the bow propped his musket between his knees and leaned his head forward. The steersman shifted less and less often.

At-mun knew his own strength. He knew that he could break the bamboo withes that bound his wrists. He knew that he could kill with his hands, and he clenched them together. He was the only man awake in the canoe, but his people would waken at a word, and they would do his bidding, since he was their prince. The other canoes were lost in the darkness. Lifting his head to the sky patterned with stars, At-mun prayed to the God of Life—and the voice of the land gave answer, sighing through the tall trees, echoing in bending fern and willowy reed. This was the time of birth, the time of renewal. This was not the time of death. At-mun leaned his head forward on his knees and slept.

Three hours after dawn the canoes reached a place where the river emptied into the sea. Far out on the throbbing water the At-mun-shi saw a ship with furled sails, riding at anchor. To them it was a great bird sent for their deliverance, and in his heart each one hailed it. The canoes were beached, and the captives were driven into a line on the shore. Some of the captors waved whips; others brandished guns as they drove the At-mun-shi to the pits.

The pits were a series of holes ten feet deep in the ground, and the captives were herded into them. Coconuts were split open and tossed into the pits, and the people, now almost crazed with hunger, grabbed at them. Loaves of coarse bread followed the coconuts, and goatskins of water. The captors then laid a rough matting over each pit, rolling heavy stones to the edge to hold the matting in place. Shade from the sun was provided, but such covering offered small protection from the rain. Once a day the matting was drawn away, and food was tossed into the pits. And for three weeks the At-mun-shi waited.

They did not wait alone. From time to time, as more raids were made into the interior, more captives were

brought back and thrown into the pits. Some were from tribes the At-mun-shi had known as friendly neighbors. Others were ones against whom they had often defended themselves. Still others were unknown. Now the captives had neither hate nor friendship in common, only an instinct to survive, though for what end no one knew.

At-mun tried to hold together those of his people with him in the pit. But as the days passed, they seemed less and less able to respond to him. The time came when the eyes looking into his had no recognition in their glance.

When the pits were full, the *White Falcon*, riding at anchor, was impatient to set sail. Her small boats had been going back and forth to the mainland for foodstuffs and stores—corn, beans and yams, fruit, coconuts, medicinal herbs, and vinegar in hogsheads. Once the stores were full, the master was ready to come ashore to do his business with the white traders. He would soon exchange his cargo of molasses and rum, tobacco and gunpowder for a cargo of slaves. But only the healthiest and largest, the youngest and ablest of all those gathered in the pits would interest him.

The captives were brought up from the pits and fastened together by twos, at ankles and wrists. They were washed and fed well; then they were shaved and their bodies oiled. They stood in a long, patient row, like animals trained at last to obey commands. The traders were pleased at what the time and treatment in the pits had done. The African tribesmen and women were now what their captors wanted them to be—merchandise that could be exchanged for merchandise.

The traders went up and down the line surveying their property.

"That tall fellow there," one said, "should be good for a barrel of rum, no less, or twenty pounds sterling."

"He'd go for more if he wouldn't hold his head up the way he does," another trader answered.

"What the pits didn't do for him the ship will," the first man replied. "He won't be holding his head up when he steps ashore at—where's the *Falcon* from?"

"Boston, but she's going to drop her cargo all along the Atlantic coast. They're needing labor at so many places that she's making half a dozen calls."

A small boat put off from the *White Falcon*, and soon the master arrived. Together with the traders he went up and down the line carefully inspecting the captives.

No one under four feet could meet with approval, and no one over twenty-five years.

When the papers were signed, three hundred and forty-five Africans who had been bought and paid for were conveyed to the ship and stowed in the hold. The head room was so low that they had to stoop to enter. The body room was so narrow that they had to lie spoon fashion, men on one side of the ship, women on the other. Wrists and ankles still chained, they would be given no food until morning. That was part of the discipline of the ship, the mate barked at them, no food unless they behaved. And if they didn't behave, then no food and the lash. But the waves slapping against the ship had more meaning than the words shouted through the hatch.

At-mun drew himself up to a sitting position and looked out through a small air chink. The sun was setting. Long lines of light across the water made the distant shore gleam. Mangroves fringed the tawny beaches, and cormorants skimmed over the waves. That was his land, At-mun thought; there he had been born and nursed and grown to manhood. Where this great bird would bear him he did not know. He only knew that he looked upon his land for the last time.

All night long, after the ship had unfurled her sails and caught the wind that would bear her on her course, At-mun stayed awake. He compelled himself to remember as far back in the past as he could that he might have something more than his body to carry into the future.

The Middle Passage from Africa to America took two months—two months of fair weather, of storms, of calm, of blistering heat, of cold that came out of the teeth of the wind. Once a day the Africans were brought up on deck for an hour. In such freedom as their shackles permitted, they were allowed to move about while their quarters were washed with vinegar. Then the hose was turned on them, and the salt water stung their naked bodies. They were fed their meager rations and sent down again.

At-mun found that as the days and weeks went by he could recall less and less of his early life.

The *White Falcon* made her first stop at the Carolinas, selling a third of her cargo. Her master was satisfied with the crossing. Of the three hundred and forty-five he had started out with, he still had more than three hundred. Disease had not spread among his cargo as it often did on a slave ship, and though some of the captives had died and a few had thrown themselves overboard, a captain expected such things. Impatiently he moved off a hundred men and women, those most in need of leaving the ship. Bathed, oiled, and clothed enough for decency, they made a good showing as they stood on the wharf at Charleston. Then he waited for a high tide and his fee. Fifteen pounds sterling he was asking for every person put ashore, though many of them would bring more when put up on the auction block, and well he knew that some of them would never reach it.

The *White Falcon* sailed slowly up the coast, putting in at different ports. On the first Sunday in July of the year 1725, the ship approached her home port of Boston. The master gave orders to furl sail and ride at anchor outside the harbor until the next morning. More than one vessel

had been forced to go elsewhere because her master had tried to land her cargo on a Sunday.

When the ship drew up to her wharf on Monday morning, twenty persons—all that remained of her human cargo—were brought up on deck. These were the strongest—least impaired by the voyage and best able to stand the rugged New England climate. At-mun was among them. Not one of the others was of the At-mun-shi. Where his people were now, At-mun did not know.

The gestures, not the words, of the mate made the Africans understand that they were to walk down the gangplank to the wharf. They moved slowly because of chains. A crowd of people, men for the most part, had already gathered near the auction block. At-mun was hailed by the auctioneer, and his chains were removed. For the first time in more than four months he could walk freely. He mounted the block. Above him gulls were dipping and soaring, coming to rest in the tall masts of the *White Falcon*, filling the air with their cries. At-mun kept his eyes on them.

"Here's a fine specimen from the Gold Coast," the auctioneer began. "Well-limbed, not much more than a boy, capable of years of hard work, lusty, strong, sound in health."

A voice shouted out from the crowd.

The auctioneer cupped his ear to hear better. "Defects? Why, none at all. Can't you see for yourself?"

Then he consulted a paper the mate had given him describing the *Falcon*'s merchandise. "Wait a moment, now. It says here that this one can't talk. Is that so?" He peered at At-mun and barked, "Come on, now. Let's hear you say something."

At-mun continued to watch the gulls.

A man dressed in gray and wearing a broad-brimmed hat stepped forward. The man went to the block and looked up at At-mun. "What is your name?" he asked.

At-mun had never heard anything come from a white man's lips but commands, curses, threats, none of which he understood. He brought his gaze from the gulls to the face of the man addressing him, for the words just spoken were different in tone. At-mun did not understand their meaning, but he understood the look in the man's eyes. He had never answered a white man. He had vowed to himself that he never would. But his lips opened, and the word that came through them was "At-mun."

The man in gray turned to the auctioneer. "Friend, will thee take thirty pounds sterling and do no bidding on this man?"

The auctioneer thought for a moment, realizing that he was being offered almost twice what he had hoped to get.

"He's yours," he said.

The money was paid. At-mun was led from the block.

"He looks an intelligent lad," the purchaser commented.

The auctioneer did not answer until he had pocketed his money. "That will wear away soon enough," he said. "Give him plenty of hard work, and you'll soon have him in the shape you want him."

"At-mun," the slave said again, wanting to add that he was a prince. But the words had gone from him. His own name and the dwindling dust of a few memories were all that he had brought with him from his homeland.

"Call him Amos," the auctioneer laughed harshly. "That's a good Christian name for a heathen." He turned and gestured to the next to mount the block.

"Come, friend," the Quaker beckoned, and the gesture was understood by At-mun.

"At-mun——" No more words came from his lips.

"Amos, now," the Quaker said and started away.

So Caleb Copeland, who had gone to the wharf not to buy a slave but to deliver a load of cloth he had woven, left the wharf with a slave and nothing in his pocket from the sale of his cloth. And At-mun, who had lost a heritage, had at least found a friend.

The African in this story was a real person, whose life story is told in the book Amos Fortune: Free Man. *Eventually Amos worked out his freedom and was able to buy the freedom of others.*

When Elizabeth Yates accepted the Newbery Award for her book in 1951, she said: "In a world such as ours today . . . it is good to be reminded of a life such as Amos Fortune's. He lived the only force that is greater than any bomb: simple affection, deep-hearted love. . . . All that he stood for in his day is vital to ours: those 'inalienable rights' whose achievement is part of the long mountain we all are climbing as we emerge from our various forms of slavery into the fullness of freedom."

Quotation from *The Horn Book* Magazine, July-August 1951. Reprinted by permission of The Horn Book, Inc., Boston.

Off for America

by POLLY ANGELL

"Up, Danny Mulvaney! Will ye sleep all day? The sun is high, and your brother Pat's already out and about."

"I be not hungry when I sleep," murmured Danny to his mother.

"Dreams put no food inside ye. Up now, laddie!"

Danny rolled out of bed and went into the next room, where a rough table stood near the fireplace. In a corner of the room his grandmother was spinning.

His mother gave him a mug of thin oatmeal, and Danny took a swallow. It wasn't much of a breakfast, but it was warm, and it felt good in his empty stomach. As Danny lifted his mug for another sip, a whining sound came from outside the door. He glanced carefully around. His mother had gone to waken his little sister, and his grandmother's eyes were fixed on her spinning. Taking his mug and a saucer, he let himself softly out of the door.

There lay a collie, a heap of skin and bones, barely able to wag his tail. Kneeling beside the dog, the boy poured the rest of his scanty breakfast into the saucer. Greedily the collie lapped it up. Then he turned his sad eyes up to Danny and licked his face.

At that moment Danny's grandfather came hobbling around the corner of the house.

"What's this that the dog be thanking ye for?" he asked.

Then the old man saw the saucer and the empty mug. Taking Danny by the ear and pulling him to his feet, he said, "With all of us starving, ye must feed the dog!"

He opened the door of the sod house and pushed the boy into the room with such force that he landed against the table. Danny's mother looked up in surprise, for Danny and his grandfather were great friends.

"It's giving his food to the dog, he is," said the grandfather. "He do be needing to have some sense knocked into him."

"I'll not let Trigger starve to death," Danny answered.

"Don't be giving food to the dog that yourself is sorely in need of," said his mother. "Let him catch rabbits."

"He hasn't the life left in him to catch a rabbit."

"Then catch one for him yourself!"

Danny's face brightened. "I'll set a snare," he said, and hurried out to the shed.

But Danny did not set his snare that day. As he came out of the shed, carrying the noose of rabbit wire, he heard a shout from the potato patch. Turning, he saw his brother Pat running toward him with hands held high above his head.

"Potatoes!" shouted Pat. "Potatoes, by the powers!"

Together the boys ran into the house with the news.

"Potatoes!" shouted Pat again, holding out his hands and proudly displaying a few small potatoes. "I dug down just to see how they were growing. Looks like the finest crop we ever had."

"The Lord be praised," said his mother, wiping her eyes. "Our year of hunger is over."

Pat laid the potatoes on the table, and his grandfather picked them up one by one. His eyes shone as if each potato were a lump of pure gold.

To most Irish farmers in the 1840's potatoes were, indeed, as good as gold. No other vegetables were raised —no onions, no carrots, no cabbages. Just potatoes. When the potato crop failed, the farmers went hungry.

Not only that—the farmers' pigs lived on potatoes, too, and it was the sale of pigs to the English that brought in money to pay the rent. So—no potatoes, no pigs. No pigs, no rent. When the potato crop failed, many a poor farmer was turned out of his sod house and forced to take to the road with his wife and children and beg for food.

"They be darling potatoes," said the grandfather, sweeping them carefully into a heap in the middle of the table. "Me heart lightens till it's like to burst from me chest. 'Tis the beginning of better days."

"Be not too hasty to rejoice," said the grandmother, raising her voice above the whir of the spinning wheel. " 'Twas just this time last year that the blight came and rotted the crop."

A silence fell on the room at memory of the blight. Then Pat spoke up triumphantly, "Have ye forgot the day it is? This be the Eve of St. John, when fire fights evil and destroys it. We'll ring the potato patch with fire."

So at sunset the members of the family made a bonfire. When it had burned down to coals, they spread the red embers around the edges of the potato patch. All night they fed the little fires so that no evil spirit would dare to pass through the fiery ring.

At dawn they tumbled into bed and slept until noon. Then Pat dug a few more potatoes to celebrate the Feast of St. John. The family dipped the boiled potatoes in salt and once more enjoyed the taste of their favorite food.

That night the weather turned hot and close. Pat tossed restlessly from side to side. Presently a crash of thunder brought him bolt upright. He heard the rain falling in a torrent. With the rain came a breath of cooler air. Pat sank back with relief and closed his eyes.

But even as he did so, a terrible fear struck him and he jumped from his bed. Last year the potato blight had started with just such weather. Was it coming again?

The world next morning was bright with sunshine, and the garden steamed under the heat. Bent double, Pat ran between the rows sniffing like a dog for the sickly smell that was the first sign of the blight. But there was no telltale smell in the potato patch, and everyone rejoiced.

111

Then came another rain, followed by a day of heat with the air hanging heavy and still. That day the blight struck. Woolly gray patches on the leaves of the plants spread rapidly through the stems to the potatoes. By morning the whole crop was an evil-smelling mess.

Old Mr. Mulvaney crawled into bed and wouldn't speak to anyone all day.

"Your grandfather has given up, Pat," said his mother at last. "You must be our man."

Pat, too, was stunned. He had spoken no word since the disaster, but now his mother's need for him stung his mind to action.

"I'll apply for a job on the Relief Works," he said.

The relief office had been set up in the village inn just after Christmas. Here the Government provided jobs for men who had no food and no money to buy any. Pat took his place at the end of the line of waiting men and looked about him. So much depended on his getting a job that he felt weak and was trembling inside. When his turn came, however, he stepped forward firmly.

"Your name?" asked the government official.

"Patrick Mulvaney."

"Age?"

"Sixteen."

"How many in your family?"

"We be six. Me grandparents, me mother, and me brother and sister, who are younger."

The government official turned to the village magistrate sitting beside him.

"Have the Mulvaneys any land?"

The magistrate looked down a list. "They rent half an acre," he said.

"Have they any cattle?"

"Six pigs, a dozen sheep, and a cow."

"Your Honor," said Pat, " 'tis an old list ye have there, surely. Last October it was, we had six pigs, twelve sheep, and a cow. In that very month we sold all but two pigs and the cow in order to pay the rent."

"So now you have a cow and two pigs," said the official. "You are better off than many of your neighbors and do not need help. Next!"

"But your Honor," Pat cried out desperately, "the landlord took the cow and the pigs for the rent we owed since last October. In May it was, and now we have no cattle at all."

"That's true," said the magistrate, who had been fumbling among his papers. "They have no cattle, and this lad is carrying the weight of a family on his shoulders."

The official hesitated a moment and then handed Pat a work ticket. As soon as Pat stepped outside the inn he realized how lucky he had been. The blight had struck every potato patch in the valley, and a mob of men was struggling to get into the relief office. There were jobs for only a handful, and the police were doing their best to drive the desperate men away.

Pat made his way around the crowd and started along the road toward home. Women and children were standing around their doorways waiting for their men to come back from the relief office. The sight left no room for joy in Pat. He felt only a deep thankfulness.

In the gathering dusk he saw a man with a pick and shovel trudging along ahead of him. He realized it must be Barney Finnegan, a neighbor. Barney was the only man along the road who already had a job on the Relief Works.

Pat quickened his steps.

"Barney," he said, as he caught up with the man, " 'tis meself will be going with ye to the job hereafter."

"Chosen from amongst all the poor souls that be mobbing the office?" Barney looked up with surprise and pleasure. "A miracle, by the powers! And miracles we all have need of."

Pat went to work with a gang that was building a road up the steep side of the mountain. On his grandfather's small patch of land Pat had done plenty of hard work, but never for hours and hours at the same thing. By the end of the first day his hands were raw and sore. He tied rags around them and kept at the work day after day until at last his hands were calloused and hard.

With his first week's wages in his pocket, he went to the store to buy food.

"A side of bacon, a bag of sweet crackers, and a stone of oatmeal," he said. A stone weighed fourteen pounds and would be enough to last for a week even though the family ate almost nothing else.

"How much money have ye got?" the storekeeper asked.

Pat spread his week's wages on the counter.

The man counted the coins and shrugged. "There's not enough for what ye want."

"How much for the oatmeal?" asked Pat, thinking the storekeeper might be trying to cheat him.

"Close to three fourths of all the money ye have there."

"Give me the oatmeal, then," said Pat, "and for the rest, as much bacon as it will pay for."

"Next time," said Pat, when he set the packages before his mother, "I will get some salt fish for a change."

But when the next payday came, the men were told that the money hadn't been received from the Government and they would have to wait another week for their wages.

Pat went to the storekeeper and asked for credit.

"The money is coming to me from the Government, so ye can rest easy," he said.

"I very much doubt that ye will get the money," said the storekeeper. "I hear the government funds are giving out. It's not myself can afford to give charity."

Barney came into the store in time to hear the storekeeper's words.

" 'Tis not charity the lad do be asking," he said. "I'll complain to the Relief Committee."

"Oh, to be sure," said the storekeeper, "if the Committee has the money, there will be no difficulty."

But the Committee had no money, and Pat got no credit. He went to work Monday morning aching with hunger. He was determined to stick it out, however, in the hope that the storekeeper was wrong and that he would get his wages at the end of the week. He did, but this time he was very careful how he spent his money and gave the storekeeper only half of it. The rest he took home to his grandfather, who put it away in his moneybag.

"I will save some every week," said Pat. "If the work stops, as the storekeeper says it will, at least we'll have a bit of a nest egg."

As it turned out, the nest egg did not go for food. On Sunday evening, as the family sat in the dooryard, Barney Finnegan came leaping over the fence.

"I've a letter from me cousin in America!" he shouted, his voice shaking with excitement. "Listen now to what he says. He has meat to eat every day in the week and white bread, too, and him only a workingman. But in America wages are high, says he. He gets seventy-five cents a day, which is almost five times what we're getting here." Barney jumped up and kicked his heels in the air. "As soon as I can save money, it's off for America!"

"Fine for yourself, Barney," said Pat's grandfather. "But what about your wife and the little ones ye'll be leaving behind?"

"On seventy-five cents a day," said Barney, "I can send 'em more than I could give 'em by staying here. Better than that, I can save enough to bring 'em all to America—and that is what I'm going to do."

Pat was dazzled by his friend's plan—dazzled, but a little frightened, too, when he thought about it for himself. To go so far away that there was never a chance to come home again, to leave his family, maybe forever! Who knew how things would go with a man in a strange country?

All night he turned the matter over in his mind. Even when he fell asleep, he dreamed about America and the money to be made there. In his dream his family was with him, and they all had plenty to eat.

Pat said nothing to his mother or to Danny, but all next day he thought about going to America. That night he talked with his mother and his grandfather about it.

" 'Twould tear the heart out of me to lose ye," said his mother, "and ye my oldest son."

"It would not be for long," said Pat wistfully.

"Who knows, now, if ye would reach America at all? The voyage is long and rough, and many a good ship has gone down with all souls on board." Mrs. Mulvaney wiped tears from her eyes.

"There is no need to take your life in your hands," said the grandfather. "We can live through the winter on the wages ye get and lay something by as well."

"And if the Government stops the Relief Works?"

"We'll go across that bridge when we come to it," said the old man firmly.

In October Pat's wages were held up again, and this time it was not for one week only but for two. Worse yet, at the end of the second week, the men were told what they had been fearing to hear—the government funds had given out. There would be no more work.

"We'll be getting our wages for the weeks we have worked?" asked Barney.

"All in good time," said the overseer.

And with this promise the men left, seeing nothing ahead but disaster. All except Barney. As he and Pat walked home together, Barney said, "By the powers, I can make it to America! There's enough now in the bag for me passage and some to spare."

"I'm minded to go with ye," said Pat. "Will ye come and talk to Grandfather and my mother?"

"I will that," said Barney.

It was not easy for Pat's mother to set aside her fears, but at last she agreed. And the grandfather, shaking his head sadly, decided that since there was no work for Pat in Ireland, America was the only hope.

The money in the leather bag was counted. There were only eleven shillings, and Pat would need twelve for his passage.

"He'll be needing something for food as well," said Barney Finnegan. "Me cousin warned me. Not a bit will ye get on the long voyage unless ye pay well for it."

Pat's grandfather frowned. "Nor should the lad go to a strange land with empty pockets," he said.

"I've two weeks wages coming to me," said Pat.

"Ye cannot wait for that, me lad," said Barney. "There's a ship sailing the end of the week. With winter coming on there'll not be many boats, nor so good a chance to get a job when we land. We should leave now."

The family sat for a moment in gloomy silence. Then Pat's mother struck her hand against her forehead.

"It's a dumb woman I am, for sure," she murmured.

Quickly she went into the bedroom and came back with a fiddle that had belonged to her husband.

"The innkeeper has long been wanting this fiddle," she said. "I'll sell it to him tomorrow." She laid her hand on Pat's shoulder. "The money, my son, will be your father's blessing on your journey."

The innkeeper paid a good price for the fiddle.

"I'll take no more than my share," said Pat, and he spread the shillings on the table and divided them into six piles.

"Be not so foolish," said his mother. "Our hearts are full of fear for ye already."

"Mind ye now," said his grandfather, "that we have a roof over our heads, and ye have not. So the dividing was not fair and even."

He took a coin from each of the five piles and added them to Pat's. Then he swept the rest into his pouch.

"We will have, besides, the wages that's coming to ye," he said. "So let your heart be easy. We will not starve."

"I'll be sending for all of ye, anyways," said Pat.

"Not for me, lad," said his grandmother. "I'd not be satisfied outside of Ireland, where I've lived all the days of me life, and she like a mother to me. Rather would I go hungry than look to a strange land for food."

"She is right," said her husband. "We are old, but the rest of ye are young, and it's in America that ye can grow and flourish."

The old man went outside and cut a bit of sod from beside the door.

"Treasure it well," he said as he wrapped it in a bit of cloth and handed it to Pat. " 'Tis a bit of the old sod that will bring ye luck and keep the memory of Ireland in your heart."

The sun was an hour high when Pat put his father's shillelagh over his shoulder and set off on the long walk to Cork harbor. Tied to the stout club were a small bundle of clothes and a much larger bundle, which held a quilt. Around Pat's neck a cord held his moneybag, and in his pocket was a small package of oatmeal cakes, which his grandmother had baked for him.

Danny, with Trigger at his heels, walked with his brother as far as Barney's cottage.

"It's a man ye must be now," said Pat.

"Will it be long before ye send for us?"

"It may be long," said Pat, "but keep a stout heart, for send for ye I will."

Barney was waiting, his wife and children huddled by his side. The little ones began to cry, but Barney stopped them, and his words were a comfort to Pat and Danny, too. "None of that, now," said Barney. "I be going after riches that will give us a fine life. So dry your eyes and think on what's to come."

A Pocketful of America

by WALTER AND MARION HAVIGHURST

At the close of a winter day more than a hundred years ago in a steep Norwegian valley, candle lights began to twinkle in the clustered houses of Nordal village. With the darkness came a cold wind and a swirl of snow. The mountains stood up huge and ghostly. At their base the water of the fiord made a blackness where the streets of Nordal ended.

Down the road from Nordmore Mountain plodded a solitary boy. He was muffled in a wool cap and a heavy coat and carried a burden slung in a snow-covered sack across one shoulder. Passing through the village streets, he trudged across the empty market square toward the lighted windows of Nordal tavern. The tavern door swung open. There was a hearty sound of voices and a glimpse of fire blazing on the broad hearth. The boy went on. He turned the corner, tramped through soft snow at the side of the tavern, and stopped at the kitchen door. His mittened hand pounded on the heavy wood.

The door opened, revealing a cook. A ruddy light fell on the snowy figure of the boy.

"What's this?" the cook cried, rubbing his hands on his long white apron. "I thought it was the fish peddler, and here it is a tramp." The cook looked more sharply at the boy, and his voice changed. "Come in, lad. It's no night to be standing in the cold."

Beside the leaping fire, where the blackened kettles hung, the boy let down the burden from his shoulder.

The adaptation of the chapter "Any Knives to Grind?" from *Song of the Pines* by Walter and Marion Havighurst has been made by the permission of the publishers, Holt, Rinehart and Winston, Inc. Copyright of *Song of the Pines* 1949 by Walter and Marion Havighurst.

He opened the tow sack and lifted out the solid disk of a
grindstone set in a short-legged wooden frame. He took
the snowy cap from his head. Snowflakes hissed on the
hearthstone, and the boy's fair hair fell over his ears.
He spoke to the cook in the brisk voice of business.

"Any knives to grind?"

"Why—you're the lad that came here with his father,"
said the cook, rubbing his apron again. "You were here
last winter. You've grown, but I remember you."

"I am Nils Thorson," the boy said.

"And where is your father? We never had such sharp
knives as he left behind him. Where is he now, boy?"

"My father was drowned last summer."

"Drowned?" The cook's voice changed. "That is bad." He shook his head, and behind him his shadow wagged slowly on the wall. "He was a good man, your father. A good knife grinder and a good man."

"He went fishing with my uncle. They were caught in a storm, and the boat was pounded on the rocks. My uncle got ashore, but my father was drowned."

Nils spoke quietly, but the terrible pictures passed vividly through his mind—his uncle staggering up the rocks half dead with fear and exhaustion, the search for his father's body in the seething tide, and the sea scourging the rocks below.

"So I took my father's grindstone, and I go from town to town." He looked up. "Few remember my father, as you did, but they give me knives or scissors to grind."

"Lad, how old are you?" the cook asked.

The boy's face lighted. "I'm fifteen today."

"Where have you come from?"

"Today? From Elvedalen, over the mountain."

The cook shook his head again. "Over the mountain, in wild winter weather. Tramping the roads like a homeless old man. Why didn't you stay with your uncle?"

"He asked me to stay, but his cottage is already full, with five children." Nils' thin shoulders stiffened. "A boy my age can make his way in the world, especially if he knows a trade. My father taught me well."

"Where do you go from here?" the cook asked.

"I go to Eidfjord and the towns in the valley."

In the blazing fire a kettle boiled over. The cook swung it out of the flames and stirred it with a long iron spoon.

Nils found a knife on the carving block. He bent over his grindstone and pressed the blade to the whirling disk. The cook took off his apron and carried platters of meat, pans of browned potatoes, and bowls of steaming pudding in to the long table in the dining room.

When Nils had sharpened all the knives he could find, the cook pushed a chair to the serving counter. "Come now and have your birthday supper; eat all you can hold."

Nils began on a big bowl of bean soup.

"There's a man in there," the cook jerked his thumb toward the dining room, "who just walked in from over the mountain, as you did. I would not suppose there were two people tramping the roads in this weather. He ate three slices of roast veal and a whole mackerel. See if you can beat that."

After the soup Nils made away with a heaping plate of roast veal and dressing and a huge white mound of potatoes with brown gravy. He finished the meal with a rich rice pudding flecked with raisins, a slice of cinnamon cake, and a mug of sweetened tea. The cold had left him now. His cheeks were flushed in the ruddy friendliness of the fire. His mouth opened in a huge, slow yawn.

"Sleepy?" said the cook. "Well, you ought to be after the walk you've had today. Curl up on the floor there by the fire and go to sleep."

Nils was half asleep when he became aware of an excited buzz of voices in the next room. Then he began to hear one quick, ardent voice above the others.

He yawned again, but his curiosity was stronger than his sleepiness. He crossed the kitchen and pushed open the door into the tavern room. The leaping firelight showed him a circle of listeners around a little man pacing restlessly in their midst. The man had quick blue eyes that seemed to catch the firelight, and around them were fine lines of sun squint—the eyes of a sailor or a traveler in wide, bright places.

Fascinated, Nils sank down on the floor, wedging the door open with his shoulder. The little man was talking about the distant country of America, its forests and prairies and rivers. He used strange names—Illinois, Wisconsin, the Mississippi. He told about unfenced land, whole empires of it, deep and fertile, waiting for settlement. His hands went out to describe wide horizons, and his voice grew soft and full of wonder.

While he talked, the circle of men in the dim tavern room forgot everything but the picture he painted in their minds. They forgot the snow deepening on the mountain roads of Norway, the long winter, and the rockslide that had ruined their best fields. They forgot the mountain edges where they carefully gathered little tufts of grass for hay and the rough hillsides where they tried to raise potatoes among the stubborn stones. Even the plump tavern keeper leaned on the counter with a happy smile on his round face and distance in his eyes.

The little man stopped in the midst of his story. "A cup of tea, please, with some sweetening in it."

The cook left the ale counter and hurried toward the kitchen door. Nils got up.

"So you're awake, lad," said the cook, "and listening. There's a man worth harking to."

"Who is he?" Nils asked. "Where does he come from?"

"Cleng Peerson, the first Norwegian who ever went to America, that's who he is. He has guided Norwegians to fine settlements in America, and now he is back again to tell about that country. They say he has a magnet in his pocket that draws people after him."

Nils edged into the tavern room and sat down against the shadowed wall.

"Listen," Cleng Peerson was saying, "I'll tell you the dream I had alone one night on the empty prairie, a day's walk from where the new city of Chicago stands."

For a moment Cleng's eyes caught the face of the boy crouching in the shadows beside the kitchen door. Nils felt his heart pounding inside his jacket as the man talked.

Cleng told how he had walked day after day on the shores of the great Lake Michigan and across the level grasslands where no settlement had come. At last the food in his sack was gone, and he grew weak from fatigue and hunger. In that weariness, at the end of a burning summer day, he fell asleep and dreamed of the broad prairie and the arching sky. He saw fine fields of corn and wheat and barley and fenced pastures dotted with fat cattle. He saw scattered farmhouses, each with its own garden. In the center of the prairie rose a steepled church.

The little man became silent. Cleng Peerson walked around the circle of his listeners, artful as an actor. He stopped, looking over the villagers' heads as if at the sunrise. "When I woke," he continued, "it was morning, and a golden light slanted over the plain. I loosed my knife from my belt." He held up the knife for them to see. The steel glinted in the firelight, and Nils Thorson, crouching in the shadows, saw that it could stand a sharpening. "I took my knife," Cleng Peerson repeated, "and dug into the prairie to see what kind of soil I had been dreaming on. Beneath the grass roots the earth was black and fine as gunpowder." His hand dived into a sagging pocket and came up with a fistful of crumbling soil. "Here—I brought back a pocketful of America. That soil is soft as flour and deep, deep."

The villagers crowded round to see. Little Cleng Peerson had to hop on the bench before the glowing fire.

There he held America cupped in his two hands, and the farmers and fishermen peered at it and studied it and tested it in their fingers as if it were gold-bearing sand.

"My dream," said the little man, "is already coming true. A hundred Norwegian families are settled now on that prairie, and others will soon be on their way." He went on to tell what a man could expect in America. Bread and pork and milk always on the table. A farm of two hundred acres of timberland—two hundred, mind you—and all that land to be had for the taking. You could pay your dollar an acre after the harvests were gathered. And in America the poorest man was as good as any other, and he needn't stay poor a season longer than he wanted to.

From the circle of listeners a deep voice spoke. "How can you get there?"

"A barque, the *Nordland,* is now in Stavanger harbor," Cleng Peerson said. "It will be sailing for New York before the month is out. It has room for more passengers."

Another listener spoke. "Will you spend the night at my house and tomorrow tell this to my brother?"

"Yes," Cleng Peerson said. "I will tell it to anybody— even the King of Norway if he would listen."

Soon everyone was gone, and the tavern grew quiet. The cook, wheezing as he put a night log on the hearth, looked startled when Nils got up from the floor.

"Ah, lad," he said, "I'd forgotten you, thinking about Cleng Peerson and his dream, though I'm too old to think about a country on the other side of nowhere." He yawned. "Too bad that talking woke you up. We haven't had so much talk in this village all winter." He yawned again. "You can sleep right here by the fire."

Lying there in the warm glow of the fire, Nils was wide awake. He thought of Cleng Peerson dreaming on a moonlit prairie in America. He thought about his birthday a year ago—tramping with his father in Romsdal province. That night his father had given him a birthday present, a clasp knife with a bright steel blade. There had been no birthday gift today. Nils moved, and his jacket seemed to bunch under his shoulder. He reached up to smooth it, and his fingers closed on something soft and dry. Then he was sitting up in the firelight, bending over the crumbled earth that Cleng Peerson had dropped on the floor. It came to him suddenly, with a pounding of his heart—here was his birthday present, a handful of America.

He put some earth in his pocket and lay down again. Soon he was asleep. He dreamed of a broad, sunlit land. In the dream a little man with sun-bleached hair came walking through the grasslands, and Nils was at his side.

A week later a boy with a grindstone slung over his shoulder tramped along the jetties in the port of Stavanger. Spring had come, and Stavanger was thronged with vessels bringing the winter catch of fish, fur, and feathers from the northern islands. Above the bay the mountains glittered white, but in the city streets the snow was disappearing. Across the market square ran countless little streams of snow water. Blue sky arched over the harbor, and gulls wheeled white in the sun.

From wharf to wharf Nils went, always asking the same question. "Is there a vessel here bound for America?" At last he stood beside a tall-masted ship with barrels and boxes disappearing in an open hatchway and sailors sewing canvas in the sun.

"Yes," said a young ship's officer at the rail, "this is the barque *Nordland,* bound for New York and sailing at daybreak tomorrow."

"Then I got here in time," Nils said.

"In time for what?" the sailor asked sharply.

Nils hitched up the grindstone on his shoulder. "In time to see if you have knives to grind."

"Well," the young sailor said, "you'll find the crew on deck. To start a voyage they ought to have sharp knives."

Nils walked up the gangway and went across the deck to where the sailors were sewing canvas. He put his grindstone down. "Any knives to sharpen?"

"Sure, lad. Right over here."

They were glad to have a fresh blade put on the knives they used so often in their work with rope and sail gear. While he whetted the blades, Nils carefully studied the ship, observing all the hatches, the crew's quarters, the sail lockers, the cook's galley halfway down the deck.

When he had whetted all the sailors' knives, he thanked them for the coins they tossed him. Then he carried his grindstone to the galley, and the cook gave him a dozen carving knives to grind. He made a deliberate job of that, so deliberate that it grew dark and time for supper before he had finished. The cook gave Nils a plate of codfish and potatoes. When the meal was finished, Nils thanked him, picked up his grindstone, and went on deck.

The crew had gone ashore for their last evening in port, and their quarters were dark and silent. Nils crouched down on deck and pulled off his shoes. He tossed them in with his grindstone and threw the sack over his back. Crouching in the heavy shadows along the rail, he stole noiselessly over the deck. Carefully he slid back the small hatch cover that opened into a sail locker. He let himself in and sank down on a mound of canvas. Sliding the hatch cover over his head, he listened. There was no sound but the creaking of the mooring lines and the slow drip-drip of snow water from the wharf. Nils curled around his grindstone and went to sleep.

He woke up once, but in that dark hideaway he could not tell whether it was night or morning. A sound of voices came, and footsteps on the deck. He wondered if the singsong voice he heard was that of Cleng Peerson, and in the darkness he felt for the handful of American soil in his pocket. He was successfully stowed away on a ship bound for America, and perhaps Cleng Peerson was aboard. With that happy thought, Nils dropped off to sleep again.

He woke suddenly, aware that a heavy foot was prodding him from his bed of canvas. Above the open hatchway he saw a group of sailors staring at him. As Nils sat up, a young officer and a weathered man in a captain's uniform appeared.

"It's the boy who came aboard to grind knives," the officer said.

132

"Come out of there," ordered the captain.

Nils climbed out. His movements were stiff and slow and his mind was still fuzzy with sleep.

"What are you doing here?" the captain asked.

"I wanted to go to America, sir."

"It costs money to go to America," the captain declared.

"I could work my way, sir," Nils said eagerly. "I would work hard."

"I don't hire stowaways," the captain said. "Put him ashore, Mr. Engstrand."

"Is Cleng Peerson aboard?" asked Nils as a young officer took his arm.

"Cleng Peerson? No, he's off in the mountains."

A minute later Nils was on the wharf. He sat there putting on his shoes, while the sailors hauled at the lines and the big white mainsail inched up the mast. The captain called from the quarterdeck, and the mooring lines were cast off. Slowly the ship slipped into the harbor. It grew smaller and smaller and then passed out of sight around a point of land.

In his pocket Nils' fingers closed on the crumbled soil. The next land the ship would sight would be America.

"Good morning, lad."

Nils looked up at an old white-haired sailor with a band of white whiskers on his chin.

"I saw you put ashore. If you could have stayed under cover an hour longer, they would have had to take you with them."

"I didn't think they'd find me," said Nils.

"Next time," the old man said, "don't hide in a sail locker. They're sure to find you there. Get under a bunk in the passengers' cabin and stay there."

"Are there any other ships going to America?"

The old sailor was whittling a piece of wood. He shook his head. "Not now. Later this season there may be. But at Bergen there's a ship loading iron. She'll be sailing for New York within a week."

"Bergen," Nils said. "How can I get to Bergen?"

"Take the road over the mountain to Olen," the old man said. "Then take the coastal boat to Bergen. It only costs two kroner. Have you got two kroner, lad?"

"Yes," Nils said. He pulled his grindstone out of the tow sack. "Sir," he said, "will you let me grind your knife? I can see it needs a fresh edging."

"So it could," the old man said, smiling. "Things have got dull since I've come ashore."

While Nils was grinding the blade, the old man pointed across the harbor. "That's the way to Olen," he said.

A week later Nils was in the busy port of Bergen, grinding knives for the men and women selling fish in the market place. Day after day he inquired about a boat for America, and at last he found a man who didn't shake his head but pointed into the harbor. "There's the *Lyngen*, loading iron for New York."

The tall-masted vessel lay in the middle of the busy basin, taking on cargo from a clumsy sailing barge. Nils watched all day, wondering how he could get out there and climb aboard the *Lyngen*. Then at evening he saw a cluster of people with trunks and chests around them, watching the *Lyngen* from the jetty. There were men, women, and children; and Nils, mingling with them, heard them talking of America. As they watched, the *Lyngen* raised sail and moved in toward the wharf. It came near, and as the prow swung round parallel with the jetty, the sail began slatting.

From the *Lyngen*'s deck a sailor threw a small line ashore, and a wharfman began hauling a dripping hawser from the water. Then a gust of wind sent the *Lyngen* forward toward a fishing smack moored halfway down the wharf. The *Lyngen*'s captain shouted from the rail.

"Clear the wharf!"

On the smack a boy and girl jumped up from a web of fish nets. Their frightened eyes went up to the big vessel.

It was bearing down upon them. "Cast off the line!" the boy called to the wharfman.

But already his hawser was straining at the mooring timber on the wharf. Two men tugged but could not free it.

"Clear the wharf!" the *Lyngen*'s captain cried again.

But the fishing boat stood motionless at its lines, and the boy and girl were trying to raise the canvas sail. Already the *Lyngen*'s bowsprit was looming above the fishing boat. In another moment the sharp stem of the vessel would crash against the small craft.

In that instant Nils darted forward, his clasp knife in his hand. One slash of the sharp blade was enough. The strands of rope parted with a snapping sound. The small boat lunged forward, with the wind in its sail. The *Lyngen* eased safely alongside the wharf.

A moment later the ship's captain strode across the gangplank and went straight toward Nils.

"That was quick thinking," he said, "and quick work. You must have a sharp blade on your knife."

"Yes, sir," Nils said.

The captain took a leather purse from his pocket. "You saved my ship from damage and from a damage claim by a thoughtless fisherman. There must be something you want. Here's a gold krone to buy it with."

"Sir," said Nils, "there is one thing I want. But a gold krone won't buy it."

"What is it, lad?"

"I want to go to America."

The captain frowned and pulled his dark beard. "You want to go to America. A boy like you—alone?"

"I'm fifteen," Nils said. "I could work my way. I have a grindstone and can sharpen knives. I can fit ax heads. I can mend scissors and umbrellas."

Again the captain rubbed his bearded chin. "We haven't any scissors or umbrellas, and there aren't any extra bunks. Can you sleep on a pile of sailcloth?"

"Yes, sir. I can sleep anywhere."

"Can you climb a mast?"

"I climbed the Maypole at Vadheim to hang the flowers after the wind blew them off."

"Can you hang on to the bobstays in a gale?"

Nils looked puzzled, but his eyes came up squarely. "I can try, sir."

"All right," the captain smiled. "Come aboard. Eight weeks from now you'll be in America."

My Land Is Fair for Any Eyes to See

by JESSE STUART

My land is fair for any eyes to see—
Now look, my friends—look to the east and west!
You see the purple hills far in the west—
Hills lined with pine and gum and black-oak tree—
Now to the east you see the fertile valley!
This land is mine, I sing of it to you—
My land beneath the skies of white and blue.
This land is mine, for I am part of it.
I am the land, for it is part of me—
We are akin and thus our kinship be!
It would make me a brother to the tree!
And far as eyes can see this land is mine.
Not for one foot of it I have a deed—
To own this land I do not need a deed—
They all belong to me—gum, oak, and pine.

From *Man with a Bull-Tongue Plow* by Jesse Stuart. Published by E. P. Dutton & Co., Inc., New York, 1934. By permission of the author.

To Have Nothing at All
by ELIZABETH COATSWORTH

To have nothing at all
Is to have much still:
One's share in the sun,
And the winds that blow,
A right in the road
That swings over the hill,
And the far horizon
That lies below.

To have nothing at all
Does not take from the mind
Its free roving thoughts
Which still know their abode,
Nor the hope that's ahead,
Nor the sorrow behind,
Nor the future that lies
At the turn of the road.

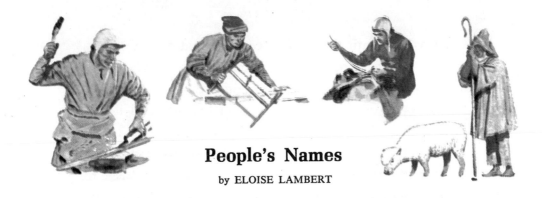

People's Names

by ELOISE LAMBERT

Names were probably among the first words to be used by human beings. Today no one gives much thought to what names mean, but if we trace them to their origins, some of our most common names reveal some amusing and unusual meanings.

While human beings lived in family and tribal groups or in small settlements, everyone had just one name. What the very earliest names were we do not know, but we can guess that in one way or another they all started out as descriptions. Sometimes a person was given a name to describe a physical characteristic that distinguished him from others. We find plenty of examples among common names: Rufus means "red," Bruno means "the brown one," Julia means "having soft hair," and Claude and Claudia mean "the lame one." Sometimes it seems that names were given by comparing an individual to an animal, although it is possible that these names were taken from animals that held places of honor on the tribal totem pole. At any rate, we find that Ursula means "little bear," Deborah is "bee" (so Debbie is "little bee"), and Mona means, at least in Spanish, "monkey."

By permission of Lothrop, Lee & Shepard Co., Inc., from *Our Language* by Eloise Lambert. © 1955 by Lothrop, Lee & Shepard Co., Inc.

It was not until the twelfth century that family names as we know them began to develop, and then they began to be used over most of Europe, including England.

The population of England was increasing, and it was evident that there were just not enough names to go around. There were so many Johns and Elizabeths and Marys and Williams that confusion arose. It is easy to see how awkward it would be if one had to say something like this: "I was talking to John the baker, when John who lives across from the village green came along and said that he had just spoken to John who has the farm below the hill, and that John, the son of David who lives down the long street, would be with us presently."

To put an end to such long explanations, a system of last names, or surnames (as they also are called), was hit upon. John the baker became John Baker; John who lived across from the village green became John Green; John who had the farm below the hill could turn into John Farmer or he might become John Underhill or John Hill; and John, the son of David who lived on the long street, could become either John Davidson or John Longstreet.

Some surnames were given to describe physical characteristics. A man named William, who was very tall, became known as William Long or Longman or Tallman or Longfellow. In the same way people were given surnames like Little, Black, Gray, Fair, or Russell, which is from an Old French word meaning "red-haired." Descriptive names were not always flattering, as we see in the case of Cruikshanks (crooked legs), Calvesnose, and Wrigglenecke, and so some did not survive.

Other surnames might describe a personality trait, like Pleasant, Smiley, Goodman, and Doolittle.

Some surnames were evolved by identifying a person through his trade or profession; here we get such names as Carpenter, Taylor, Shepherd, Miller, Goldsmith, and, of course, Smith, which has become the most common of all English surnames.

Another class of surnames was built up around the place from which a person came. A man moving to a new community from London might be given the last name London; one from Scotland might be called Scott. In this class belong names like French, Welsh, Glasgow, and Frankfurter (from Frankfurt).

Of all different types of surnames, however, perhaps the first to be formed were the ones we call *patronymics,* a word that means "of the father's name." Patronymics came about by distinguishing between a William who was the son of John and another William who was the son of Richard: William John's son and William Richard's son. Later these became William Johnson and William Richardson.

The Scots and Irish formed their patronymics by using the prefix *Mac* or *Mc* (which means "son of" in Celtic) in front of the ancestor's name, giving us MacDonald, McGregor, MacHenry, and MacArthur.

For centuries many of the first names given to children were taken from the Bible. Girls' names like Mary, Elizabeth, Ann, Sarah, Rebecca, and boys' names like David, Joseph, Peter, Paul, and John were used in Europe and brought to this country.

These old traditional names are still popular in the United States today. There are over four million women and girls who have the name Mary and over six million men and boys who are named John. As Americans we must remember that the same names came to our country in many different forms. John has come in the French form Jean, the Spanish Juan, the German Johannes and Hans, the Russian Ivan, the Italian Giovanni, the Welsh Evan, and the Irish Sean or Shawn.

The most common family names in the United States are Smith, Jones, and Brown, and they, too, have come here in foreign dress. For example, Smith is the German Schmidt, the Dutch Smit, the French Ferrier, the Spanish Herrero, the Italian Ferraro, the Hungarian Kovacs, and the Polish Kowalczyk. Many other common surnames also came from foreign countries: Carpenter and the German Zimmerman mean the same thing; so do Baker and the French Boulanger and German Becker.

It is natural for newcomers to our country to be unwilling to change names that they have worn with honor in their native lands. But if the names are long and difficult for American speakers, in the course of time they almost certainly undergo a change of some sort. Either they are translated, and German König becomes King and Czech Vlk becomes Wolf, or they are pronounced as if they were English, and German Köster becomes Custer.

It is fairly safe to say that behind every personal name there is a story or a meaning. For Americans, living in a country that is a melting pot, the stories are probably longer and more involved than for other people.

Whenever I Say "America"

by NANCY BYRD TURNER

Whenever I say "America"
I say so many things!—
Something shouts in the syllables,
Something echoes and sings.
Maybe it's hope, maybe it's pride,
Maybe it's only love,
Maybe it's just a kind of hail
To the flag that flies above,
The flag that flies so broad and bright
From dawn to setting sun,
And takes the wind and takes the light—
The flag our fathers won!

Whenever I say "America"
Old pictures come to me
Of lone prows pushing slowly on
Across a stormy sea;
Of men and women who knew no rest,
Toiling with heart and hand;
Of covered wagons rocking west
Into an unknown land;
Of freemen striving, striving still
In Freedom's old, hard way . . .
Whenever I say "America"
So many things I say!

To the City of Golden Hills

by VANYA OAKES

Hip Wo was alone in the Shop of Ten Thousand Profits. Senior Uncle had stepped out to discuss some matter with Neighbor Chang, leaving Hip Wo to unpack the box of rice bowls that had arrived that morning from Canton. Hip Wo unwrapped another bowl and held it up to see if there were any imperfections. He would have to light the bean-oil lamp; the light was too dim with all but one panel of the folding shop front closed to keep out the damp chill of the Hong Kong winter.

He placed the small lamp on the counter and continued his careful inspection of each bowl. Behind him bowls and plates were stacked on shelves that reached to the ceiling, making a mosaic of the glazed beauty he had come to love in the six months he had served as an apprentice in the Shop of Ten Thousand Profits.

The adaptation of the chapter "Hip Wo Receives Important News" from *Footprints of the Dragon* by Vanya Oakes has been made by the permission of the publishers, Holt, Rinehart and Winston, Inc. Copyright of *Footprints of the Dragon* 1949 by Vanya Oakes.

He had almost finished his scrutiny of the bowls on the counter when a gentleman in a heel-length gown of dark silk stepped across the threshold.

"The owner of the shop, is he here?" asked the man.

For a moment Hip Wo was startled speechless. Why, it was none other than Li Lai-tong, he whose brush was considered to make the finest characters in all of South China. Never did Hip Wo think to see him in the Shop of Ten Thousand Profits.

Hip Wo hastened to extend the customary courtesies to the honored customer. "He who owns the shop, my father's brother, has left for but a moment," he explained. "I am only an apprentice, but if the honorable gentleman will be seated, I will fetch my uncle."

"No need, no need. I will await his return." And so saying, Li Lai-tong seated himself.

Hip Wo hurried to the teapot that always stood waiting beside Senior Uncle's abacus. He started to pour the pale green liquid into a cup, then stopped. No ordinary cup would do for so exalted a customer. He reached beneath the counter for one of the finer lidded tea bowls kept for honored visitors, poured the fragrant tea, and placed it on a table at the elbow of the noted scholar.

"A fine piece of porcelain, this is," commented the visitor, his fingers gently caressing the smooth surface.

"In my uncle's shop are to be found many of the finest porcelains," declared Hip Wo proudly. "At the moment we have a pair of dragon bowls, truly things of beauty. Would you care to see one?"

"Indeed, yes," assented Li Lai-tong.

Hip Wo climbed quickly up the ladder to the highest tier of shelves. With great care he brought down a box and placed it on the table beside the tea bowl. He slipped free the mother-of-pearl clasp and reverently lifted a gleaming object from its nest of cotton.

"Ah, indeed a thing of beauty!" exclaimed the scholar.

Of white porcelain it was, almost crystal-clear, decorated with two green five-clawed dragons that floated in clouds. The dragons were so alive they seemed about to step off the bowl.

"It is said that one of the finest makers of porcelain in the city of Peiping fashioned its beauty," said Hip Wo. "But with the coming of the troubles and the fighting throughout the land, its owner fell upon evil times. And so, in due course, this one and its mate found their way to the city of Hong Kong. My uncle plans to sell them, but as yet he cannot bring himself to part with them."

"Most honored sir! A thousand apologies that the young one disturbs you with his chatter." So engrossed had Hip Wo been in his story that he failed to notice that Senior Uncle had appeared in the doorway.

"A fine apprentice you have here," replied Li Lai-tong. "One with a true love for beauty."

Hip Wo flushed with pride at these words of praise. As he returned to his task, he heard Senior Uncle murmur, "A pity. For in the Land of the Barbarians such an appreciation for beauty will be wasted."

In the Land of the Barbarians!

The Outside Country known as America, to which Hip Wo was soon to go, what would it be like? When would he be going? He wondered about the future, his future. Six moons ago he had left his home village, much harrowed by famine and fighting. How much longer would he remain in Hong Kong, living with the family of Senior Uncle, working in the shop?

The following day, while the family still sat at morning rice, the cracking and spluttering of firecrackers from the direction of the harbor announced that a steamer from America was arriving.

"It comes! The ship from the City of Golden Hills. It comes!" shouted Hip Wo.

He dashed out into the street, still holding his rice bowl and chopsticks. His friend Wong, son of Tailor Wu, was already running toward the water front. "Wait a minute," Hip Wo called after Wong.

Then Hip Wo rushed back into the shop and placed the bowl on the table. "I go now to watch the ship from America arrive," he told Senior Uncle.

"What manner of talk is this?" Senior Uncle wanted to know. "The sun not yet high in the sky, and you speak of leaving the shop."

"Not every day does a ship arrive from the City of Golden Hills," pleaded Hip Wo.

"Go, then," Senior Uncle relented, "but return in time for noon rice."

Hip Wo sped down the cobblestone street after Wong, running so fast that his queue bounced as in a great wind. He caught up with his friend and led the way through a short cut, through an alley so narrow that the cloth signs on bamboo poles made a canopy overhead that shut out the sky. In and out among the baskets of the vendors the boys darted. Hip Wo, dodging a pile of cabbages, just missed a charcoal stove with sizzling chestnuts and banged head-on into a farmer who was carrying two baskets of geese on a bamboo pole.

The geese squawked, the owner of them sprawled in the muddy street screaming, and people stood all around shouting and laughing. One of the geese escaped and ran hither and thither and no place at all.

Hip Wo dashed after the goose and managed to grab it by one of its feet. "Here is your silly goose," he shouted to the farmer, thrusting it back into its basket. "Come on, Wong, or we will be too late."

Reaching the street that led to the docks, the boys were halted again. The way to the shore was blocked by a procession of coolies carrying all manner of produce destined for San Francisco—boxes of China's famous tea, earthen ginger jars, hides, and lumber.

As soon as the procession had passed, Hip Wo and Wong sprinted across to the water front.

"It is not too late!" shouted Hip Wo.

The ship from America was just entering the harbor, little spurts of smoke puffing from its single funnel. Closer and closer it came, picking its way carefully among the age-old junks and the smaller craft, the sampans and floating houses and shops.

"But what is the thing in the middle, sticking up, that sneezes smoke?" Hip Wo asked in astonishment. Having arrived in Hong Kong from a village near Canton only a few moons before, he had never seen a steamer.

"Why, as everyone knows, that comes from the fire inside the ship. It is what makes it cross the ocean like the wind," Wong explained in a very superior fashion, as one explains the simplest thing to a country bumpkin.

"To think of it!" gasped Hip Wo, full of wonder.

The boys stood there with the hundreds of others who had come to see the ship arrive and watched until it disappeared among the bamboo-matted sails of the junks.

"Come, Hip Wo, there is work to be done. We must go back," urged Wong.

When he reached the shop, Hip Wo was informed that Senior Uncle had gone out on urgent business. It was nearly time for noon rice when he returned, looking somber and stern.

When the chopsticks were laid down at the end of the meal, Senior Uncle took from his pocket two pieces of paper. All sat silently, knowing that the head of the family was about to make an important announcement.

Senior Uncle cleared his throat. "I shall read to you first what is to be read in all the tea houses.

" 'To the countrymen of Ah Chow! There are laborers wanted in the land of Oregon and California, in the United States of America. There is much inducement to go to this new country, as they have many great works which are not in our own country. They will supply good houses and plenty of food. They will pay you $28 to $30 a month after your arrival and treat you considerately when you arrive. There is no fear of slavery. All is nice. The ship is going now and will take all who can pay their passage. The money required is $54.' "

Senior Uncle laid the paper down and addressed Hip Wo directly. "As you know, Hip Wo, it was decided that you should go to this land called America as soon as the necessary arrangements could be made. All is now in readiness. I have today paid the $54 for your passage and have here the ticket." He held up the second piece of paper. "You leave upon the vessel that arrived today when it starts its return journey to the City of Golden Hills."

Hip Wo was stunned. Although he had understood, of course, that the family had decided he was to travel to the Outside Country called America, it had not seemed possible that it would really happen.

"He is too young to go so far!" his aunt murmured.

"What nonsense!" snorted Senior Uncle. "He has seen fifteen summers already. And big and strong he is, ready for a man's work."

Hip Wo knew, without any doubt whatever, that it was a good thing for him to go to America. Yet later, when he was fastening the wooden shutters for the night, he was filled with sudden dismay. Senior Uncle's shop-house, with the shop downstairs and sleeping quarters above, seemed so secure, so familiar. He would miss the neat rows of bowls and Senior Uncle peering sternly at him over the writing brushes and the abacus. And the chatter of his aunt and his girl cousins as they bent over their fine embroidery. And above all, the delicate porcelains he had grown to cherish. *Ai-ya!* Did he really want to go?

Hip Wo sighed. Yes, certainly he should go. But to leave China! To go so far away—why, he might never again see the early morning mist rise from the rice fields; never watch Big Horn, the family water buffalo, sitting in his noon mud bath; never sit, as he often did, watching the junks unfurl their proud sails. He tried to picture what the Outside Country would be like. Would it have rice fields? Mountains, like the ones in China?

Panic seized Hip Wo. He couldn't go—he couldn't leave what he had known all his life to travel to a barbarian country, far away! He stood there, outside the shuttered shop, his face burning as if he had the "inside fire," his hands and feet clammy cold. Should he go and tell Senior Uncle that he would, after all, remain here?

No, decided Hip Wo, he would think it over. For hour on hour he walked, not even aware of where he was. He was jostled by coolies, pushed to one side for a wheelbarrow of pigs, but he noticed none of it. He watched some street acrobats but did not see what he looked at. As he stumbled along he said to himself, again and again, "I cannot go, but I must. It is the thing to be done."

Suddenly Hip Wo realized that he was in front of a temple. He stepped through the gateway and crossed the quiet courtyard.

Within the dim recess of the temple the image of the Buddha smiled serenely down into his lifted face.

Hip Wo recalled another time, not long ago, when he had stood thus in the small village temple to which his father and mother had taken him before he came to Hong Kong to live with Senior Uncle.

"Remember," his father had said, "remember always the meaning of your name, Hip Wo—Mutual Help and Concord. Let these be your aims through life, for without both, the family goes to pieces; and without the family, as the sage has said, the individual is, indeed, lost."

Those words echoed through Hip Wo's mind. *Mutual Help and Concord*—that was not only his name, he realized in a flash of insight, but a signpost. The thing to be done was that which would best fulfill his name. With many mouths to be fed in Senior Uncle's house, and so much of his village destroyed by floods and bandits, he could help restore peace and prosperity to the family by journeying to America and earning there many silver dollars. It was the best way, then, as Senior Uncle had decided. And as he turned back across the courtyard to the gate, Hip Wo felt that peace had come to him.

In the next circle of days Hip Wo and all the household were busy making things ready for his departure. Second Cousin wove for him a new straw sleeping mat, while the two girls made a *pu-gai,* a quilt padded thick with cotton to keep him warm on the coldest of nights. New clothes were fitted for him, not many, but of strong cotton stuff that would wear for many, many moons. And a fine padded jacket as well was ordered by Senior Uncle. "I am informed," he stated, "that where you will work it will be as cold as in North China."

Then one afternoon Senior Uncle summoned Hip Wo and told him that he could choose, from all the stock in the shop, his bowls for rice and tea, bowls that he would, as is the custom, carry everywhere with him. After Hip Wo had chosen thick, strong pottery with a design of bamboo trees that reminded him of a grove near his home village, Senior Uncle took down from its place on the highest shelf one of the dragon bowls.

"This, too, take with you on your journey to the new country. One must have beauty near one." Senior Uncle spoke gruffly, but Hip Wo knew what it meant for him to part with one of his most treasured possessions.

"Oh, Uncle, it is too much," protested Hip Wo. "The bowl might get broken. It is so delicate."

"Guard it, Young One. It is well to have beauty from one's own country to look upon in a strange land."

"Maybe one day, when I have earned many of the silver dollars, maybe then I will have a shop as fine as yours and sell things of such beauty as the dragon bowl in the new country," Hip Wo replied.

"It is possible. 'Patience and a mulberry leaf will make a silk gown,'" Senior Uncle said, quoting one of his favorite proverbs.

And so it came to the last day, the day before Hip Wo would leave for America. Senior Uncle granted him permission to spend the afternoon saying farewell to his friends. Wong he saved until the last, and it was with heavy footsteps that he entered the small tailor shop.

"Come," Wong greeted him, "come with me. I have for you a present."

Together they entered the cupboard-sized room where Wong and his brothers and sisters slept. From a camphor chest Wong took a very small parcel.

"For me?" asked Hip Wo, wondering what it could be. He unwound the rice paper, and there in the palm of his hand rested a diminutive carving of Ma Chu, the Goddess of Sailors, and her two assistants, Favorable Ear Wind and Thousand Mile Eye.

"It may well be that the Barbarians on whose ship you will travel to America do not fully understand the importance of Ma Chu," Wong stated gravely. "Therefore, I thought it wise for you to carry with you this small image of her to protect your path across the water."

Hip Wo could find no words to express his gratitude. "I shall keep Ma Chu in the pocket of my jacket," he promised. "Every moment she shall be with me."

"Do so, and no harm can befall you," Wong said.

Hip Wo knew that he must take his leave of Wong. The entire family gathered in front of the shop, shouting, "Peace on your journey, peace on your journey!" as Hip Wo started sadly toward Senior Uncle's shop.

But as he reached home, he forgot his sadness. What were those wonderful odors that poured out to greet him! Hip Wo had thought that on his last night there might be, with the usual rice and vegetables, a bit of salt pork, perhaps, or shreds of chicken. Never had he imagined there would be the much prized duck-hung-in-the-oven, that delicious boneless duck that he had tasted only once before, on a New Year when the crops had been unusually good in the village. With it were stacks of the thinnest and softest pancakes, called thousand-layer biscuits, and a dish of water chestnuts and bamboo shoots.

Hip Wo stood there beside the table, speechless, unable to believe his eyes or his nose. "Why—why it is like the feast for the New Year," he finally gasped.

"Only once in one's life does one voyage to the City of Golden Hills," observed Senior Uncle, smiling.

As he picked up his chopsticks, Hip Wo felt tears of gratitude stinging his eyes. He would repay Senior Uncle's kindness a thousand times over, he vowed. He would work unceasingly to add to the honor and prosperity of the family.

Homeless Birds

by MARY ANTIN

*Under the Czars, the Jews in Russia were persecuted
bitterly, and many of them began to emigrate to America.
The letters they sent back spread word that in the United
States there were freedom and opportunity for all. By
1910 more than a million Jews had arrived.*

*One of the immigrants was a small ten-year-old girl,
Mary Antin. Mary Antin told the story of her life in a
book called* The Promised Land, *from which this descrip-
tion of her school days is taken. To her this new land
was "like a nest to homeless birds," as she was to
express it a little later in one of her first attempts at
poetry.*

Father himself took my brother and sister and me to
school on the first day. He would not have delegated that
mission to the President of the United States. He had
awaited the day with impatience equal to mine, and now
he took long strides in his eagerness, the rest of us running to keep up.

At last the four of us stood around the teacher's desk.
In his broken English, my father gave us over to her
charge, with some word of his hopes for us that his heart
could no longer hold. I think that Miss Nixon was struck
by something unusual in the group we made. My little
sister Dora, who had golden curls and eyes like violets,
was as pretty as a doll. My brother Joseph, with black
hair and fine eyebrows, stood up straight before the

Adapted from *We Came to America*, an anthology selected and edited by Frances Cavanah.
Copyright © 1954 by Frances Cavanah. Published by Macrae Smith Company. Condensed
from *The Promised Land* by Mary Antin, copyright © 1912 by Houghton Mifflin Company.
Copyright © 1940 by Mary Antin. Published by Houghton Mifflin Company.

teacher, his cap in his hand. Next to him stood a wide-eyed, starved-looking girl—myself.

But the figure that most drew attention in the group was my father, with his earnest face and eloquent hands and voice full of feeling. I think Miss Nixon guessed that by bringing his children to school my father felt that he became part of America.

I was put into the baby class, but as soon as I could understand what the teacher said, I was advanced to the second grade. There were about half a dozen beginners in English, in age from six to fifteen. Miss Nixon made a special class of us. She aided us so skillfully in our efforts to "see a cat" and "hear a dog bark" that we turned over page after page of our readers, eager to find out how the world looked, smelled, and tasted in the strange English speech.

I shall never have a better chance to make public my love for the English language. I am glad that American history runs, chapter for chapter, the way it does; for thus America came to be the country I love so dearly. I am glad, most of all, that the United States began by being English, and thus gave me this beautiful language in which I think.

Whenever the teachers did anything special to help me, my gratitude went out to them. Dear Miss Carrol of the second grade would be amazed to hear what small things I remember.

Says Miss Carrol, looking straight at me, "If Johnnie has three marbles, and Charlie has twice as many, how many marbles has Charlie?"

I raise my hand for permission to speak. "Teacher, I don't know vot is *tvice*."

Teacher beckons me to her and whispers to me the meaning of the strange word, and I am able to write the correct answer. It's all in the day's work with her; to me it is a special act of kindness.

My third-grade teacher became a friend whose approval was always dear to me. I remember to this day how Miss Dillingham and I worked over the word *water*. I could not seem to make the sound of *w;* I said "vater" every time.

Patiently my teacher invented ways to get my stubborn lips to say that *w;* and when at last I could say *village* and *water* rapidly without misplacing the two initial letters, that memorable word was sweet on my lips. We had conquered, and Teacher was pleased.

Just before locking up her desk one evening, Miss Dillingham gave me a volume of Longfellow's poems. It was a thin volume, but to me it was a bottomless treasure. I had never owned a book before. This book I already knew and loved because Teacher had read from it.

By the middle of my second year in school I had reached the sixth grade. After Christmas we began to study the life of George Washington, and it seemed to me that all my reading had been idle until then. When the teacher read to us out of a big book, I sat rigid with attention, my hands clasped on my desk. I gazed with adoration at the pictures of George and Martha Washington till I could see them with my eyes shut.

As I read how the patriots planned the Revolution and then set up the republic, it dawned on me gradually what was meant by *my country*. The people all desiring noble things and striving for them together, giving their lives for each other—all this it was that made *my country*.

It was not a thing that I understood; I could not go home and tell my sister about it, as I told her other things I learned at school. But I knew one could say *my country* and feel it, as one felt *God* or *myself*. When we stood to sing "America," I shouted the words.

As the day approached when the school was to honor George Washington's birthday, the halls resounded with patriotic songs. On the day of the celebration I recited a poem that I had written. I dug the words of that poem out of my heart, squeezed the rhymes out of my brain, forced the missing syllables out of their hiding places in the dictionary. Where was I to find rhymes for such words as *tyranny, freedom,* and *justice?* Even the name I wished to celebrate was difficult. Nothing rhymed with *Washington.*

I was not a heroic figure when I stood up in front of the class to praise the Father of his Country. Thin, pale, with a shadow of short black curls on my brow, I must have looked frightened. My pronunciation was faulty, but I had the courage of my beliefs. I was face to face with forty fellow citizens in clean blouses and extra frills. I must tell them what George Washington had done for their country—for *our* country—for me.

I can laugh now at my clumsy poem, but to the fellow citizens sitting in rows in front of me it was no laughing matter. I fixed their eighty eyes with my single stare and gave them verse after verse. The children listened. They had to. A special note ran all through my poem,

for I made myself the spokesman of the Jews, the "luckless sons of Abraham," saying—

". . . like a nest to homeless birds
Your land proved to us, and therefore
Will we gratefully sing your praise evermore."

The boys and girls, who had never been turned away from any door because of their father's religion, sat in their places as if fascinated. But they woke up and applauded when I was done.

The poem was repeated, by request, before several other classes. Later it was published in the Boston *Herald*. When the paper with my poem in it arrived at our house, we all pounced upon it at once. The poem was hard to find, but when we found it, it looked wonderful. And my name was at the bottom!

After the excitement in the house had subsided, my father took all the change out of the cash drawer and went to buy up the *Herald*. He did not count the pennies. He just bought *Herald*s, all he could lay his hands on, and gave them to our friends and relatives—to all who could read and to some who could not. For weeks he carried a clipping from the *Herald* in his pocket, and few were the occasions when he did not manage to introduce it into the conversation.

Pleased as I was with my fame—and nobody but me knew how exceedingly pleased I was—I had a sober feeling about it all. I enjoyed being praised, but what gave a divine flavor to my happiness was the idea that I had publicly borne testimony to the goodness of my hero and to the greatness of my adopted country.

164

The Warm of Heart

by ELIZABETH COATSWORTH

The warm of heart shall never lack a fire
However far he roam.
Although he live forever among strangers
He cannot lack a home.

For strangers are not strangers to his spirit,
And each house seems his own,
And by the fire of his loving-kindness
He cannot sit alone.

Reprinted with permission of the publisher from *Five Bushel Farm* by Elizabeth Coatsworth. Copyright 1939 by The Macmillan Company.

Miss Liberty

by WILLADENE PRICE

On a cold October day in 1886, a million Americans, including the President of the United States, braved a rain to attend the dedication of the Statue of Liberty in New York. Of those who looked upward at her serene face there were few who realized that she had survived a good deal of hardship. It had taken her twenty years to reach her pedestal.

National Park Service Photo

By permission of the author and *Boys' Life*, published by the Boy Scouts of America.

It was in the summer of 1865 that a group of Frenchmen met to discuss how France might take part in the anniversary celebration of American independence. One of the guests was Auguste Bartholdi, a young sculptor from Alsace. Bartholdi wrote down much of what was said that day. Looking over his notes later, he read, *If a monument should rise in the United States as a memorial to their independence, I should think it only natural if it were built by united effort—a common work of both our nations.* The young man began to dream. But it was years before he saw his dream come true.

While busy making a name for himself as an artist in Paris, Bartholdi was ever aware of his dream of a monument for America. He even became friendly with a little group of Americans who lived in France, so that he might learn more about their hopes and dreams for their country.

Then suddenly France was at war with Prussia. The sculptor's native province, Alsace, was put under German rule. More than ever, America became for him a haven of peace and hope.

After the French defeat, America had supplied food for a hungry France, and now Bartholdi spoke out for a French gift to America. It was to be presented at the centennial celebration of the signing of the Declaration of Independence, which was to be held in Philadelphia. He proposed a statue of liberty so large that it could "be seen from the shores of America to the coast of France." Backed by the enthusiasm of other Frenchmen, Bartholdi set off for America to talk about his plans.

As he approached the shores of the United States, he was so stirred by feelings of peace and security that for the first time he was able to put on paper his idea for a statue. He named the woman in his drawing Liberty Enlightening the World.

Bartholdi toured the United States for five months and interested President Grant, the poet Henry Wadsworth Longfellow, and many others in his project. He returned to a France that was still recovering from war wounds. It took some time to start a campaign to collect funds to build the statue. Meanwhile the people of America were to supply the pedestal on which the statue was to be mounted when it arrived.

Bartholdi put twenty men to work ten hours a day on his colossal Liberty. It was no longer just a work of art; it became an engineering feat. A nine-foot plaster model of the statue was first reproduced four times its original height. Then, section by section, the thirty-six-foot model was enlarged to its existing scale. Copper sheets of about the thickness of a silver dollar were pressed into wooden patterns and hammered into shape by hand.

Liberty's copper body took shape over a steel and iron skeleton designed by Gustave Eiffel, who later built the famous Eiffel Tower in Paris. By 1876 only the right arm, holding the torch, was ready for the centennial celebration in Philadelphia. The arm in itself was a magnificent display. It was forty-two feet long, with eight-foot fingers, and twelve feet in diameter at the point of greatest thickness. The arm required twenty-one huge crates for shipping.

The money to pay for Miss Liberty trickled in from the French people, and she grew slowly in the yard of a gigantic workshop in Paris. In the summer of 1882, her thirty-five-foot waistline took shape. To celebrate, twenty men sat on her knee and ate luncheon. A platform had been erected at the level of Miss Liberty's knee for this occasion. On it was a gaily decorated table. Food was hauled up from below by a rope and a pulley.

By Christmas, Miss Liberty began towering over the French housetops.

Soon cranes gingerly lifted her left arm, which clutched a giant law book inscribed July IV, MDCCLXXVI, and the arm was riveted into position.

The cranes went down again for the magnificent head, which had been on display at an exposition in Paris, and it, too, was riveted into position.

Some people say that the serene face of Miss Liberty bore close resemblance to Bartholdi's mother. Others say his model was his wife.

To complete the statue, the right arm, bearing the torch, was shipped back from America and also put into place.

On July 4, 1884, the completed Miss Liberty, in all her copper glory, was formally presented to the American ambassador in Paris.

People in the United States seemed to be in no hurry to arrange her homecoming. A group of Americans who lived in Paris were so embarrassed by this indifference to the statue that they decided to express appreciation to France with a gift.

G. Sirot Photo, Paris

They ordered the making of a small Miss Liberty, exactly like the original. It was presented the day before the original statue set sail at last for America. Later a bronze model of the miniature was made. It now stands on an island in the Seine River in the heart of Paris.

When Miss Liberty arrived on Bedloe's Island—now called Liberty Island—her pedestal was still not ready. The 214 crates in which she was packed had to be stored in a warehouse. A Pedestal Fund Committee, organized long before the arrival of the statue, was still $100,000 short of enough money to complete the pedestal.

A newspaperman came to the rescue of Miss Liberty. He was Joseph Pulitzer, owner of a New York paper called *The World*. "*The World*," said Mr. Pulitzer, "is the people's paper, and it now appeals to the people to come forward and raise this money. The $250,000 that the making of the statue cost was paid in by the masses of the French people—by the workingmen, the tradesmen, the shop girls, the artisans—by all, irrespective of class or condition. Let us respond in like manner. . . . If we all go to work together with a firm resolve and a patriotic will, we can raise the needed money."

The money came in—five cents, fifty cents, dollars, and more dollars. Much of it came from school children. In a few months *The World* had collected $102,006.39.

When the 225-ton Goddess of Liberty had finally risen to her majestic height of three hundred feet from pedestal to torch, President Grover Cleveland officially welcomed her with the promise that "We will not forget that Liberty has here made her home."

For many years the Statue of Liberty, her once shiny copper robes now mellowed to a soft green by age, has been a symbol of home to Americans. Hundreds of thousands of persons visit the statue each year. Soldiers of two world wars homeward bound have wept with joy at the sight of her. She has also meant home and freedom to millions of immigrants approaching our shores.

At the left of the entrance to the statue is a bronze tablet inscribed with the poem "The New Colossus," by Emma Lazarus. The poem says:

Not like the brazen giant of Greek fame,
With conquering limbs astride from land to land;
Here at our sea-washed, sunset gates shall stand
A mighty woman with a torch, whose flame
Is the imprisoned lightning, and her name
Mother of Exiles. From her beacon-hand
Glows world-wide welcome; her mild eyes command
The air-bridged harbor that twin cities frame.
"Keep, ancient lands, your storied pomp!" cries she
With silent lips. "Give me your tired, your poor,
Your huddled masses yearning to breathe free,
The wretched refuse of your teeming shore.
Send these, the homeless, tempest-tost to me,
I lift my lamp beside the golden door!"

Universe

by ELEANOR FARJEON

The Universe is all the skies
Reaching far beyond your eyes.

The Universe is all the seas
Spreading in unseen degrees.

The Universe is all the earth
Besides the spot that gave you birth.

If you can with your small eye
Know one star in all the sky:

If, of all the seas there be,
From one beach you know the sea:

If, of all the land on earth,
You can know one meadow's worth:

You might do a great deal worse
To understand the Universe.

ROUND EARTH
AND OPEN SKY

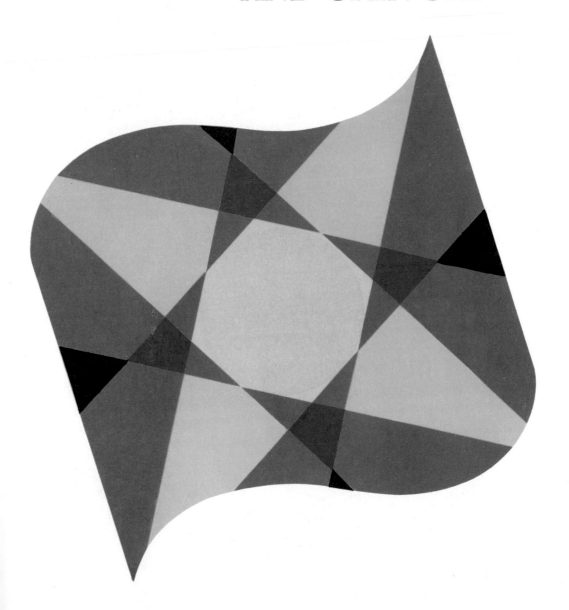

Stormbound

by JIM KJELGAARD

Allan hurried across the ice toward the forest, fighting a panic that rose within him. The tree line, which should have been starkly clear against the snowy background, was almost obscured. He saw it not as a forest whose separate trees were distinct but as a blurred whole that at times almost disappeared behind swirling drapes of snow.

The storm seemed to have burst upon him silently and with no warning whatever, but Allan knew that was an illusion. He was to blame for being caught. If he had been less intent on watching his new dog Stormy trail a trapped mink, he would have realized a storm was breaking. While he was tracking the mink, Allan had

From *Stormy* by Jim Kjelgaard. Copyright © 1959 by Jim Kjelgaard. Published by Holiday House, New York.

learned a good deal about the dog he had found just the day before on the icebound lake, but now it was too late to return home. The storm was gathering fury by the second. If it caught him out on the ice, he would be unable to see a single landmark; he might walk in a circle until exhausted. His only hope lay in the forest, where he could wait out the storm under some sort of shelter. He'd camped out before in winter and had been not only safe but comfortable. This was different only because of the storm, he told himself.

With Stormy beside him, Allan left the ice and plunged into knee-deep snow. He forced a way through the willows that lined the banks of Balsam Creek and ducked into a grove of bushy hemlocks, which broke the strength of the snow-driving wind. Looking about and wondering what to do next, he noticed the dog.

A shadow in the semigloom, Stormy was sitting on his haunches a little to one side and looking steadily at Allan. Unaccountably Allan thought of a picture he had seen in some thriller magazine. It was a black leopard at twilight, and its body blended so well with the darkness that it seemed part of it. Its glaring yellow eyes were fixed on something as it deliberated the next move.

Allan felt uncomfortable. There was no threat in the dog's attitude, but Stormy was intent in the same way the leopard had been. Allan could not rid himself of a feeling that the dog was studying him. They were facing a crisis, one not without danger, and Allan sensed that the dog was deliberately waiting to see what he would do next.

Wrenching his eyes from Stormy, Allan slipped the snowshoes from his shoulder, stuck one upright in the snow, and started digging with the other. He worked fast, using the snow he removed to build a wall on all four sides. At the same time he was cautious. His digging might uncover a dead snag or stump on which the snowshoe could be broken. He found no such obstacle, and when the toe of his snowshoe brushed cushiony hemlock needles, he widened the hole already dug into a pit several feet across. He glanced quickly at Stormy and away again.

A week from now he'd remember and doubtless smile about the time a dog sat in judgment to see how he would react to a dangerous predicament. But at the moment he could not rid himself of the notion that Stormy was really studying him and did want to know what he would do about the problem that faced them. Suddenly he felt a warm bond between himself and the big mongrel.

He leaned his snowshoes against the side of the pit, broke a trail through the snow to the nearest hemlock, and stooped to run his hands up and down its lower trunk. Such small, closely growing evergreens always had dead twigs on the bottom. As Allan found them, he broke them off and wrapped them in his jacket, which he laid in the snow. Then he plunged farther into deep snow for more wood.

He did not want to cut any of those trees immediately adjoining his pit, for they would help soften the wind and turn the snow, but presently he found one he could take. Allan was about to cut it with his belt hatchet when he saw a small, dead tree so close that its brittle branches intertwined with the green of the living hemlock. Bracing his back against the green one, and helping maintain a balance by thrusting his left leg into the snow, Allan placed his right foot against the dead tree and rocked it forward. He let it swing back and rocked again, increasing the tempo and each time shoving the dead tree farther. After a moment it snapped and tumbled in the snow.

Allan dragged the dead tree to the pit and used the blunt end of his hatchet to smash the brittle branches from the parent trunk. Then he chopped an eighteen-inch length from the trunk itself and, laying an end of the remainder on it, broke the rest of the trunk into suitable lengths by jumping on it.

He went back for his jacket, laid the twigs it had protected in the bottom of his pit, and slipped into the jacket. Going to his knees, he removed the outer layer of paper from the two sandwiches he had brought with him from home. Upon it he arranged dead twigs no bigger than matchsticks. Carefully he added larger pieces of wood. Then, unbuttoning his jacket and holding the left side out to form a windbreak, he struck a match and applied it to the paper. The paper flared. Flame crackled through the twigs and ate its way into the larger pieces of wood. Allan added the rest of his dead tree, and the leaping fire burned a bright hole in the semigloom.

Following the path he had broken, which was already partly snow-filled, Allan returned to where he'd cut the dead tree and looked back. The fire was plainly seen. Looking back every few steps, Allan plowed through the snow until, when he looked over his shoulder, the fire was only a dull glow through sheets of swirling snow. He cut another tree, dragged it to his pit, broke it up, and went out again.

With the fire as a hub, his wood-gathering excursions became the spokes of a wheel. Never traveling out of sight of the fire, he cut trees and dragged them back. Allan took all the dead trees he found—and green wood as well, because it burned longer. He cut or smashed the branches off with his hatchet and used the green ones to carpet the floor of his pit. The trunks he stood against the snow wall that surrounded him, for future use.

The storm was now reaching its peak, and all about, snow whirled furiously down. Busy gathering enough wood to last, Allan had paid no attention to the time, but he thought that most of the day was gone. However, when he tilted his watch beside the fire so that he could see the dial, he discovered that it was only half-past three.

Allan settled himself by the fire and took stock of his situation. Rarely did storms like this one last longer than twenty-four hours. But every now and again they raged for periods of three days to a week. Should this be such a storm, Allan knew that he was in for serious trouble. He had wood and shelter but no food except his two sandwiches.

For all that, he was calm, almost serene. This was what life was like in the Beaver Flowage. It was a wild, raw, and sometimes dangerous land, but even in crisis Allan loved it. There was something elemental here. It had nothing to do with lives so well ordered that those

who lived them always knew exactly what they would be doing on any given day. It was a country for the wild ducks and geese, the deer, the fish beneath the ice, the dog across the fire, and the sportsmen who came every year to fish or hunt. As he sat beside his fire, Allan knew that the fish sportsmen caught and the waterfowl they bagged were only part of the lure that drew them. They came also because they were weary of conformity and easy living. Allan understood completely, because he himself could never leave the Beaver Flowage. Born to the elemental, he could not live without it.

By the fire's light he skinned the mink Stormy had trailed, thrust the limp pelt into his jacket, and speculatively regarded the carcass. Then he grimaced and threw it out in the snow. At best it was a few ounces of meat permeated with foul musk. Even Stormy wouldn't want it. A moment later he climbed out of the pit, thrust his hand into the snow where the mink carcass had landed, and recovered it. This was a time for thinking, and in lightly throwing the carcass away he had not thought. Seating himself in the pit again, he looked at the dog lying on the other side of the fire.

Stormy was lying with his head on his paws and his unblinking eyes fixed on the fire. Allan's fleeting smile was warm. Almost any other dog would have been crowding anxiously near and looking to his master for reassurance. Stormy was meeting the situation like a wolf and making the best of it. He seemed to have no intention of looking to anything or anybody except himself. Allan had the feeling that Stormy could never be bent or beaten into any conventional mold. But he also thought that if he should ever be fortunate enough to win the big dog's allegiance, he would win all of it.

Turning his mind back to their stormbound plight, Allan took his knife from his pocket, opened the pliers that folded into the handle, and snipped the chain from the trap in which the mink had been taken. He snipped again, so that the end link formed a hook. Closing the pliers and opening the file blade of his knife, he filed a needle point on the hook. Then, removing his leather belt, he sliced thin strips from either side and tied them together to form one six-foot length. He tested it for strength by snapping it between his fingers, and when the leather thong did not break, he tied one end securely to the trap chain.

Next he took off his boots, stripped off the outer of the two pairs of wool socks he wore, and again bent to work by the fire's light. He opened the awl blade of his knife, pierced a sock, and carefully began to unravel it. It was slow and tedious work, but he was going nowhere for a while; there was plenty of time.

Allan tied the strands of yarn together, rolled them into a ball, and began on the other sock. He tied those strands to the first ones and, when he was finished, thrust the ball of yarn into his pocket. He had a plan. If it did not work, nothing was lost. If it did, no matter how long the storm lasted, he and Stormy would see it through. But night had fallen in earnest now. He could do nothing except wait for morning.

Allan took the sandwiches from his pocket, removed one, and put the other back. He cut the one in half.

"Chow time, Stormy," Allan announced, holding out one half.

The big dog rose, came around the fire, accepted and ate his half of the sandwich, and went back to lie in his original bed. While Allan chewed his share of the sandwich, he concentrated on the dancing flames.

Only a fool would deliberately invite a predicament such as this, but now that he was in it, Allan found it not all bad. Petty worries were far away and insignificant. The world consisted of himself, his new dog, the fire, and the storm that kept them prisoners.

Presently he leaned his head on his upraised knees and dozed until he was awakened by cold. The fire had subsided to a mass of glowing coals that somehow seemed to defy the storm. Allan rose, added wood to his fire, and on sudden impulse divided the remaining sandwich with Stormy. Now he had no food at all, but he remained unworried. He sat down to doze until cold should again awaken him.

Morning came, but rather than a brightening of the day, it was more a lessening of the night. Wind-driven snow continued to fall so fast that only those trees within twenty-five feet or less were visible. The snowbank Allan had erected around his pit was covered with ten inches of new fall, beautiful but sinister.

Stormy rose, rid his black fur of snow with a single vigorous shake of his body, and waited expectantly. Allan got up and stretched, ready to carry out his plan formed during the night.

Storms such as this always came from the northwest. To reach Balsam Creek, which lay southeast, Allan had only to go with the wind. He built his fire so high that leaping flames began to melt the surrounding snowbank. Satisfied that it would last, he put a foot-long piece of wood in the game pocket of his jacket, laced his snow-shoes on, caught up the mink carcass, and with Stormy following in the path he broke, started toward the creek.

Every few steps he looked back. When he was thirty feet from the fire, which he still saw plainly, he tied one end of the yarn to a tree and continued, unrolling the ball as he went. He traveled slowly, for the yarn was fragile and he dared not risk breaking it. Presently the tips of the willows bordering Balsam Creek bent beneath his snowshoes, and then he was on the creek itself.

Allan anchored the end of his yarn with the stick of wood he'd brought along, unlaced his snowshoes, and laid the piece of wood on one of them. With the other he methodically began to dig through the snow. He did not hurry or even attempt to lift any heavy weight of snow, for his very life depended on the snowshoes, and he dared not break them. Reaching ice, he widened the hole in the snow to give him room to move about.

Taking his hatchet from its sheath, he knelt and scarred the ice, averting his face as a stinging shower of ice pellets struck him. Stormy looked on with interest as Allan continued to chop. Twenty minutes later he removed a square foot of ice eight inches thick, and the slow water of Balsam Creek rose partway into the hole. Allan lay prone to look into the creek.

The day was half dark and half light, but he could see the creek's sandy bottom because the water here was only two or three feet deep. After a moment a school of shiners darted past. Then he saw a thin film of silt that could have been caused only by some disturbance upstream, and he crossed his fingers. All the signs looked hopeful.

Taking the chain and thong from his pocket, Allan strung a piece of the mink's red carcass on his improvised hook and lowered it through the hole. He wrapped the thong loosely about his wrist and sat quietly. It was a calculated rather than a fretful waiting. There were times to hurry, but there were also times when haste defeated the objective.

About ten minutes later, as though of its own volition, the leather thong began to slide into the water. Allan let it go, knowing that he had read the signs correctly. Small fish had sought a haven in these shallow waters. Big pike, hungry most of the time and ravenous in winter, were hunting them. A pike had taken Allan's bait, and now everything must be done exactly right. The chain and thong would hold even a big fish, but at best the hook was makeshift. For one thing it was too small, and for another it had no barb. Almost the only chance of landing a fish lay in letting whatever had the bait swallow it before setting the hook.

Allan let the thong play out to the last possible inch, then jerked it. Instant resistance told him that he had his quarry, but it was still possible to pull the hook out if he was not careful or if he used too much strength. Allan merely held on, took up the slack when there was any, and let the fish tire itself in a series of savage rushes. Then, inch by inch, he shortened the thong and worked his catch up to the hole he'd chopped in the ice. Fifteen minutes after he'd set the hook, he lifted a big pike through the hole.

For a moment he sat enthralled, too happy even to move. It seemed a long while ago that the storm had broken and he had run for shelter; he almost seemed like another person. Now he knew that no matter what happened, he would never again be afraid of weather. He had won because he had refused to lose.

"We'll eat now, Stormy," he told the dog.

Putting on his snowshoes and swinging the pike over his shoulder, Allan picked up the stick to which his yarn was attached and followed the strands back to where he could see the fire. The snow still whirled and the wind still blew, but now there was no threat in either. The storm was merely something to be waited out until he could return home.

He half slid and half stepped into his pit, built up the fire, and cleaned and beheaded the pike. The offal he saved; cannibal pike would bite on it as readily as they would on anything else if he needed to go fishing again. Allan sliced his fish down the back and stripped the firm white flesh away from the backbone.

Unexpectedly, Stormy rose and walked around the fire. He nudged Allan's thigh with his shoulder and flicked his tongue out to brush the youth's cheek. When Allan ruffled Stormy's ears, the big dog's tail wagged happily.

Stormy had finally chosen his master.

Lone Dog

by IRENE RUTHERFORD McLEOD

I'm a lean dog, a keen dog, a wild dog, and lone;
I'm a rough dog, a tough dog, hunting on my own;
I'm a bad dog, a mad dog, teasing silly sheep;
I love to sit and bay the moon, to keep fat souls from sleep.

I'll never be a lap dog, licking dirty feet,
A sleek dog, a meek dog, cringing for my meat,
Not for me the fireside, the well-filled plate,
But shut door, and sharp stone, and cuff, and kick, and hate.

Not for me the other dogs, running by my side,
Some have run a short while, but none of them would bide.
O mine is still the lone trail, the hard trail, the best,
Wide wind, and wild stars, and hunger of the quest!

Wind-Wolves

by WILLIAM D. SARGENT

Do you hear the cry as the pack goes by,
The wind-wolves hunting across the sky?
Hear them tongue it, keen and clear,
Hot on the flanks of the flying deer!

Across the forest, mere, and plain,
Their hunting howl goes up again!
All night they'll follow the ghostly trail,
All night we'll hear their phantom wail,

For tonight the wind-wolf pack holds sway
From Pegasus Square to the Milky Way,
And the frightened bands of cloud-deer flee
In scattered groups of two and three.

Elsa Gets an Education

by JOY ADAMSON

In the northern part of Kenya a game warden, George Adamson, shot a lioness in self-defense. Later he discovered that she had been nursing a litter of three cubs. He took the cubs home with him, and they became part of the household. Two of them were sent to a zoo before they were fully grown; the third, Elsa, remained with the Adamsons as pet and friend. The time came, however, when it seemed best to return Elsa to the wild life for which nature intended her. Mr. and Mrs. Adamson knew of an area where there were almost no people or livestock but where game was abundant, especially lion. Plans were made to release Elsa in this place, and this is what happened.

It took us seventeen hours to reach our destination, where we were met by a friend who was the game warden of the district. We pitched camp on a site overlooking a vast plain of open bush country. The air was fresh and brisk. In front of our camp grassland sloped toward the plain, on which herds of Thomson's gazelle, wildebeest, zebra, antelope, and a few buffaloes were grazing. It was a game paradise. We took Elsa for a stroll, and she rushed at the herds, not knowing which to follow. In every direction there were animals running. As if to shake off the effects of the long journey, she lost herself among these new playmates, who seemed astonished to find such a strange lion in their midst—one who rushed to and fro without any apparent purpose. Soon, however, Elsa had had enough and trotted back to camp and her dinner.

Our plan was this: We would spend the first week taking Elsa around the new country, getting her used to the animals, many of which belonged to species that she had never seen. During the second week we intended to leave her out at night and to visit and feed her in the mornings when she was sleepy. Afterward we would reduce her meals, in the hope that eventually she would kill on her own or join a wild lion.

The morning after our arrival we took off Elsa's collar. She hopped onto the roof of our Land Rover, and we drove off. After only a few hundred yards we saw a lioness walking parallel to us downhill, and we rode closer to her. Elsa displayed much excitement, jumped off her seat, and cautiously followed this new friend. But as soon as the lioness stopped and turned around, Elsa's courage failed her, and she raced back as fast as she could to the car. The lioness continued her walk, and we soon detected six cubs waiting for her on a small anthill in tall grass.

Later we passed through herd after herd of antelope, whose curiosity seemed to be aroused by the sight of a Land Rover with a lion on it. Elsa watched carefully but did not attempt to leave the car unless she spotted an animal off guard, grazing with its back toward her or fighting. Then she would get down quietly and creep forward, taking advantage of every bit of cover. As soon as the animal showed any suspicion, Elsa would freeze.

Joy Adamson

Or sometimes she pretended to be uninterested and licked her paws, yawned, or even rolled on her back until the animal was reassured. Then she would start stalking again. But however cunning she was, she never got close enough to kill.

The little Thomson's gazelles teased Elsa unfairly, relying on the unwritten law of the bush that a superior creature will not attack a smaller one except for food. These urchins of the plain challenged her and simply asked to be chased. But Elsa ignored them and with dignity put them in their place.

Buffaloes and rhinos were quite another matter. They *had* to be chased. One day, from the car, we watched a buffalo cantering across the plain. Perhaps his curiosity was aroused by seeing a lion on a Land Rover. Quickly Elsa jumped to the ground and, using the cover of a bush, set out to stalk him. The buffalo had the same idea and also used this cover—but he started from the opposite direction. We waited and watched until we saw them nearly collide. The buffalo bolted, with Elsa bravely following him.

On another day we came upon a rhino standing fast asleep, with his head buried in a bush. Elsa stalked him very carefully and succeeded in nearly rubbing noses with him. Then the poor beast woke, gave a startled snort, spun around on himself, and dashed into a nearby swamp. There he churned up the water and gave Elsa a shower bath. She splashed after him, and the pair disappeared from our sight. It was a long time before Elsa returned, wet but proud.

She loved climbing trees. Sometimes when we had looked in vain for her in the high grass, we found her swaying in the crown of a tree. More than once she had difficulty getting down again. Once, after making the branch she was on bend alarmingly under her weight, she fell onto the grass over twenty feet below. She was most embarrassed at her loss of dignity. Although she always enjoyed making us laugh when she meant to do so, she hated being laughed at when the joke was against her. Now she walked quickly away from us, and we gave her time to regain her self-respect.

One morning we followed circling vultures and soon found a lion on a zebra kill. He was tearing at the meat and paid no attention to us. Elsa stepped cautiously from the car, miaowing at him, and then, though she did not get any encouragement, advanced carefully toward him. At last the lion looked up and straight at Elsa. He seemed to say, "How dare you, woman, interfere with the lord while he is having his meal? You are allowed to kill for me, but afterward you have to wait till I have had my lion's share; then you may finish up the remains." Poor Elsa returned to the car as fast as she could. The lord continued feeding. We watched him for a long time, hoping that Elsa might go back to him, but nothing would induce her to leave her safe position.

Until now we had always given Elsa her meat already cut up so that she would not associate her food with living animals. Now we needed to do the opposite. We shot a buck for her, wondering if she would know how to open it, since she had had no mother to teach her. We soon saw that by instinct she knew exactly how to open the carcass. She gnawed the meat off the bones with her molars and rasped it away with her tongue.

Once we knew that she could do this, it was time for us to let her do her own killing. The plain was covered with ideal hide-outs for any animal. All that the lions had to do when they wanted a meal was to wait under cover of a bush until an antelope approached downwind, rush out, and get their dinner.

We now left Elsa alone for two or three days at a time, hoping that hunger would make her kill. But when we came back, she was always waiting for us, and she was always hungry. It was heartbreaking having to stick to our program, which we now realized was going to take longer than we had expected. All Elsa wanted was to be with us and to be sure of our affection, but we knew that for her good we must persevere.

We increased the number of days Elsa was left on her own, and we reinforced the thorn fences around our tents to prevent her from visiting us when she was hungry.

One morning when Elsa was riding with us, we located a lion who seemed in a good mood. She stepped off the Land Rover, and we left the pair alone. That evening, while sitting in our thorn-protected tent, we suddenly heard Elsa's miaow, and before we could stop her, she crept through the thorns and settled down with us. She had walked eight miles back and obviously preferred our company to that of the lion.

The next time we took her a longer distance away from camp. As we drove along, we met two young lions sitting on the grass in the open. They looked to us like ideal companions for Elsa, but by now she was very suspicious of our tricks and would not leave the car. We went on until we met two Thomson's gazelles fighting; this sight caused Elsa to jump off, and we drove quickly away, leaving her to learn more about wild life.

It was nearly a week before we returned to Elsa. We found her waiting, very hungry. She was full of affection. We had tricked her, broken faith with her, done much to destroy her trust in us; yet she remained loyal. We dropped some meat that we had brought, and she immediately started to eat it. Suddenly we heard growls and saw two lions trotting toward us. They were obviously on the hunt, and they approached very quickly.

Poor Elsa took in the situation and bolted, leaving her precious meal. At once a little jackal appeared. He lost no time in taking his chance and began to take bite after bite of Elsa's meat, knowing that his luck was not going to last long. This proved true, for one of the lions advanced steadily upon him, uttering threatening growls. But meat was meat, and the little jackal took as many bites as he could until the lion was practically on top of him. Even then he tried to save his meal, but size prevailed over courage, and the lion was the winner. Elsa watched this scene from a distance and saw her first meal in many days being taken away from her. The two lions took no interest in anything but their food and completely ignored her. We took her back to camp with us.

While we were in camp we had some human visitors. A Swiss couple, having heard that we had a lion cub, came to see it. I think they had imagined something small that could be picked up and cuddled. Seeing the three-hundred-odd-pound Elsa made them pause, and it was a little time before they got out of their car and joined us at lunch. Elsa, courtesy itself, welcomed the strangers, and only once swept the table clear with her tail.

After this they could not have enough of her and had themselves photographed with her from every angle.

We had been in camp for four weeks, and although Elsa had spent half that time in the bush, she had not yet started killing for herself. Now the rains began, and every afternoon there were heavy showers.

The plains were under water, and most of the game had gone to a few bits of ground that were higher and drier than the rest. Elsa loved one little hillock that was studded with rocks, and we chose it as her experimental headquarters.

After about a week of torrential rains we waded the eight miles to the hillock where we had left her. As usual, she was waiting for us, overjoyed to see us, and greeted us each in turn by rubbing her head and body against us repeatedly. She was nearly crying. We decided that though it would interrupt her education, we could not leave her out in such weather.

Next day she was in great pain; her glands were swollen, and she had a temperature. We made her a bed of grass in the annex to my husband's tent, and there she lay, panting, listless, and pathetic.

For a time we did not think that she would recover. She was rapidly losing her beautiful golden color, her coat was dull, and on her back she developed many white hairs. Her face became ash-gray. She had difficulty in dragging herself from the tent into the sparse sunshine. The only hopeful sign was her appetite, and we gave her as much meat and milk as she wanted, although both had to be fetched from a long distance.

During her sickness Elsa became even more dependent on us and tamer than ever. Most of the day she lay across the opening in our thorn fence in a position that enabled her to watch all that went on inside the camp and outside on the plain as well. At mealtime she preferred having the boys step over her as they brought in our food rather than having to move from her place. The staff laughingly ran the gauntlet while balancing full soup plates, getting spanked by Elsa in a friendly way as they passed over her.

It was now plain that the climate in this region was against Elsa, that she might not be immune to local infections. Besides this, she was different in appearance from the local lions—much darker in color, with a longer nose, bigger ears, and generally much larger. In every way she belonged to the semidesert and not to the highlands, where we had tried to make her adjust. It was evident that we must try to choose a better home for her.

It was not easy to find an area that had a suitable climate, permanent water, enough game to supply her with food, and no tribesmen or hunting parties. Eventually we discovered such a paradise and received the Government's permission to release a lion there. As soon as the rains ceased, we decided to go there.

Camp was struck and everything loaded into the cars— everything except Elsa. She chose that very day to disappear into the bush. We hunted for her everywhere, in the Land Rover and on foot, but without success. We feared she might have been killed. For two days and nights she kept away, except for one short visit, during which she rushed up to us and rubbed her head against our knees, as though to tell us, "I just came back to tell you not to worry." Then she was off again. When she finally returned, she was badly scratched. It needed much patience to make her jump into the truck.

A three-month experiment was ended. We failed in our first attempt to release Elsa, but we had learned a great deal, and so had she. A few weeks later, in a more congenial place, Elsa was accepted by a pride of lions, and we left her in her natural home.

Joy Adamson

Enough for Everyone

by PHILIP HARKINS

After a year of learning to scuba dive, Eric Compton, a senior in high school, went to Mexico with his father on a fishing trip. Mr. Compton stayed in a hotel, but Eric lived with the family of a young Mexican skin diver, Chico. One day the boys decided to explore a sunken boat and to fish under water.

Eric and Chico dived, fins up. Eric had a spear gun with a power head. Chico carried another kind of spear gun known as a crossbow that shot a steel spear with great force under water.

Down the two divers went, their air hoses hissing re-assuringly. They coasted onto the wreck flutter-kicking to a smooth landing on its sloping deck. Their aqua-lungs, face plates, and swim fins gave them a feeling of power. They were supermen from another planet, assert-ing their superiority at sea.

Chico swam into the shadowy cabin of the sunken ship and disappeared. Eric waited. Should he enter, too, or stand guard, just in case? *Crash!* Something hit Eric, something big, hard, and heavy. He saw a huge olive-green blur, and then nothing. Chico swam out of the cabin. Which way did it go? his gestures asked.

Eric didn't know. He pointed up. His simple signal said, "Let's surface and talk this over."

They broke the surface near the rubber raft which they had paddled out to the wreck. Eric detached his mouth-piece and held on to the raft with one hand. "What was it?" he asked.

"Garupa," said Chico and stretched his arms to show great size.

"Good," said Eric. This was fine. A large grouper, probably about a hundred pounds. That was just about right—big but not too big. The power head would take care of it handily.

The aqualungs were functioning normally; the power head with its .38 blank cartridge was loaded. Everything was set for an exciting underwater game of hide-and-seek. Eric would go first with the power head.

Before going, he thought he would take a look. What he saw made his heart skip. Swimming slowly out of the shadow at the stern of the sunken boat was a steely blue monster with a wicked threat in its powerful tail and a fin raised like a pirate's flag. Out it came slowly, foot by foot—six, seven, eight—a blue shark!

Eric signaled to Chico with his finger and hoped it wasn't shaking as he pointed down. Even as he pointed, Eric was figuring out his strategy. The shark hadn't seen the boys. They could float motionlessly on the surface and hope that the monster would go on its way. Or they could climb aboard the rubber raft and move it slowly shoreward, taking turns guarding the rear.

Which strategy would Chico favor? Perhaps he had another plan, a different sort of retreat.

Retreat? Chico was turning to Eric, taking the power head from hands that were semiparalyzed, putting in its place his spear gun. Chico was not going to retreat; he was going to attack!

Still in a daze, Eric said to himself, "I must stop him!" But it was too late. Chico had dived and was on his way down. Eric could not retreat now; he could not even consider it. He had to stand guard there at the surface or join the attack. Suppose the shark attacked first? Suppose it slashed at Chico and inflicted a severe wound before he could fire the power head? It would then be up to me, thought Eric, to rush to the aid of this foolhardy teammate. Eric was annoyed, scared—and intrigued.

Chico was moving in fearlessly. He was about twenty feet from the blue shark and he kept on going. He was fifteen feet away. How close, thought Eric fearfully, is he going to get?

The shark turned slowly and saw the diver. It looked him over calmly, as if it were sizing him up and deciding how to dispose of him.

Eric, floating motionlessly above the drama, had almost forgotten to breathe. Suddenly he saw a telltale white wake. Chico had fired the power head. Up from the depths came the *blup* of the underwater explosion. There was a great burst of bubbles. The shark, struck amidships, charged its attacker. Chico dodged deftly.

Never had Eric seen such a show. And it was far from over. The breakaway gear was just going into action; the shark's rush had tripped the trigger on the float. Released and inflated, it was floating up to the surface.

The line was paying out at a rapidly rising rate—ten, fifteen, twenty feet. And the wounded shark was flashing up toward the surface.

Toward me! thought Eric. Move! With a great effort he forced himself out of his trance and aimed his spear gun. Aim above the eyes, at the brain, Eric told himself.

He was just about to fire when the shark suddenly veered off and rushed out to sea, the spear still firmly imbedded in it and the line from the float pursuing it. And here was Chico surfacing and grinning.

"Good hit, *no es verdad?*" said Chico with enthusiasm.

Eric ignored the remark. "The float!" he commanded. "Grab the float!" Quickly they flutter-kicked to it.

"The raft!" cried Eric. "Get in!" They helped each other and clambered aboard just in time. The line to the shark was becoming taut.

"Hold on!" cried Eric. They braced themselves. The dart, deeply imbedded by the power head, held its own. The float and the stout line to the shark were anchored to the raft by two pairs of strong hands. But the boys could not anchor the raft. Slowly at first, then with gathering speed, they put out to sea on the strangest voyage Eric ever had made.

They could feel the brute strength of the monster vibrating through the line that they grasped. Eric was thankful that the line had been tested to five hundred pounds, for it was becoming a towrope. The ferocious power of the shark, eight fighting feet of it, was their tugboat. Up and down over the swells they went, bodies braced, holding on for dear life.

"Hola," cried Chico. It was quite evident that he was delighted with the adventure.

"Loco," said Eric. "Absolutely *loco!"*

"Who is crazy?" said Chico indignantly.

"You," said Eric.

"Me?" Chico looked hurt. "Oh no! I know what I do. You wait—you see."

"O.K." said Eric. He tried to smile. "I'll wait." What else can I do? he said to himself.

The monster was veering off now to the left, starting a wide circle. Would the line hold? Would the boys be able to hold on? Eric's hands were already beginning to ache. Perhaps they should spell each other at the job. He turned to Chico.

"I have it," he said. "My turn."

Chico grinned in understanding and released his grip on the line. Eric immediately felt the full force of the shark's strength. He felt his hands being pulled from his arms, his arms from his shoulders.

A little later Chico took his turn on the straining line. Eric reloaded and refit the power head. He now had time to think.

What a mad voyage this was—towed through tropical waters on a rubber raft by a huge blue shark! Suppose the shark came about, capsized the raft, and threw them into the water?

Why not cut the monster loose? Why not? Because he, Eric, was committed to this adventure. It was his dart that was in the shark, imbedded by his power head. If it hadn't been for the power head, the dart probably would not have gone in deep enough to hold against the terrific tension. It was his line that was equal to the great strain. His equipment was making it possible for this scuba diving team to fight the shark. For better or worse, Eric owned an interest in this wild venture.

The voyage had now lasted a half hour according to Eric's waterproof watch, but Chico had lost none of his exuberance. Out to sea they went and back again. Each time it was Chico's turn at the towrope, he reminded Eric of a jaunty cowboy riding a bucking bronco.

Eric was weary. Why had they embarked on this voyage? Why had Chico taken that shot at the shark? "Why?" Eric finally asked the question aloud.

"I want it," said Chico slowly and with conviction. "My family wants *el tiburón*. It is good to eat."

"Good to eat!" Eric repeated the incredible phrase.

"Sure," Chico smiled. "Blue shark cooked in smoke, very good. *Mucho*. And much of it to eat. Enough for everyone. My three brothers, my three sisters, my father, my mother, everyone."

For a minute Eric said nothing. The blue shark was food, enough food for an entire family. How could I have been so slow in catching on? he asked himself. He shook his head at his own short-sightedness. He had been so interested in "local color" on this fishing trip that he had overlooked the heart of the matter. Chico's family had a hard time getting enough food to eat.

"Look!" cried Chico. "Look!" He was hauling in the line. The shark was giving up the fight.

Eric and Chico pulled together. Slowly the strong, wet line came in and coiled on the bottom of the raft—fifty feet of it, seventy-five. When would that great steely shape appear? How much life was left in it?

All at once they saw it, lurking in a sun-swept billow. They cried out together, *"Mira!* Look!"

It was enormous and it was still able to move. It gathered up its remaining strength for one last lunge and charged to the raft. Amazed at his own calmness, Eric lifted the power head he had reloaded. He waited until the shark was well within range. Then he fired.

The spear found its mark. On impact the cartridge exploded. The blue shark staggered in a bloody froth of bubbles. With a flick of its ebbing strength the shark struck the raft with its huge tail. The raft tipped on its side, hung for a moment as if undecided, then slapped down, right side up, on the swell.

There was a second slap—Chico's hand on Eric's sunburned back. *"Magnifico!"* Eric winced at the slap and hardly heard the compliment.

The shark was dead. It was a solemn moment. Death, even the death of a shark, cast its spell.

Paddling firmly, Eric and Chico towed the shark in. As they neared the shore they coasted in on a small avalanche of white surf. A wave picked up the shark and rolled it onto the beach. They dragged it up farther and inspected it.

"Magnifico," said Chico again. Eric knew now that his teammate wasn't admiring the prehistoric monster. He was estimating it as a provider of food for his family.

The shark was too heavy to lift into the truck the boys had driven to the beach. Out came Chico's knife to dissect the monster. Nothing of this great prize was going to be wasted, ·not even the fin. This was no longer a shark. It was food, and each chunk of it was being neatly wrapped in a piece of old newspaper.

Chico and Eric loaded their gear and drove off. Chico was singing as they turned off the road into the two ruts that marked the driveway to his home. Suddenly a burro confronted the truck. On it sat Elena, Chico's sister, and beside it stood his brother Manuel. Chico greeted the trio with triumphant blasts on the horn and cries of "Come and see!"

Other members of the family came running. Now all the children were lined up, staring, pointing, and chattering. Then out of the adobe house came Chico's father and mother to join in the joyful welcome. Chico demonstrated how Eric's gear had made the great catch possible. Dark eyes full of awe and admiration looked from the gear to its owner and back again.

But there was work to be done. The food from the sea had to be carried in to the fire to be cooked and smoked and preserved. Chico's brothers and sisters formed a human conveyer belt that quickly emptied the truck of its valuable cargo.

In a short time a call came from the kitchen. "Supper! Supper!" Everyone trooped in. There was soup with a most unusual taste.

"Does it taste good?" Chico asked.

"*Si*," said Eric politely. "What is it?"

Chico grinned. "*El tiburón azul.*"

The blue shark! Made into soup—so soon!

Chico laughed. "Only the fin. Tomorrow night we have the big feast. Blue-shark steaks!"

"*Bueno!* Good, good!" said Eric, with as much enthusiasm as he could muster.

211

First American in Space

by ALAN B. SHEPARD, JR.

Lift-Off

I honestly never felt that I would be the first man to ride the Mercury capsule. I knew I had done well in the tests, and I thought there was a good chance I would get one of the early flights. But I had conducted my own private poll and frankly figured that one of the others would probably go first. I got the word that I had been selected in the room at Langley where we had done a lot of our homework. The only people present were the seven of us astronauts and the director of the Space Task Group.

After my name was read off, I did not say anything for about twenty seconds or so. I just looked at the floor. When I looked up, everyone in the room was staring at me. I was excited and happy, but it was not a moment to crow. Each of the others had wanted to be first, himself, and now that chance was gone. But with grins on their faces covering what must have been great disappointment, all of the fellows came over and congratulated me.

The public thinks that a countdown starts when someone starts counting from ten down to zero. Actually, everything is a countdown. You are always aiming at some specific launch date on the calendar. And the countdown really begins when the first two pieces of metal are put together, months before the launch is even scheduled.

For me the countdown started with quite a bit of homework. I stuck close to the capsule as the workmen put it together, piece by piece, and then hung around to watch as the engineers tested it, section by section. I was more familiar with that capsule when it was all over than I have ever been with any other piece of hardware in my life.

A capsule is quite a bit like an automobile. No two identical models ever drive exactly the same. Each one has its own delicate differences and small deviations. Sometimes an ammeter in one capsule will read zero, when actually it is pulling two amps. In another capsule it may be just the reverse. You can cope with these deviations if you know about them ahead of time. It's like driving a car with a soft brake or a little play in the steering wheel. You have to allow for it. In *Freedom 7* I detected a slight difference in the way the control stick responded when I moved it in some test runs. The stick seemed to be a little stiffer than the ones I had gotten used to in the trainers. But there was nothing alarming about this. The capsule checked out very well. The technicians knew that *Freedom 7* would be manned, and they gave it a lot of special attention.

To make sure that all of the equipment was in working order before the actual flight, I went through forty separate dry runs in which everyone rehearsed his own role, from beginning to end, and kept an eye on all the gauges, signal lights, and fuses which controlled each sequence and showed how the gear was working. In addition to checking out the equipment and crews, I was also checking myself out—and so were the NASA doctors. As the first American to go through this sort of thing, I had to pay an unusual amount of attention to my own inner thoughts as the pressures began to mount.

Once in a while the thought of making an unsuccessful flight would get to be too much, and I could feel it in my stomach. I was not going around shaking, but there were some butterflies. There was so much work to do, however, that I never took time out specifically to worry.

On the morning of May 2, 1961, when I was first scheduled to go, a heavy rain was falling, and flashes of lightning were playing around the launching pad. The mission was postponed.

That afternoon, while the technicians drained the corrosive fuels out of the Redstone with blasts of hot air and rechecked all of the circuits for another try, I took a short nap and answered some of my mail. Then I drove out to a deserted beach to do some running to keep in trim and went to Cape Canaveral, now called Cape Kennedy, to see the capsule.

This time things looked very good. There was a real feeling of "go." We were getting pretty fair weather reports, and I felt glad that I was going to be able to give it a whirl.

At the scheduling meeting Thursday morning there were some serious things that had to be said, but there were some good jokes, too. Late that evening, after I had made a few simulated runs in the trainer as a last-minute refresher, John Glenn and I went out on the beach to chase a few crabs around. Things were businesslike in the hangar that night. Everyone realized that there were strong feelings present, but they were not brought out.

I went to bed at ten. John Glenn slept in the same room, and before we turned in, we went over a few last-minute changes in the recovery-ship signals so I would know what to expect. I went off to sleep in ten or fifteen minutes. There were no dreams or nightmares or charging around on the bed. I woke up once, about midnight, and went to the window to check on the stars. I could see them, so I went back to sleep.

A little after 1:00 A.M. on May 5, I got up, shaved and showered, and had breakfast. John was most kind. He asked me if there was anything he could do, wished me well, and went on down to the capsule to get it ready for me . The medical exam and the dressing went according to schedule. There were butterflies in my stomach again, but I did not feel that I was coming apart or that things were getting ahead of me. A little after four we left the hangar and got started for the pad.

When we reached the pad, the count appeared to be a little behind. Apparently the crews were taking all the time they could and being extra careful with the preparations. Gordon Cooper, who was stationed in the blockhouse that morning, came in to give me a final weather briefing and to tell me about the exact position of the ships in the landing area. He said the weathermen were predicting three-foot waves and 8- to 10-knot winds.

When it was time to ride the gantry elevator, I paused at the base to take a look at the Redstone. I sort of wanted to kick the tires—the way you do with a new car or an airplane. I would probably never see that missile again. I enjoy looking at a bird that is getting ready to go.

216

The Redstone with the Mercury capsule and the escape tower on top of it is a particularly good-looking combination, long and slender. And this one had a decided air of expectancy about it. It stood there venting white clouds and rolling frost down the side. In the glow of the searchlight it was really beautiful.

After admiring the bird, I went up in the elevator and walked across the narrow platform to the capsule. I walked around a bit, talking briefly with Gus Grissom and with John Glenn. Some of the crew looked a little tense, but none of the astronauts showed it.

At 5:20 I disconnected the hose which led to my portable air conditioner, slipped off the protective galoshes that covered my boots, and squeezed through the hatch.

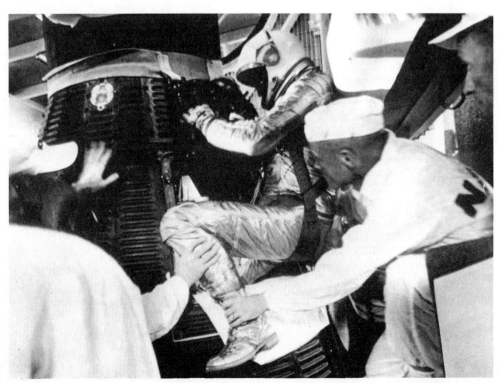

Then I linked the suit up with the capsule oxygen system, checked the straps which held me tight to the couch, and removed the pins that kept some of the switches from being pushed or pulled by accident. I passed these outside.

John had left a little note on the instrument panel, where no one else could see it but me. It read, *No Handball Playing in This Area.* I was going to leave it there, but when John saw me laugh behind the visor,

he grinned and reached in for it. I guess he remembered that the capsule cameras might pick up that message, and he lost his nerve. No one could speak to me face to face now. I had closed the visor and was hooked up with the intercom system.

At 6:10 the hatch went on. I was alone. I watched as the latches turned, to make sure they were tight.

This was the big moment, and I had thought about it a lot. The butterflies were pretty strong now. "OK, Buster," I said to myself, "you volunteered for this thing. Now it's up to you to do it." I had anticipated the nervousness I felt, and I had made plans to counteract it by plunging into my pilot preparations. There were plenty of things to do to keep me busy, and the tension slacked off.

The gantry rolled back at 6:34, and I lay on my back seventy feet above the ground, checking the straps and switches and waiting for the countdown to proceed.

I passed some of the time looking through the periscope. The view was fascinating. I could see clouds up above and people far beneath me on the ground. When the sun rose, it came right into the scope, and I had to crank in some filters to cut down on the glare.

I had a long wait and could hear all the talk of the engineers and technicians on the intercom. When I had been locked in the capsule almost four hours, I put a remark of my own into the intercom. "Why don't you fix your little problems and light this candle?" I said.

The last few minutes went perfectly. Everyone was prompt in his reports. I could feel that all the training we had gone through with the crews was really paying off down there. I had no concern. I knew how things were supposed to go, and that is how they went. About three minutes before lift-off the outside flow of cooling gas was turned off. At two minutes before launch I set the control valves for my suit and cabin temperature and had a quick check of my radio communications. Electronically speaking, my colleagues were all around me at this moment.

At the count of 5 I put my right hand on the stop watch button, which I had to push at lift-off to time the flight. I put my left hand on the abort handle, which I would move in a hurry only if something went seriously wrong and I had to activate the escape tower.

I think I braced myself too much while I was given the final count. Nobody knew, of course, how much shock and vibration I would feel when I took off. I was probably a little too tense. But I was really exhilarated and pleasantly surprised when I answered, "Lift-off, and the clock is started."

There was a lot less vibration and noise rumble than I had expected. It was extremely smooth—a gentle, gradual rise off the ground. There was nothing rough about it. But there was no question that I was going, either. I could see it on the instruments, hear it on the headphones, feel it all around me.

It was a strange and exciting sensation. And yet it was so mild and easy—much like the rides we had experienced in our trainers—that it seemed very familiar. I felt as if I had experienced the whole thing before.

NASA Photo

While the World Watched

For the first minute the ride continued to be smooth. My main job just then was to keep the people on the ground as informed as possible. It was no good for them to have a test pilot up there unless they knew what he was doing, what he saw, and how he felt every thirty seconds or so. I did quite a bit of reporting over the radio about oxygen pressure and fuel consumption and cabin temperature and how the G's were mounting slowly, just as we had predicted they would. I do not imagine that future spacemen will have to bother quite so much about some of these items.

I was scheduled to communicate about something or other for a total of seventy-eight times during the fifteen minutes I was to be up. And I had to manage, or at least monitor, a total of twenty-seven major events in the capsule. This kept me rather busy.

One minute after lift-off the ride did get a little rough. This was where the booster and the capsule passed from sonic to supersonic speed. The spacecraft started vibrating here. Although my vision was blurred for a few seconds, I had no trouble seeing the instrument panel.

The engine cutoff came right on schedule, at two minutes and twenty-two seconds after lift-off. Nothing abrupt happened, just a delicate and gradual dropping off of the thrust as the fuel flow decreased. I heard a roaring noise as the escape tower blew off. I was glad I would not be needing it any longer. After reporting events on the instrument panel, I heard a noise as the little rockets fired to separate the capsule from the booster. This was a critical point of the flight, both technically and psychologically. I knew that if the capsule got hung up on the booster, I would have quite a different flight, and I had thought about this possibility quite a lot before lift-off. There is good medical evidence that I was worried about it again when it was time for the event to take place. My pulse rate reached its peak here—138.

Right after leaving the booster, the capsule and I went weightless together, and I could feel the capsule begin its slow, lazy turnaround to get into position for the rest of the flight. It turned 180 degrees, with the blunt or bottom end swinging forward now to take up the heat. It had been facing down and backward. The periscope went back out again now, and I was supposed to do three things in order: (1) take over manual control of the capsule; (2) tell the people downstairs how the controls were working; and (3) take a look outside to see what the view was like.

The capsule was traveling at about 5000 miles per hour now, and up to this point it had been on automatic pilot. I switched over to the manual control stick. I found out that I could easily raise or lower the blunt end of the capsule and make the capsule twist slightly from left to right and back again, just as I wanted it to. Finally I took over control of the roll motion, and I was flying *Freedom 7* on my own. This was a big moment for me, for it proved that our control system was sound and that it worked under real space-flight conditions.

It was now time to go to the periscope. I had been well briefed on what to expect, but no one could be briefed well enough to be completely prepared for the astonishing view I got. To the south I could see past the Florida Keys; north to clouds that just obscured Cape Hatteras. Across Florida I could see west as far as Pensacola. In a cloudless area I identified Andros Island and Bimini. The colors around these ocean islands were brilliantly clear, and I could see variations between the blue of deep water and the light green of the shoal areas near the reefs. It was really stunning.

But I did not just admire the view. I found that I could actually use it to help keep the capsule in the proper attitude. It was good to know that we could count on handling the capsule this extra way, provided, of course, that we had a clear view and knew what we were looking at.

224

All through this period the capsule and I remained weightless. And though we had had a lot of free advice on how this would feel—some of it rather dire—the sensation was just what I expected it would be: pleasant and relaxing. I was completely comfortable, and it was something of a relief not to feel the pressure and weight of my body against the couch. The ends of my straps floated around a little, and there was some dust drifting around in the cockpit with me.

At about 115 miles up—very near the highest point of my flight—the countdown for the retro-firing maneuver began. This had nothing directly to do with my flight from a technical standpoint. I was established on a ballistic path, and there was nothing the retro-rockets could do to sway me from it. But we would be using these rockets as brakes on the big orbital flights to start the capsule back toward Earth. We wanted to try them on my trip just to see how well they worked. We also wanted to test *my* reactions to them and check on the pilot's ability to keep the capsule under control as they went off. I used the manual control stick to tilt the blunt end of the capsule up to an angle of 34 degrees above the horizontal. At five minutes and fourteen seconds after launch, the first of the three rockets went off, right on schedule. The other two went off at five-second intervals. There was a small, upsetting motion as our speed was reduced, and I was pushed back into the couch a bit by the sudden change in G's. But each time the capsule started to get pushed out of its proper angle by one of the retros going off, I found that I could bring it back again without any trouble at all. I was able to stay on top of the flight by using the manual controls, and this was perhaps the most encouraging product of the entire mission.

In the long plunge back to Earth, I was pushed back into the couch with a force of about 11 G's. This was not as high as the G's we had all taken during the training program, and I remember being clear all the way through the re-entry phase. I was able to report the G level with normal voice procedure.

The temperature climbed to 1230 degrees Fahrenheit on the outer walls of the capsule, but it never went above 100 degrees in the cabin or above 82 degrees in my suit. The life-support system worked without a hitch. By the time I had fallen to 30,000 feet, the capsule had slowed down to about 300 miles an hour. At 15,000 feet a ventilation valve opened up on schedule to let cool, fresh air come into the capsule.

The next thing I had to sweat out was the big 63-foot chute, which was due to break out at 10,000 feet. If it failed to show up on schedule, I could switch to a reserve chute of the same size by pulling a ring near the instrument panel. I must admit that my finger was poised right on that ring as we passed through the 10,000-foot mark. But I did not have to pull it. Looking through the periscope, I could see the antenna canister blow free on top of the capsule. Then the drogue chute went floating away, pulling the canister behind it. The canister, in turn, pulled out the bag which held the main chute and pulled *it* free. And then, all of a sudden, after this beautiful sequence, there it was—the main chute stretching out long and thin. It had not opened up yet against the sky. But four seconds later the huge orange-and-white canopy blossomed out above me. It looked wonderful right from the beginning. I stared at it hard through the periscope for any signs of trouble. It was drawing perfectly. It was letting me down at just the right speed, and I felt very much relieved. I would have a nice, easy landing.

I opened the visor in my helmet and disconnected the hose that keeps the visor sealed when the suit is pressurized. I took off my knee straps and released the strap that went across my chest. The capsule was swaying gently now, back and forth under the chute. I knew that the people back in the Control Center were anxious about all this, so I sent two messages of "All OK."

At about 1000 feet I looked out through the porthole and saw the water coming up toward me. I braced myself in the couch for the impact, but it was not at all bad. It was no more severe than the jolt a Navy pilot gets when he is launched off the catapult of a carrier. The spacecraft hit and flopped on its side, so that I was leaning over on my right side on the couch. One porthole was completely under water. I hit the switch to kick the reserve parachute loose. This would take some of the weight off the top of the capsule and help it right itself. The same switch started a sequence which deployed a radio antenna to help me signal my position. I could see the yellow dye marker coloring the water through the other porthole. I could not see any water seeping into the capsule, but I could hear all kinds of gurgling sounds around me. Slowly and steadily the capsule righted itself.

As soon as I knew the radio antenna was out of the water I sent off a message saying that I was fine.

I took off my lap belt and loosened my helmet so I could take it off quickly when I went out the door. And I had just started to make a final reading on all of the instruments when the helicopter pilot called me. He seemed in a hurry to get me out. I heard the hook catch hold of the top of the capsule, and then the pilot called: "You've got two minutes to come out."

I called the pilot back and asked him if he would please lift the capsule a little higher. He hoisted it up a foot or two. I told him that I would be out in thirty seconds.

I took off my helmet and took a last look around the capsule. Then I opened the door and crawled to a sitting position on the sill. The pilot lowered the horse-collar sling; I grabbed it, slipped it on, and then began the slow ride up into the helicopter.

NASA Photo

On the way to the carrier I felt relieved and happy. I knew I had done a pretty good job. The Mercury flight systems had worked out even better than we had thought they would. And we had put on a good demonstration of our capability right out in the open, where the whole world could watch us taking our chances.

It took the helicopter seven minutes to get me to the carrier. When we approached the ship, I could see sailors crowding the deck, applauding and cheering and waving their caps. I felt a real lump in my throat. I started for the quarters where the doctors would give me a quick once-over. First, however, I went back to the capsule, which had been lowered gently onto a pile of mattresses on the carrier deck. I wanted to retrieve the helmet I had left behind in the cockpit. And I wanted to take one more look at *Freedom 7*. I was pretty proud of the job *it* had done, too.

Stars

by SARA TEASDALE

Alone in the night
  On a dark hill
With pines around me
  Spicy and still,

And a heaven full of stars
  Over my head,
White and topaz
  And misty red;

Myriads with beating
  Hearts of fire
That aeons
  Cannot vex or tire;

Up the dome of heaven
  Like a great hill,
I watch them marching
  Stately and still,

And I know that I
  Am honored to be
Witness
  Of so much majesty.

230

Is Anybody Out There?

by JOHN RUBLOWSKY

When you look up at the stars and study their movements across the heavens for a long time, you cannot help noticing that most of the stars move in a regular and orderly way. In the Northern Hemisphere they appear to rotate clockwise around the North Star, which is called Polaris by astronomers.

Most of the stars move in this orderly manner, but some do not. Some of the brightest stars in the sky seem to wander about aimlessly. You would have to watch them very carefully over a period of many years before you could find any order in their movements.

More than two thousand years ago the ancient Greeks noticed these restless stars. They called them planets, which was the Greek word for wanderers, and they made up fanciful stories about them. They named these wandering stars after their gods and goddesses. One of these planets seemed to glow with an angry orange color in the summer sky. This planet was named Mars, after the Greeks' terrible god of war.

It was a very good name, for Mars, as we shall see, is an angry planet. This small, cold, dry, and mysterious world has been the cause of more angry argument among astronomers and other scientists than has all the rest of the solar system.

Mars is no stranger to man. It is 35,000,000 miles from Earth, close enough for our powerful telescopes to give astronomers a good look at this celestial neighbor.

From *Is Anybody Out There* by John Rublowsky. Copyright © 1962 by John Rublowsky. Published by Walker and Company, New York. Permission to reprint also granted by Constable Young Books Ltd., publishers of the English edition, *Life on Other Worlds*.

It would seem, then, that a planet so close and so easy to see shouldn't be the cause of any arguments—we should know all there is to know about Mars. But, as is often pointed out, scientists have found that the more they learn about something, the more there is to learn. And we have learned a great deal about Mars.

Astronomers have seen the march of the seasons on this planet. They have watched the melting of the polar icecaps and the spread of bands of colors across the face of Mars that accompanied the melting. These colors change exactly the way vegetation on Earth changes. In the Martian spring they appear light green, then dark green, then yellow, and finally brown as the seasons move through spring, summer, fall, and winter. Most astronomers agree that there is life on Mars.

And why shouldn't there be life on Mars? Scientists are quick to point out that both Earth and Mars lie within the so-called life belt of the solar system. By this they mean that both planets are close enough to the sun to receive its life-giving radiations and far enough away so that they are not scorched by its heat.

Like Earth, Mars has a mild temperature range. During the Martian summer, temperatures along the equator reach a balmy 87 degrees Fahrenheit. Winter temperatures at the Martian poles rarely drop below minus 125 degrees Fahrenheit. This isn't too rugged a temperature range. In fact, there are many plants on Earth that could survive in this kind of climate.

Like Earth, Mars is wrapped in a thick blanket of atmosphere, which astronomers have measured and found to be at least sixty miles deep in the denser parts. This atmosphere stretches up another two hundred miles before it disappears into the near vacuum of space. We suspect that oxygen is present in this Martian air; so is a trace of water vapor and of carbon dioxide. Furthermore, water is present on the surface of Mars in one form or another. This can be easily seen in the form of icecaps that grow and shrink with the seasons, just as Earth's northern and southern icecaps grow and shrink.

Well, you might ask, if we know so much about Mars, where do all those arguments come in? They all center around the question of *intelligent life*.

Some astronomers hold that the life on Mars has to be very simple, probably nothing more complicated than lichens and mosses. They point out that Mars is actually very different from Earth, so different that it would be impossible for a complicated organism, not to mention intelligence, to have evolved there.

First of all, the atmosphere of Mars is so thin as to be almost no atmosphere at all when compared to Earth's. Careful examination of this Martian atmosphere has revealed that it is just about equal to the atmosphere eleven miles above the surface of Earth.

The temperatures on Mars, which seemed mild at first glance, present some serious problems for any kind of life form that is struggling to evolve intelligence. During the Martian day, temperatures soar to a comfortable 85 degrees. But this is only during the day. Because the atmosphere of Mars is so thin, it cannot hold heat as our atmosphere on Earth does. Within an hour after sunset, the Martian temperature drops to 100 degrees below zero, even in the middle of summer.

Mars is a dry world. Although there is water present, most of the planet, as seen through a powerful telescope, is made up of barren stretches of reddish deserts. Over these deserts giant sandstorms sometimes block out huge portions of the Martian surface and howl angrily over the landscape in strong, dry blasts. The Martian air is so dry that if a man were to try breathing it without protection, he would scorch the membranes in his nose and throat. An artist's version of a desert on Mars is shown on the opposite page.

We see then that Mars, which at first looked inviting, is really a very rugged world. Compared to it, our own barren Antarctic is a pleasant garden, a truly balmy little corner of the solar system. It would seem that those astronomers who say there can be no intelligent life on Mars are right. Mars seems much too harsh and angry a world to be able to support more than the simplest kinds of hardy plants.

But let us look again. Is it really impossible for an intelligent life form to have evolved on this cold, forbidding world?

This is where all the argument over Mars comes in. The trouble is that astronomers are able to see this planet too well and at the same time not well enough. We can see Mars well enough to learn a great deal about its atmosphere, temperatures, and other physical conditions. However, there is too great a distance between Mars and Earth to study any of the details on the Martian surface.

The problem is made worse by the fact that we look at Mars through not one but two obscuring atmospheres. Everything that has ever been seen on Mars has been seen by looking through one veil and into another.

The atmosphere of Earth is always in motion. Winds blow, hot air rises, cold air sinks, clouds form, and dust obscures our view. Light is shaken up and refracted as it passes through our atmosphere.

Under the best seeing conditions, in observatories on the tops of high mountains that are above most of our atmosphere, details on Mars are still very hard to see. When Mars is in an ideal position, an experienced astronomer may get as much as thirty or forty seconds of clear viewing time at a stretch—if he is lucky. And then conditions on Mars may not be ideal. The astronomer's view could be ruined by the Martian atmosphere. This happened in 1956, when Mars came closer to Earth than it will come again until 1971.

Although seeing conditions were good in many observatories on Earth that summer, they were not good on Mars. A giant sandstorm on the planet raised a cloud of dust that hid a large part of the Martian surface.

Photographs of Mars do not help much, either. Even those taken with the best telescopes, with the best cameras, with the best film, and under the best seeing conditions have shown us little more of Mars than a fuzzy round blob. Although these pictures are excellent for analyzing the Martian atmosphere, they cannot give us any fine surface detail. This detail, most important in connection with the question of intelligent life on Mars, can be seen only under ideal conditions by experienced observers for no longer than a few seconds at a time.

Exactly what do these mysterious details show? And why have they been the center of so much argument?

Almost a hundred years ago an Italian astronomer named Giovanni Schiaparelli was studying Mars with a new and powerful telescope. Mars at the time was close to Earth, and seeing conditions one night were almost perfect. Suddenly, as Schiaparelli stared at the planet, a network of fine, straight lines that stretched for miles across the Martian surface came into focus. He could hardly believe his eyes. At first he thought it was some kind of optical illusion or a fault in his telescope. In all his years of studying the heavenly bodies he had never seen anything like this.

Quickly he checked the lenses and mirrors of the telescope and found nothing wrong. He peered through the viewing piece again. There they were—long, straight lines, arranging themselves in a network that stretched across the entire face of the planet. Schiaparelli estimated that some of the longer lines ran for more than fifteen hundred miles and had to be at least twenty-five miles wide.

What could have made such a strange feature? Straight lines do not occur in nature, not such long, straight lines, anyway. If they were not made by nature, then they must have been made by a purposeful intelligence, the astronomer reasoned.

When Schiaparelli announced his findings, he started a controversy that still continues. All over the world astronomers turned their telescopes on Mars. Some of them saw Schiaparelli's "canals," and some saw nothing at all.

In America, Percival Lowell, then one of America's foremost astronomers, became champion of Schiaparelli's discovery. He, too, saw the canals and accepted them as evidence of intelligent life on Mars.

On the basis of his observations, Lowell published an elaborate theory about Mars and its canals. They were, he said, giant irrigation systems constructed on a planet-wide basis by an intelligent race that was faced with a terrible natural catastrophe. Mars was gradually losing both its water and its atmosphere. The Martians realized this and were fighting back, exactly the same way men on Earth would fight to keep their planet livable.

Lowell's theories captured the imagination of the general public. Newspapers wrote sensational stories about Martian men. Books fanned this interest.

Scientists, of course, did not like this kind of attention. Perhaps as a reaction to the unscientific clamor, most scientific opinion tended to go against the ideas of Lowell and Schiaparelli. After a time the popular furor died down. Astronomers, though they still kept looking at Mars, discounted the whole idea of canals and intelligent life there as fancy.

Then, just when it seemed that the whole question was forgotten, a strange thing happened. Dr. Edison Pettit of the Mount Wilson and Palomar observatories, a highly regarded astronomer with a long-term interest in Mars, brought the subject of Martian canals back into discussion.

For a long time Dr. Pettit had made it clear that he did not believe in Lowell and Schiaparelli's canals. He based his stand on the simple fact that, though he had spent hundreds of hours staring at Mars through some of the finest telescopes in the world, he had never seen the smallest sign of a single canal. As far as he was concerned, if there were canals on Mars, he would certainly have seen them. He placed himself squarely in the ranks of those who did not think the canals existed.

One night Dr. Pettit was studying the Martian surface. Suddenly the atmosphere above his lenses became very still and clear. In all his years of observing Mars he had never experienced such perfect seeing conditions. There, before his eyes, the fine network of long, straight lines described by Lowell and Schiaparelli came into focus. Before he left the telescope that night, Dr. Pettit saw geometric markings all over the visible portion of Mars.

Dr. Pettit freely admitted that he had been wrong. He reported that he had seen the canals. They had appeared to him exactly where other observers had said they were, and they looked exactly the way those observers had said they looked.

Today there is no longer any question about the existence of the canals. Since Dr. Pettit's observation, many other astronomers have seen and recorded them. In 1956, despite heavy dust storms on Mars that year, a photograph was made in a South African observatory that clearly showed one of the largest canals.

Let us see, then, what we can learn from these strange canals. Roughly, they form patterns that crisscross the entire surface of the planet. Straight lines, some of them more than a thousand miles long, lead from one area to another, crossing at angles. We know that they are connected with the Martian vegetation cycle, because they darken with the melting icecaps and follow the same pattern of color changes that occurs in the dark Martian plains. It is certain that they are not made by large surface faults on the planet, because there are too many of them. At least forty-five separate lines have been seen and mapped. Some Martian canals are pictured below.

The theory that they are canals, constructed by an intelligent race in order to conserve a dwindling water supply, fits most of what we know about Mars. But scientists do not like to make hasty decisions. Before they will say positively that there is, or was, intelligent life on Mars, they need more proof. Why, they ask, have we been unable to see any other sign of intelligent life? A race intelligent enough to construct such a great irrigation system surely would be able to offer us some other sign of themselves.

Some astronomers believe that the Martians have done exactly that. Mars has two moons, and some astronomers think that these moons may be the handiwork of an intelligence of a high order. Indeed, these two tiny satellites, Deimos (terror) and Phobos (fear), are in many ways the strangest things in the entire solar system.

First of all, they are both very small. Phobos, the larger, may be all of ten miles in diameter, and Deimos, half the size of Phobos, is no more than five miles wide. Not only are they small, they are also very light—so light that astronomers say they must be hollow. A solid body of their size, even if it were made up of the lightest elements known, would still be too heavy to follow the orbital paths that these two mysterious moons do.

They are also very close to Mars. Deimos circles the planet in an orbit 14,500 miles high; Phobos goes no higher than a mere 5800 miles. But this is not the only strange thing about these orbits. Both of them are almost perfect circles. No other bodies in the solar system ever travel in circular orbits.

Both moons travel very fast. Deimos goes around Mars five times every four days. But Deimos is a slow-poke compared to Phobos, which speeds around the planet three times every day. It goes around so fast that it would appear to an observer on Mars to rise in the west and set in the east.

This is unusual behavior for a respectable pair of moons. It piqued the interest of I. S. Shklovsky, a noted Russian scientist, who turned a keen eye on these two moons and came up with some startling theories.

First of all, Shklovsky showed that the moons could not have been asteroids that were somehow captured by the gravitational field of Mars, as some astronomers believed. If they were, their orbits would have to be very different from what they actually are. Shklovsky also showed that they could not have been chunks of matter that were somehow pulled away from the parent body. Again, their orbital paths would have been very different from what we can see and measure.

The Russian scientist then went on to show that the two moons cannot be very old. Their orbits are decaying, that is, they keep inching closer and closer to Mars and have been doing so ever since they started to spin around the planet.

Shklovsky discovered another interesting fact about the circular orbits of both Deimos and Phobos. He discovered that their orbits are also equatorial. They circle around the equator of Mars. Shklovsky pointed out that both of these moons are in exactly the simplest orbital path that could be achieved artificially. In other words, they are placed exactly the same way we would place an orbiting space station above the earth.

But Shklovsky still was not finished. He looked back into history and discovered even more mystery concerning these moons. Deimos and Phobos were discovered only in 1878. This is much later than the discovery of the moons of Jupiter and Saturn and of many other objects that are much harder to see.

Before 1878, though Mars had been studied and watched very carefully, no one had ever seen its two moons. After 1878 astronomers all over the world saw them. And they saw them through the same telescopes they were not able to see them with before.

Why, then, were these moons not seen before 1878? Simply, answers Shklovsky, because they weren't there to be seen. They were seen only after they had been launched into orbit by a race of thinking creatures.

And so the controversy over intelligent life on Mars continues. Arguments and counterarguments are offered by the scientists, and Mars remains the most baffling member of the solar system.

But it will not remain baffling forever. Someday a spaceship launched from Earth will finally solve the riddle. First, instrumented probes will reach across the vast gulf of space that separates us from Mars. They will be followed by manned ships, and when the first astronauts step onto the ground of Mars, we will know whether or not Mars is, or was, the home of an intelligent race.

The ones who live are the ones who
    struggle.
The ones whose soul and heart are filled
    with high purpose.
Yes, these are the living ones.

VICTOR HUGO

A great man is made up of qualities that
    meet or make great occasions.

JAMES RUSSELL LOWELL

Great lives never go out. They go on.

BENJAMIN HARRISON

DREAMERS AND DOERS

"I Have Not Yet Begun to Fight"
The Story of John Paul Jones

by CLAYTON EDWARDS

Those of you who have seen pictures of the steel battle-
ships and atomic submarines of the United States Navy
may find it hard to believe that this mighty fleet was born
in the shape of a few wooden sailing ships. One of the
commanders of the first American war vessels was John
Paul Jones. He was a great naval hero whose courage
and daring stand out in history and in the great traditions
of the Navy.

John Paul Jones was born in Scotland in 1747, but his
name was then John Paul. He was the son of a poor gar-
dener. When he was a boy, he liked to visit a small
seaport near his home and look at the ships. Many sailors
came to this port, and they made friends with the alert
youngster who was always asking them questions about
ships and seamanship. As a result of their friendship
John Paul was a handy sailor at a very early age.

"I Have Not Yet Begun to Fight" is adapted from "John Paul Jones" from the book
A Treasury of Heroes and Heroines by Clayton Edwards, by permission of the copyright
owners, Platt & Munk, Publishers, New York.

John Paul was only twelve years old when he became the apprentice of a merchant who traded with Virginia. On his first voyage John Paul sailed for that colony, where his brother was then living. From time to time in the next few years he stayed with his brother, and he learned to love America. When he was only nineteen years old, he sailed for Jamaica as first mate of a vessel engaged in the slave trade.

But this young sailor did not like the slave trade. After two years he left his vessel in Jamaica and became a passenger on a ship that was sailing for Scotland. On the way home, by a strange chance, both the captain and the mate died. An expert navigator was needed, and John Paul offered to guide the ship into port. The owners paid their debt by giving him command of their ship on the next voyage to Jamaica.

Luck and ability had taken John Paul a long way in a little time. But now he had a series of misfortunes that included mutiny on one of his ships. For a time he disappeared completely.

He was next heard from in the American colonies, bearing the longer name of John Paul Jones. At the outbreak of the American Revolution he offered his services to the Continental Congress, and soon the Naval Committee of Congress called on him for information and advice.

A few vessels were gathered together, and Paul Jones obtained a commission as senior lieutenant on the flagship of the tiny fleet. He was the first man to hoist an American flag over an American man-of-war. The flag was very different from the modern Stars and Stripes.

It was the Grand Union Flag, with thirteen red and white stripes and the British Union Jack.

Paul Jones was soon promoted to the rank of captain, and he sailed for the West Indies to prey upon British shipping. His knowledge of the waters was so thorough and his skill as an officer of such high quality that in forty-seven days he captured sixteen vessels.

The Congress was delighted, and Jones was given command of another ship. This time he sailed northward along the coast of Nova Scotia. There he captured twelve fishing vessels.

His name was now well known in the rebellious colonies. By order of the Congress he set out to cruise about the coast of England and destroy English ships. He had enjoyed the honor of raising an American flag for the first time over an American war vessel. Now he had the honor of being the first naval officer to sail under the Stars and Stripes, which flew for the first time in naval history above Jones' ship, the *Ranger*.

Paul Jones had a plan for action much bolder than the orders he had received from the Congress. He decided to attack the town of Whitehaven, which he had known when he was a boy. In the depth of night the *Ranger* stole into the entrance of the harbor and dropped anchor. Two boats put off from her with muffled oars. Paul Jones was in command of one, and his lieutenant Wallingford in charge of the other.

Jones ordered Wallingford to set fire to the shipping on the north side of the town, while he with his men would advance upon the nearby fort and spike the guns.

The fort was an old one. The garrison was completely surprised and gave in without a struggle. Jones and his followers quickly spiked the guns of the fort and, taking their prisoners with them, hastened back to the boats. Here they learned that Wallingford had failed to set fire to the ships in the harbor. So Jones himself took coals from a house and with the aid of a barrel of tar succeeded in setting fire to one of the ships that was tied to the wharf.

While England was still buzzing over the boldness of this raid, Jones performed another daring act. Following a raid on an estate in Scotland he attacked a twenty-gun British sloop of war and captured the vessel. With the British cruisers in search of him everywhere, he took his prize to a French port. Here he underwent heartbreaking delays in getting money to pay his men and in obtaining a new command.

At last John Paul Jones was given charge of an old merchant ship whose name he was allowed to change to suit his pleasure. In honor of Benjamin Franklin, who was an admired friend, Jones called his new ship the *Bonhomme Richard*. This was the French translation of "Poor Richard," the name that Franklin used when he wrote in his popular almanacs. In August 1779, Jones sailed the *Richard* on what was to be one of the most famous cruises in American history.

Four ships accompanied the *Richard,* but they had French officers and were to be independent of Jones' command. This peculiar state of affairs greatly reduced the efficiency of the little squadron. The crew of the *Richard* was such a mixed bag that even Jones' stout heart must have sunk when he saw his men together. Among them were many French peasants, who had never seen a vessel before, and English prisoners of war, who had to be kept in order by the armed force of his more loyal men. That Jones was able to mold this mass of undisciplined men into a stanch crew is proof of his genius for leadership.

The lack of unity in command soon began to show. Two of the ships left the squadron and returned to France.

As the remaining three vessels were cruising near Flamborough Head, they sighted a large convoy of British merchant vessels guarded by two warships. One of these was the *Serapis*, a ship with almost twice as many guns as the *Bonhomme Richard*. The convoy was sighted well on in the afternoon, and the squadron closed with it at about sunset.

As the sun was going down, the *Serapis* approached the *Bonhomme Richard* and hailed her with the cry "What ship is that?"

"I don't hear you," answered Jones, who was maneuvering his vessel so that his opening broadside would take the decks of his opponent. And when the *Serapis* hailed again, the *Bonhomme Richard* opened fire with all the guns she could bring to bear upon the enemy.

It was a severe blow, but the *Serapis* returned fire promptly. Almost at the first broadside from the English, the American ship, too, was severely crippled. Two of the old cannons of the *Richard* exploded at the first shot, killing and wounding many and tearing a large hole in the hull of the ship. Both ships continued firing, and as they approached each other, a cloud of dense white smoke hid the scene from the wondering folk on shore.

The best chance for the weaker vessel was to close with its opponent, and Jones maneuvered until he had a good chance to make the *Richard* fast to the *Serapis*. The jib boom of the Britisher had swung across the deck of the *Richard,* and Jones with his own hands made it fast to the mizzenmast of his ship. The two ships were now locked together and so close that when the guns were loaded, the cannoneers had to lean into the ports of the enemy vessel to drive the ramrods home.

All the advantage seemed on the side of the British warship. One after another, the American guns were silenced. Attempts by Jones to board the enemy ship were unsuccessful. As the *Richard*'s batteries were put out of commission, the men came to the main deck and manned the remaining guns.

By this time conditions below deck on the *Richard* were very desperate. Water was pouring into the hold. Great breaches were made in the hull, and the ship had been set on fire several times. But Jones fought on. One of his petty officers, thinking in the confusion that Jones had been killed, raised a cry for quarter. It was heard on the British ship.

"Have you surrendered?" called Captain Pearson, commander of the *Serapis*.

Jones climbed into the rigging of his ship so that the British and his own men would hear his answer clearly. "I have not yet begun to fight!" he shouted in a battle cry that has echoed through history.

In spite of Jones' defiance, the situation of the *Richard* seemed hopeless. The English believed that a few more broadsides would bring them victory. And then suddenly the battle was turned. An American sailor had crawled along the yardarm of the *Richard* to a mast of the enemy ship and had dropped a hand grenade. The grenade plunged through a hatchway and fell upon some loose powder and a row of charges for the cannon on deck. A terrific explosion split the air. At once smoke and flame ran through the vessel.

The colors of the *Serapis* were lowered. A little later her captain came aboard the *Bonhomme Richard* and surrendered his sword to John Paul Jones, who courteously returned it.

The *Bonhomme Richard* did not survive the battle won by her crew. The ship was so severely damaged that every man had to be transferred to the *Serapis*. When Jones sailed into a Dutch port, he had more than five hundred British prisoners in his charge. These included two captains.

The battle sealed the fame of John Paul Jones. The Congress commended him for gallantry, and General Washington sent a complimentary letter.

The long war with England ended, and the United States became a nation. Even though John Paul Jones did not go back to America to live, he remained an American citizen. He considered this the greatest honor of any that had come to him—that he could call himself a citizen of the republic for which he had fought often and well against extremely great odds.

John Paul Jones and the Flag

The fourteenth of June is a red-letter day on the calendar and a red-letter day in American history. It is Flag Day, the birthday of the Stars and Stripes.

The Stars and Stripes was born in a resolution of the Continental Congress on June 14, 1777. On that day the Congress resolved: "That the flag of the thirteen United States be thirteen stripes, alternate red and white; that the union be thirteen stars, white in a blue field representing a new constellation."

On the same day, in the same place, the Continental Congress ordered another important piece of business. It gave command of an American vessel to a British-born sea captain, John Paul Jones.

The two events were only accidentally connected. Members of the Congress had no way of knowing that in one historic hour they had brought into being both a flag and a great American hero.

The birth of the Stars and Stripes on the day he got his orders did not escape the attention of John Paul Jones. Perhaps he had a nose for destiny. Perhaps he merely had the seafarer's habit of noticing everything. No matter what the reason, his mind put the two events together, and in his journal he wrote one of the most beautiful things that has ever been written about the flag: *That flag and I were twins; born in the same hour. . . . We cannot be parted in life or death. So long as we float, we shall float together. If we must sink, we shall go down as one.*

L'Enfant's Great Plan

by DAVID BRUCE

When the United States became a nation, it had no capital city, and no one knew just where the capital should be. In the eastern part of the country there were many cities that had grown old or become famous in its colonial history—Boston, New York, Philadelphia, Yorktown, Annapolis, Trenton. Any of these cities would have welcomed the chance to become the seat of the new government. The citizens of each of them felt that their city had a right to be selected for the honor. The clamor became so loud and the feelings of rivalry so strong that Congress finally settled the matter. It authorized President Washington to select a site for a capital city on the banks of the Potomac River, in a place where no city had ever been before.

The spot chosen was the one on which the city of Washington stands today. The beautiful city that has grown there with its handsome buildings and memorials is the work of many men. But the basic plan on which it has developed was the grand design of one man. He was Major Pierre Charles L'Enfant, a young Frenchman.

Pierre L'Enfant was born and educated in France. His father was an artist, a well-known painter of battle scenes. It was a longing for battles that brought the young man to America, but he wanted to fight in them, not to paint them. L'Enfant was twenty-three years old when he arrived in America. He was trained in engineering and architecture, but he came with the sword of a lieutenant in the French army and he meant to fight for the liberation of the American colonies.

L'Enfant arrived during a lull in the fighting, and it took some time to find what he was looking for. Soon there were signs that the action of the war would start again in the southern colonies. In the south he found action enough to satisfy the most ardent of patriots. He was severely wounded at Savannah and captured by the British at Charleston. After an exchange of prisoners, he was back with the American armies and continued to serve as an officer and an engineer.

The war was long, and the colonies needed all the help they could get in their military struggles. Major L'Enfant put his talents to use in the building of fortifications. He trained troops in military discipline. He was well liked by his brother officers. At Valley Forge he was introduced to General Washington and made a portrait sketch of him for another famous Frenchman—the Marquis de Lafayette. And he saw enough of the country that was being born and of its new ideas of liberty and equality to want to make America his home.

Pierre Charles L'Enfant was living and working in New York when Congress announced its decision to build a capital city on the banks of the Potomac River. There were few men in the United States at that time with the kind of experience and training that fitted them for the task of designing a complete city in an undeveloped area. Major L'Enfant knew with the certainty of genius that he was one of them. He believed in the future greatness of the young nation he had helped bring to being. In a design for the capital city of that nation he could express what he believed.

Without delay he wrote to President Washington and asked for the privilege of taking part in the great new project. *Your Excellency will not be surprised,* he wrote, *that my ambition and the desire I have of becoming a useful citizen should lead me to wish a share in the undertaking.*

President Washington thought well of the gifted Frenchman. The necessary arrangements were made. Major L'Enfant was to go as quickly as possible to the site of the proposed city, survey the land, and make a plan, indicating on it where the principal government buildings might be located.

Travel in the days of George Washington was a chancy thing. Major L'Enfant started his journey by stagecoach, but the stage broke down on the way. Impatient to get on with his journey, the Major covered the rest of the distance on foot and on horseback. He arrived in Georgetown, one of several towns near the proposed site of the Federal City, in a rain. The purpose of his visit became quickly known. People who didn't hear it from the Major himself could read about it in the newspaper.

On March 12, 1791, the Georgetown *Weekly Ledger* carried this notice:

> Wednesday evening arrived in this town Major Longfont a French gentleman employed by the President of the United States to survey the lands contiguous to Georgetown, where the Federal City is to be built. His skill in matters of this kind is justly extolled by all disposed to give merit its proper tribute of praise. He is earnest in the business and hopes to be able to lay a plan of that parcel of land before the President upon his arrival in this town.

The writer of the notice spelled the major's name as he heard it pronounced—and he came as close to the French pronunciation as anyone could who did not know the French language.

The rain and mist that greeted Major L'Enfant on his arrival lasted for several days. They did not keep him from plunging into the task President Washington had asked him to do.

He rode on horseback over the land where the Potomac River and the Eastern Branch met—and what did he see? To any eyes the land would have been a fair land. It sloped in even rises to gentle hills. There were trees, swamps, fine springs here and there, and at the season when the Major saw it, there probably was a brightness of wild flowers on the new green of the underbrush. There were almost no houses—just an occasional farm in the fifty square miles that came under the searching gaze of the artist-engineer.

This is all there was for Major L'Enfant to look at, but he saw much more. With the artist's eye of his imagination he saw on this rolling ground a spacious city. The city he saw was complete with noble buildings, heroic monuments, splashing fountains, busy markets, theaters, mansions, colleges, and public gardens—all joined by a beautiful pattern of the broadest streets and avenues that any man had yet imagined for a city anyplace in the world.

The Major could see the "Federal House," as he called the building that was to house the Congress, on a "pedestal" of land that stood "waiting for a monument."

At a distance from it, his mind created the "President's Palace," and at a third point he imagined a superb statue of George Washington.

Major L'Enfant was a dreamer, but he was not a fool. Though he saw his city as clearly as if it actually rose from the tangled acreage of the federal area, he knew it would take a long time to come into existence. *It will be obvious,* he had written to Washington, *that the plan should be drawn on such a scale as to leave room for that aggrandizement . . . which the increase of the wealth of the nation will permit it to pursue at any period, however remote.*

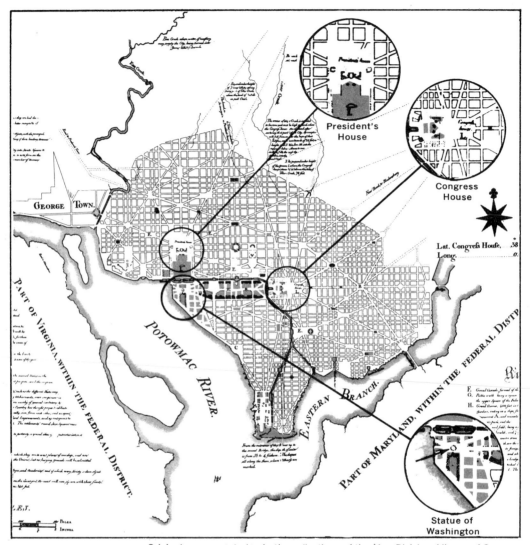

President's House

Congress House

Lat. Congress House, 38
Long. 0.

George Town.

PART OF VIRGINIA, WITHIN THE FEDERAL DISTRICT.

POTOWMAC RIVER.

EASTERN BRANCH.

PART OF MARYLAND, WITHIN THE FEDERAL DISTRICT.

Statue of
Washington

Original manuscript plan in the collections of the Map Division, Library of Congress

    The Major knew his plan was for a distant future. But he had no doubts that what he planned for would happen. His dream was not shared by the men with whom he had to work to get it started.

262

As soon as the general outlines of the plan for the Federal City were known, opposition to it began in murmurs. Men of affairs took one look at the measurements of L'Enfant's avenues and the sites for public buildings and decided the Frenchman was daft. Land was too valuable to be squandered in this spendthrift way. It is strange that men could have had such a miser's view of land when a continent stretched beyond them.

Few men questioned the Major's ability. Fewer still believed in his common sense. The feeling against him and against his plan mounted, though President Washington respected L'Enfant's ability and defended his work.

Then something altogether unfortunate happened. One of the property owners in the federal area had been warned by the Major that a house he was building would stand in the way of one of the new avenues. The man persisted. The Major was courteous but firm. At his order, the rising structure was torn down before the eyes and over the protests of the owner.

To some this action was willful; to some it was crazy; and to all it seemed against the law. It was the beginning of the end of L'Enfant's services to his adopted country. In vain was he reminded that he was to take orders from a commission appointed to direct the work on the Federal City. The Major agreed in principle but objected in practice. The President regretted. The proud Major resigned.

Perhaps L'Enfant dreamed too high and too far ahead. Certainly he dreamed too fast for his vision to be shared by the people around him. He spent the rest of his life on lesser tasks and died, a disappointed man, in the home of friends who sheltered him in the years of his poverty. His body was buried under a tree. He had never been fully paid for the work he did for the young nation whose destiny he saw so clearly.

The grandeur of L'Enfant's idea for a federal city may not have been understood by the times in which he lived —but a great idea seldom dies. In the Major's own lifetime the Capitol building and the President's Palace, which we now call the White House, were built on the sites he had chosen for them. Though their forms have changed, they occupy the same spots today.

It is to L'Enfant also that the city of Washington owes its broad streets, spacious avenues, and parks. The main avenues radiate from the Capitol like the spokes in a wheel.

The growth of our capital city had its ups and downs, but it grew in size, as L'Enfant knew it would, and as it grew, it often followed the pattern which L'Enfant had seen for it. A hundred years after he made his plan, people knew that basically he had been right.

Recognition came late to the proud French genius who chose to live in this country because he was fired by its ideals. By act of Congress he was taken from his lonely grave in 1909 and buried in Arlington National Cemetery among the nation's heroes. At ceremonies to honor the Major the United States Secretary of State said: "It is not a change in L'Enfant that brings us here. It is we who have changed, who have just become able to appreciate his work."

Washington Monument by Night

by CARL SANDBURG

The stone goes straight.
A lean swimmer dives into night sky,
Into half-moon mist.

Two trees are coal black.
This is a great white ghost between.
It is cool to look at.
Strong men, strong women, come here.

Eight years is a long time
To be fighting all the time.

The republic is a dream.
Nothing happens unless first a dream.

The wind bit hard at Valley Forge one Christmas.
Soldiers tied rags on their feet.
Red footprints wrote on the snow . . .
. . . and stone shoots into stars here
. . . into half-moon mist tonight.

Tongues wrangled dark at a man.
He buttoned his coat and stood alone.
In a snowstorm, red hollyberries, thoughts, he stood alone.

Women said: He is lonely
. . . fighting . . . fighting . . . eight years . . .

The name of an iron man goes over the world.
It takes a long time to forget an iron man.

The Man Who Named Old Glory

by ALICE CURTIS DESMOND

Willie Driver went to school in Salem, Massachusetts, until he was thirteen. Then his widowed mother apprenticed him to a blacksmith.

Willie hated blacksmithing, but he stuck it out for a year. Coming home one day, black from coal dust, he burst out, "Mother, why won't you let me go to sea?"

Mrs. Driver wept. So many sailors left Salem and never came back! But Willie gave her no peace until she let him ship as a cabin boy on a vessel bound for Italy.

Before sailing, Willie was called into the owner's office. His duties were explained to him, and he was handed five dollars, one month's wages in advance.

"You probably won't earn that," grumbled the owner. "All boys on their first voyage eat more than they earn."

Willie merely bowed politely and left. But he said to himself, "I'll show him that there's one boy in the world who can earn all that he eats and more, too."

On his return from the voyage Willie was called into the office again. This time he was greeted with a handshake. He was given the balance of his wages and twenty-eight silver dollars as a bonus.

William Driver made many voyages after that. In 1831, while still a young man, he became captain of a brig, the *Charles Doggett*.

The night before Captain Driver sailed, his mother gave him an American flag. "For your new ship," she said. "I made the flag myself."

The next morning the skipper's first act on climbing aboard was to fasten his flag of thirteen stripes and twenty-four stars to the halyards and send it aloft. As it broke out to the air, William cried, "That's the most glorious flag I ever saw. I'll call her Old Glory!"

This was Captain Driver's last voyage. When he returned home he found his wife very ill, and he moved with her to Nashville, Tennessee. But he never forgot the sailor's life that he loved, and he treasured the flag that had gone with him on his last voyage.

On special occasions through the years Captain Driver hung Old Glory over the doorway of his house. Then in 1861 Tennessee seceded from the Union, and it was dangerous to display the Union flag. One day, after Old Glory was shot at, the flag disappeared.

In 1862 Nashville was captured by the Union army and a small Union flag was hoisted above the Capitol. Standing in the crowd, Captain Driver said to an officer, "I'd like to see Old Glory flying up there instead of that little flag. May I get it?"

So Captain Driver, with a corporal's guard, went to his house. He ripped open a quilt on his bed and lifted Old Glory from the hiding place into which he had sewed it. Every night he had slept beneath it.

William and his most precious possession were escorted back to the Capitol. In spite of his sixty years, William climbed the dome and put up his flag himself.

Today the flag of William Driver, the first American flag to be called Old Glory, is on display in the National Museum at Washington, D.C.

New York City Department of Public Works Photo

Builders of the Bridge

by D. B. STEINMAN

In 1831 a German engineer named John Roebling came to the United States to make his fortune in the new land. He settled near Pittsburgh with other German immigrants, and there he married and had a son whom he named Washington Augustus. John became an American citizen. To his great satisfaction he obtained a job on the Sandy and Beaver Canal. When that was finished, there were jobs of surveying for other canals and for the railroads that were coming into Pennsylvania.

On these jobs John Roebling became interested in the way people were transferred from one canal to another when a hill was in the way. The canal boats were placed on flatcars and hauled over tracks up and down the incline by a rope. The hemp ropes that were used were clumsy and often broke. At one time Roebling saw a rope give way while some cars were being pulled up a mountainside. Two men were crushed in the wreck.

This accident started John thinking that there ought to be a stronger and more durable material than hemp for

Adapted from *Famous Bridges of the World,* by David B. Steinman. Copyright 1953 by D. B. Steinman. Reprinted by permission of Random House, Inc.

these ropes. If he could make rope out of iron wire, which would be flexible enough to bend without breaking, it would be much stronger than other ropes and only about one-fourth as thick. Above all, it would have a much longer life. But how could such rope be made? No one in America had ever heard of such a thing.

Developing his own methods and equipment, John Roebling started to make wire rope. In the meadow back of his home, he built a ropewalk. He bought quantities of iron wire and taught his neighbors how to twist it into a rope of seven strands. He invented a twisting machine, operated by hand.

The finished product exceeded his highest hopes, and a new industry was born. Roebling's wire rope was used with great success on the canal portages, the places at which the canal boats had to be hauled overland.

John did not rest here. He thought of the aqueducts built on the canals to carry the canals across rivers. He wondered why these structures could not be suspension aqueducts, with cables of his new iron rope. He built four of these suspension aqueducts, and they, too, were successful.

The wire-rope industry grew, and soon it needed larger quarters. So Roebling moved to Trenton, New Jersey, set up a factory there, and prospered.

In spite of his great success, John Roebling was not content. His real ambition was to build suspension bridges. During his student days in Germany he had visited a town to see with his own eyes a small chain bridge that was under construction. It was the first suspension bridge in that part of the world. He was fascinated by it.

In that moment he decided his lifework. He wanted to be a builder of suspension bridges, and he was going to build them better and bigger and stronger than any previously imagined.

Roebling had to wait a long time to start on his lifework. In 1851, twenty years after he arrived in America, he was given a contract to build a railroad bridge at Niagara Falls—a suspension bridge. At that time suspension bridges for railroads were unheard of. Roebling built his record-breaking span out of wire and wood. It proved a success and stood for forty-two years until a bridge designed to carry heavier loads replaced it.

Meanwhile Washington Roebling was growing up. The oldest of six children, he was a serious boy. Much of the time he was away at school, studying engineering. Until he was an adult, Washington never really knew his famous father.

At last the father and son formed a partnership, just as the Civil War broke out. Washington joined the Army, built bridges for the troops, and rose to the rank of colonel. When the war ended, he went to Cincinnati and supervised the construction of a suspension bridge his father was building over the Ohio River.

No sooner was this bridge finished than John Roebling was called to New York City to discuss the building of a bridge over the East River—a bridge that would connect Brooklyn and Manhattan Island. Washington and his wife were sent to Europe, where they were to look at every suspension bridge and learn all about the pneumatic caisson, a new method of sinking foundations that John

intended to use in the construction of Brooklyn Bridge. Washington stayed abroad a year.

At home John Roebling worked hard to survey the site of the proposed bridge and to draw up the plans. An artist's rendering of his original design was made to show how the completed bridge would look. It took time and hard work to convince politicians and the public that his plans were practicable. By the summer of 1869 everyone was convinced that the bridge could be built, and the money had been subscribed. Actual work was about to begin.

Then, on the morning of July 5, John went to survey one more time the location of the Brooklyn tower. So engrossed was he in the work that he did not notice a ferryboat was docking at the pier on which he was standing. The vessel jammed against the pier, and John's foot was crushed. He was taken at once to Washington's home in Brooklyn, and the toes of the foot were amputated. But lockjaw set in, and the great engineer died.

In spite of this tragedy, the building of the bridge had to go on. Washington took over his father's job as chief engineer and devoted all his time to the work.

Because the foundations for the towers of the bridge had to go far below water to secure a firm resting place, the pneumatic caissons that Washington had investigated in Europe were used. Only a few years before, James Eads had introduced them in America in the building of his St. Louis Bridge.

The Brooklyn pier of the bridge had to be sunk to a depth of only forty-four feet, but the Manhattan pier had to go down to seventy-six feet. As this part of the work progressed, more and more men suffered from caisson disease. This crippling and even killing disease was one of the risks of working in the compressed atmosphere of the caisson. Workmen called it "the bends." Three men working on the Brooklyn Bridge died from it.

All this while, Washington Roebling drove himself relentlessly; he worked day and night in the caisson. One afternoon he was carried up unconscious and lay all night near death. In a few days he seemed well again and returned to the caisson. This time he collapsed and was carried up paralyzed. At the age of thirty-five he became an invalid for life.

But Washington Roebling did not give up. From his sickbed he directed every detail of the building of the bridge. Notes and drawings were carried to the workmen by his wife, Emily, who had become his assistant. He taught her engineering so that she could understand the problems and could talk the engineers' language. From the windows of his house, Washington himself watched the progress of the work through field glasses.

Brooklyn Bridge was remarkable not only for the early use of the pneumatic caisson, but also because it was the first bridge on which steel wire was used. Steel was then a new structural material; it was lighter and stronger than wrought iron. But it had to be tried out. Engineer Roebling was convinced that it was the material of the future, and so he went ahead. He had every wire galvanized as a safeguard against rust, and this, too, was something new. The four cables of the bridge, nearly sixteen inches in diameter, took twenty-six months to spin.

But the work on the bridge did not proceed smoothly. There were fires, accidents, lack of funds, dishonest contractors, and political troubles. Just a year before the bridge was completed, there was an attempt to displace Washington Roebling as chief engineer. His wife went before the American Society of Civil Engineers and read a statement recounting her husband's sacrifices and accomplishments. Her courage and sincerity won the full support not only of the engineers but of the public as well.

On May 24, 1883, almost fourteen years after it was started, the bridge stood finished. It was a fine day for a celebration. Thousands of people lined the streets to watch the parade, which started at Twenty-third Street and moved down Broadway to the bridge. Bands, carriages, horses, flags—all added to the splendor of the parade. And among the notables were the President of the United States, Chester A. Arthur, and the Governor of New York, Grover Cleveland. As these people walked across the bridge, heavy cannon boomed, boats blew horns, and whistles and bells added to the joyous sound.

276

After the speeches the distinguished guests marched through the streets of Brooklyn to Washington and Emily Roebling's home. The two had watched the celebration from their windows with field glasses. While the officials were inside congratulating the engineer and his wife, cheering crowds stood on the street corner.

When night fell over the city, torches, bonfires, and lanterns lit up the sky. And from the huge towers of the bridge fell showers of fireworks. But the brightest sight was the sixteen-hundred-foot main span itself, illuminated by eighty powerful electric lamps, Edison's new invention! At midnight the bridge was opened to the public, and within twenty-four hours, 250,000 people crossed over it.

The Brooklyn Bridge became one of the most famous bridges in the world—a superb example of a union between beauty and strength.

John Roebling did not live to see his masterpiece, but he had supreme confidence in its greatness. When it existed only on his drawing board, he wrote of it: "The work, when constructed in accordance with my designs, will not only be the greatest bridge in existence, but it will be the great engineering work of this Continent and of the age. Its great towers . . . will be entitled to be ranked as national monuments."

Roebling's serene prophecy came true. Today the Brooklyn Bridge is listed as a National Historic Landmark by the United States Department of the Interior.

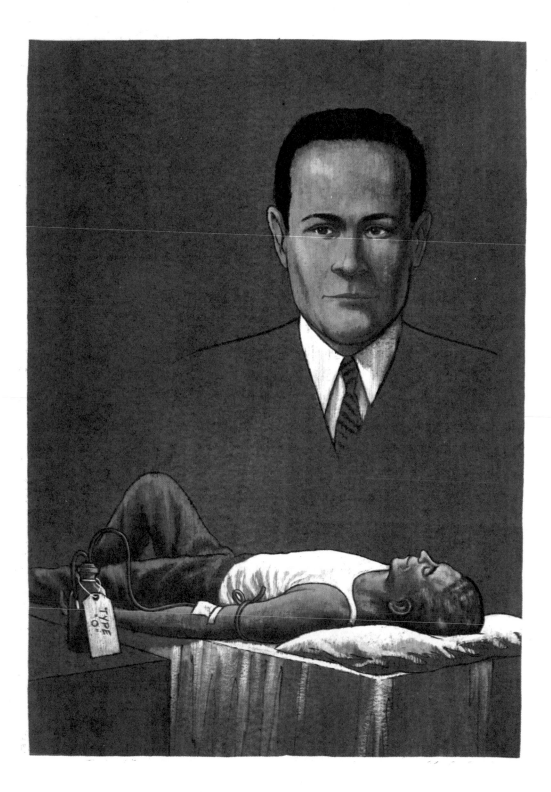

A Precious Gift:
The Work of Dr. Charles Drew

by RHODA TRUAX

Dr. Charles R. Drew, Medical Supervisor of Blood for Britain—a project for supplying blood plasma to Great Britain in World War II—paused for a moment to look in on the first important step of his new undertaking. This was the giving of blood. The project Dr. Drew was supervising was the first of its kind. It would serve as a model for other cities and, with modification, for the armed services and hospitals. Dr. Drew was constantly on the alert for ways to improve techniques.

The blood donor he was watching lay on his back on a cot. His left arm was connected by a tube to a bottle standing on a little table by his head.

"Everything's all right, isn't it?" the man asked as the nurse came over to him, his voice a shade too casual.

"Everything's just fine, Mr. Osgood," the nurse said to him.

The nurse's manner, Dr. Drew observed, was excellent, as was that of all the nurses and doctors who were volunteering their services. They were matter-of-fact, as though this was a simple routine affair, as, indeed, it was. Yet they conveyed the impression that the donors were doing something admirable, and this was also true. It was important to treat the donors properly. No stirring appeals for volunteers could be so effective as word-of-mouth reports by those who had given blood without finding the process unpleasant.

The response of volunteers was more than gratifying. The first blood for the project had been collected from doctors and nurses on August 16, 1940, the day the bombing of London began. Within a month, mainly because of appeals to churches, synagogues, and various organizations, 1723 people had given blood. Early in September the aerial blitzkrieg against London had begun, and by October 26 there had been 8699 donors. The number was steadily increasing.

This was excellent, but it increased the problems of the project and its director. More workers were needed to take the blood, to make tests, to process the blood, to bottle, pack, and ship it. Each step was crammed with questions that had to be answered.

Which was safest and most practical—whole blood, serum, or plasma? Should plasma, once decided upon, be dried or sent in fluid form? Should the white and red cells be removed by the slow method of letting them settle to the bottom? Or by the faster and more expensive method of using a centrifuge? What were the best methods of testing for infected blood before pooling it?

These and many, many other questions had to be answered at the same time that large quantities of safe plasma were being sent to England. Dr. Drew, who was a research scientist as well as a surgeon, mourned because there was not time to investigate all the possibilities of this tremendous project.

But now the nurse was speaking again to the blood donor Dr. Drew had been watching. He turned his attention back to her.

"We've almost finished, Mr. Osgood," she said. "Just lie still a few minutes, please."

Mr. Osgood was apparently not inclined to follow instructions. He sat up quickly and turned his head to look at the flask that the nurse was placing on a rack. "Well, what do you know! Did I give all that?" he asked. The question began in a booming voice but trailed off. The nurse caught him as he was about to fall back, and she eased his head onto the cot again. Without appearing to hurry, the Doctor brought the smelling salts.

"I don't know what got into me," the man said after a minute or two. "I never passed out in my life."

"I'm afraid you sat up a little too suddenly," the nurse told him. "And besides, it's often the huskiest men who get upset at the sight of blood. We had one in here the other day who was an all-American football player. He fainted dead away."

It was always difficult for Dr. Drew to realize that many people reacted with horror at the very thought of blood. He found everything about it fascinating: its physical and chemical composition; the way it wound through the entire body in about a minute, its red cells carrying oxygen to all the tissues; the way the white cells and plasma protected the body against infection.

Yet in spite of all that is known about blood, superstitions persist. "It's in his blood to act that way," people remark. They explain differences between people by supposed differences in their blood.

It is true that the blood of all individuals is not alike. There are four different types, and the differences can be very important; but they have nothing to do with racial, religious, or national groupings. Each of the four blood types includes people of all colors and nationalities. The blood of a Norwegian can differ from that of his own relatives and "match" that of a Japanese or an Indian.

It was strange, Dr. Drew thought, that people could know this scientific fact and yet continue to talk about "Jewish blood" or "colored blood." He realized that a great many of his fellow citizens would not want to accept a transfusion of his blood because he was a Negro.

As a surgeon, Dr. Drew was particularly interested in transfusions as a means of preventing and treating the condition known as shock. Following a serious operation or injury, a patient's blood pressure would often drop. His pulse would become weak and his skin cold and clammy. He would collapse and perhaps die. A transfusion could work wonders in such a case.

Dr. Drew had been interested in blood research for a number of years. In 1938 he was engaged in blood research at Columbia University. Two years later his thesis, *Banked Blood,* was published.

There could have been no more timely subject. World War II had broken out. Some of the nations, recognizing the importance of transfusions to the wounded, had established some mobile units to collect blood and others to give transfusions.

The British lost most of their units in the retreat at Dunkirk. Their situation was now critical, as was that of France, Belgium, and Holland.

As the need for help grew more and more desperate, the Blood for Britain project was planned and formed in New York. Dr. Drew, who was then teaching at Howard University, was asked to serve as full-time director. He was, the board felt, "best qualified of anyone we know to act in this important development . . . a recognized authority on the subject of blood preservation."

Dr. Drew would have preferred staying at Howard University, teaching Negro medical students. He loved surgery, and he felt that his people needed him. On the other hand, a Negro in such an important position could help in the struggle against prejudice and discrimination.

Charles Drew knew well what prejudice was. As a student he had heard the crowds cheer for him and three other Negroes on the track team as they piled up crucial points in a meet. After the cheers had died away, an embarrassing situation had arisen in connection with a banquet for the track team: no large hotel could be found that was willing to serve Negro athletes. Would they mind, they were asked, eating by themselves at the college? If Dr. Drew should ever be tempted to believe that applause made him special, he would hear in his memory the words "Would you mind . . . ?" as they hung over the table where four members of the team sat by themselves in absolute silence.

But he had other reasons for accepting the position. It would enable him to help win the war and to save lives. Lives were already being saved. Dr. Drew wished that every adult could see a transfusion. Then more people would donate blood to fill the needs of peace as well as of war. Perhaps the old feelings about blood would change. A man might look at a total stranger and say to himself: Maybe my blood is flowing in his veins.

The night after Mr. Osgood gave his blood, a storm blanketed the British coast. Enemy aircraft were all grounded, and the tired people of London hoped for a good night's rest.

Shortly before dawn, however, the clouds lifted and the German planes crossed the Channel in a great wave. Warning signals of a raid were unheeded by people who were too drugged by sleep to hurry to shelters.

Most of the bombs fell on the poorest sections of London. One of them scored a direct hit on an old three-story building not far from the Thames River.

Alec Macintosh lived on the ground floor with his daughter and his daughter-in-law and her baby. He had been awake, for who could sleep through the screaming of the sirens, the anti-aircraft fire, and the bombs?

After the explosion he was out on the street, surrounded by the wreckage of his home, staring up at the sky that was crisscrossed by the probing fingers of searchlights.

Air Raid Precaution workers and neighbors moved hurriedly around him.

"Rose is inside!" he cried suddenly. "Rose and the baby. Sarah's working the night shift, but Rose and the baby are inside. You've got to get them out."

"Easy now, mate," a rescue worker told him. Then the worker turned to some young men and said, "Lend a hand here, lads. A woman and child are inside."

A woman neighbor, carrying a bucket of sand, called out, "It's Tom's wife. She's in there somewhere."

"Let me help," Alec cried. "I'm all right now."

"Well then, we can use a hand. Hold that beam while I set a prop here," someone directed.

The wavering glow from the searchlights came through a gaping hole in the ceiling. It revealed something white under the wreckage—a woman and a child. In a few minutes the men got them out, and then, in a lull, they heard the baby cry. The child was uninjured, having been protected by her mother's body.

"I'll take the baby. It's me, Lizzie Wells, and I'll take care of the poor little thing," said a neighbor.

Alec nodded, wondering who would take care of the baby later, with no mother and with Tom in the hospital since Dunkirk, where he had lost a leg. Alec was sure Rose was dead, for he had touched her hand and found it cold and clammy.

"Make way for the Sister."

A nurse knelt down beside Rose Macintosh. Sharply she gave orders. "This girl's alive. Fetch the doctor at once. He's down by the corner."

Within a few minutes the doctor had taken over. Alec stood with a hooded flashlight, directing its beam on the ground where Rose lay covered. The doctor stopped the bleeding from the gash in her arm. Now he inserted into her other arm a needle to which a tube was connected.

He stood up, raising his hand to hold up something to which the tube was attached. Alec saw that it was a bottle of colorless fluid.

When the flask was empty, the doctor said, "That's it," and knelt beside the young mother. Alec could scarcely believe it, but Rose's face had changed. There was a little color in it, and her eyelids fluttered.

"My baby . . . my baby."

"Your baby is safe. And you'll be all right soon, too." The doctor turned to Alec. "Keep her quiet and warm till the stretcher-bearers come and take her to the hospital. Bad case of shock, but the plasma picked her up."

"Plasma?"

"Blood plasma from the United States," the doctor said. "It's coming in regularly now, and they say we can count on an increased supply. Makes all the difference on a night like this."

Close by there was the explosion of another bomb. There's all kinds of people, Alec told himself. Those that drop bombs on us who never did them any harm, and those who send us their own blood. He looked down at the shadows where his son's wife lay, wondering who it could have been that saved her life. Whoever it was, he thought, I wish I could shake his hand and thank him and call him brother.

In 1950 the following notice appeared in a magazine:
DIED. Dr. Charles Richard Drew, 45, pioneer in the collection and use of blood plasma. . . . For supervising New York's blood donations to bombed Britain and directing the first Red Cross collection unit for the United States armed forces, he won the 1943 Spingarn Award for the highest achievement by an American Negro.

"Proteus," the Mighty Dwarf:
Charles Steinmetz

by WILLIAM HERMAN

In Breslau, Germany, on the night of April 9, 1865, a humpbacked lithographer stared down at a tiny replica of himself.

Even in the sprawling, awkward position in which the baby lay, the father could see that the left leg was twisted and shorter than the right one. The child's head seemed grotesquely large for the small body. Already noticeable on the baby's back was the beginning of a hump.

"Karl August Rudolph Steinmetz," he whispered sadly. "My son!"

The father could not know then that a giant mind was locked in this dwarfish baby. He could not suspect, staring down at the frail body, that one day this puny infant would harness the roaring power of the mighty Niagara in America and tame the demon that was electricity. Certainly he could not know then that a "Modern Jove" was born to him.

Little Karl was just beginning to play with building blocks when his mother died. To Breslau came his *Grossmutter*—his grandmother—to care for him and to heap love and affection on this awkward child.

Grossmutter told him stories from the Bible. One of his favorites was the dramatic tale about the lighted Temple of Solomon. One day he heaped his building blocks one atop the other until he had created his own image of the beautiful Temple.

But the Temple of Solomon, *Grossmutter* had said, was a lighted temple. He solved the problem by sticking a burning candle in with his blocks. Now there was light!

The small wooden blocks were smoking when his *Grossmutter* rushed into the living room. Quickly she blew out the candle and doused the blackened blocks with water.

"No, no, no!" she scolded, after hearing his explanation, "you must not light the Temple!"

"It is Solomon's Temple," insisted Karl. "Solomon's Temple was lighted!"

"It was a different kind of light."

"What kind?"

"It was a light that doesn't burn."

"Well, what kind of a light is that? I want to know."

Grossmutter shook her head. The child's questions were too much for her.

"I.can't tell you," she answered.

When Karl was five years old, his grandmother bundled him up and sent him off to school. In the beginning his teachers did not think he was a particularly bright youngster. They found him dull-witted and slow to learn. However, by the time Karl was old enough to enter the Gymnasium, a combination of junior high school and high school, his interest was quickened by the riddles and puzzles of arithmetic, and he began to develop his keen mind.

Soon he was reveling in knowledge. Ancient history fascinated him; Greek, Latin, and Hebrew attracted him; but it was mathematics, with its mental gymnastics, that captivated him.

Almost at once he took his place at the head of his class. When it was time for graduation, the brilliant eighteen-year-old Karl Steinmetz was as far above the other students in mental stature as he was below them in physical height.

Proudly he prepared for the ceremony of graduation. It was traditional for the graduating students to be given an oral examination on a platform before their parents. Karl bought a formal dress suit for the occasion. What a proud moment it would be when he stood before everyone as the head of the class!

On graduation day a strange notice appeared on the bulletin board:

> Karl August Rudolph Steinmetz, by reason of his
> exceptional scholarship, is not required to submit
> to the oral examination.

And so Karl sat in the great audience and listened to the second-best student answering questions and gaining applause that rightfully belonged to him, Karl Steinmetz. He turned to a friend sitting beside him and said softly, "He had the luck to be not quite good enough to be excused from the examination."

Sadly Karl laid the new dress suit away. The notice, he knew, bestowed unusual honor, but he had been separated from the others. Had he been singled out because he was only four feet tall? The hurt was deep.

The new suit became a symbol of the difference between himself and others. Never again, though he was to receive great honors and speak before awed crowds, was he to own or wear a dress suit.

When Karl enrolled in Breslau University, electricity was not much more than a plaything of the laboratory. There was no course in electricity. But the young, eager student was strangely excited by it. What was this mysterious power about which so little was known? "It is not a science," a professor assured him. "It is only a scientific toy."

Young Karl thought otherwise. In far-off America, it was rumored, a man named Edison had already invented a light based upon the principles of electricity. Someday, Karl told one of the students he tutored, electricity would run the world!

It was not only electricity that goaded his mind to intense activity and questions. There were the mysteries of astronomy, the beauties of language, the lessons of history, and the challenge of mathematics to stimulate him.

"Why? Why? Why?" he kept asking. And the professors were as helpless to answer many of his questions as his grandmother had been years before. They agreed that the youth had a brilliant mind but thought he was a problem with his endless questions.

Karl was invited to join the Mathematical Society, to which only students with the keenest minds belonged. Never one to pass up companionship, he gladly accepted. On the day of initiation he knelt before the president of the club. A "fitting name" was to be bestowed upon him.

The president stared down for a moment at the gnome-like little figure. A smile wrinkled his lips. "I dub thee Proteus," he said grandly, patting the kneeling young man on the shoulder. "I dub thee Proteus, wise man of the sea and teller of tales; Proteus, with the gift of prophecy, who knows the answers to all the riddles of the universe."

Karl winced. He had not forgotten the characters in Greek mythology. Proteus, the little humpback of the sea, no bigger than a man's hand! You needed but to capture him and hold him tightly, and he would answer all your questions and even foretell the strange and wonderful things that were yet to come.

"Proteus," Karl whispered. It was a fitting name.

At this time in Germany many students were interested in bettering the life of the German people. Karl was among them. It was dangerous to criticize the Government. Those who did so were often put in prison.

The college dean tried to warn Karl, but it was already too late. One night, a few weeks before he was to receive his degree from the university, a friend brought him a message. The police were about to arrest him.

Karl left Germany forever.

He fled to Zurich, Switzerland, where he enrolled at the university. He barely supported himself by writing articles on astronomy and electrical engineering. Frequently he had to omit a meal.

More and more he was thinking of that wonderful new world across the sea. His interest was quickened by an American friend, Oscar Asmussen, with whom he shared a room.

"America is growing; building is going on all over," Oscar said. "It is a world needing engineers. Believe me, Karl, it is the place for you!"

"How can I go?" Karl asked. "I have no money."

"I'm returning home soon. If we go steerage, I'll have enough for both of us," Asmussen suggested. "What do you say?"

"I will pay you back," Karl agreed, deeply moved. "Every penny of it!"

Late in May 1889, the two young men boarded a ship for America. As they paced the decks for the next eight days, they talked of their plans and their hopes. Asmussen taught the little German his first words of English.

But Karl Steinmetz was a sad-looking sight when the ship docked in New York harbor. He had caught a cold. His eyes were red; his cheeks were swollen; his nose was running, and he sniffed.

The inspector looked at him scornfully. This swollen-faced, humpbacked little dwarf was hardly a desirable specimen.

"Do you speak English?"

"A few," Steinmetz said.

"Have you any money?"

"A few."

It was the only phrase this penniless wayfarer from a foreign land could remember. He shook his head uncertainly as the inspector snapped more questions. "A few —" he whispered in bewilderment and stared pleadingly at his companion.

"I'm sorry," the inspector said. He motioned toward the hold where the undesirable aliens were being held for return to the countries they had left.

It was Asmussen who saved the day. He pleaded his friend's case, telling of his background and education. He promised to be responsible for Karl Steinmetz and to see that he got a job.

The inspector finally nodded. As he watched the humpbacked figure shuffle down the gangplank, he frowned, as if he now suspected he had made a mistake in admitting this little foreigner.

The twenty-four-year-old Steinmetz went to the Edison plant, where he applied for a job as an engineer. The foreman took one quick look at the unprepossessing figure. "No work," he said curtly. "There seems to be an epidemic of engineers coming here from Europe."

At another company Karl had better luck. The owner was himself a German, and also a political fugitive. He studied the young man carefully for a moment. *"Sprechen sie Deutsch?"* he asked kindly.

Karl's face broke into smiles. A torrent of language welled up in him, and for two hours the men talked about themselves and about science. They talked about transformers, storage batteries, mathematics, and magnetism. Karl now had a job.

Promptly he took out his first citizenship papers. Five years later, when he received his final papers, his research in electricity had already made him world famous.

Karl August Rudolph Steinmetz was too Germanic a name for his new country. He was an American citizen now, starting out all over again in another world, an American world he loved. He would have a new name, too, an American name. The American version of Karl is Charles. He did not need the August and Rudolph.

Charles Steinmetz, he wrote.

The name looked incomplete. A middle name was needed. But what? His mind leaped back to his happy student days.

"Proteus," he whispered fondly and wrote his full new name, a name that would never be forgotten in the history of science—*Charles Proteus Steinmetz*.

When Steinmetz came to the United States, electric motors were just beginning to be put into use. There was still much to be learned about them. Most baffling of all the engineering problems was the loss of power in an electric motor. The power that is put into a motor does not all come out in driving the machine to which it is attached. Some is lost in the form of heat. How much? No one yet knew. Electric motors were built "largely by hope and by guess," as the engineers put it.

Steinmetz solved this problem. Today every electric motor that is built, whether for great generators or for a little electric mixer, uses the principles of his solution.

In the same year that he solved this problem, one of the most important events of his life occurred. The General Electric Corporation was formed and bought the company that had given Steinmetz his first job. The sale included courtesy right to the mighty brain of Charles Proteus Steinmetz.

Soon after he joined the engineering staff of General Electric, Steinmetz helped design the dynamos and generators that harnessed the power of Niagara Falls. Then he turned his attention to the problem of transporting electrical current from its source across miles of space on power lines.

This problem, too, he solved. Great dynamos hummed, and electrical current began to give new life to the industry of the New World. A new way of living, the golden age of electricity, came into being.

In the last years of his life Steinmetz turned to the study of lightning. One day the leading scientists of the country were invited to attend a demonstration in his laboratory in Schenectady, New York. Dynamos and generators purred in corners of the room.

In the center of the room, on a large copper plate, was the replica of a village. Near the display, insulated glass plates hung suspended by wires.

"The rain cloud," Steinmetz explained, pointing to the plates. "We are approximating the conditions of a thunderstorm."

He flicked a switch. The guests waited intently. A blinding bolt of electricity leaped from a condenser. Then a crash filled the room. Smoke swirled, and when it cleared away, the tiny village had been destroyed.

"Gentlemen," Steinmetz said softly, "you have seen the lightning."

He had conclusively demonstrated that the fury of the lightning bolt could be controlled.

An engineer looked at the lightning generator and said to Steinmetz, "No greater generator will ever be built."

The scientist smiled.

"I will begin building one tomorrow."

The One-Girl Team from Texas

by RUSSELL FREEDMAN

"Before I was even into my teens," Babe Didrikson once said, "I knew exactly what I wanted to be when I grew up. My goal was to be the greatest athlete that ever lived. I suppose I was born with the urge to get into sports and the ability to do pretty well at them."

Everyone in Babe's family seemed to have athletic ability. There were nine of them, just enough for a base-ball team—Ole and Hannah Didrikson and their seven children. Babe, who was christened Mildred Ella, was next to the youngest. She was born in Texas, where her parents had settled after coming to this country from Norway.

Ole Didrikson was a cabinet-maker and a furniture refin-isher. He couldn't afford to give his children many luxu-ries, but he was a firm believer in good, healthy exercise, and at least he could do something about that. He built a gymna-sium in the back yard, out of old pieces of steel pipe and other odds and ends.

Although everyone in the family was athletic, there was one thing about Babe that set her apart from her brothers and sisters. She was the most fiercely competitive of them all. When she played a game, she played to win. And when she said she wanted to be a great athlete, she meant it. "All my life," she once remarked, "I've had the urge to do things better than anyone else."

The urge to do things better than anyone else motivated Babe in every area of her life. She approached her schoolwork as if it were a contest. Some subjects came hard for her, but she managed to maintain a high grade average all the way through school. She was outstanding in her home economics classes, partly because she and her sisters made all their own clothing at home. In class, Babe once worked for weeks on a blue silk dress, determined to turn out the best dress ever made in that school. She did. The dress won a prize at the Texas State Fair.

But Babe's competitive spirit found its most rewarding outlet in sports. Here she proved she could excel. To begin with, she had to prove herself. When she was still a youngster, and still called Mildred or Millie, the boys in her neighborhood hated to see her advancing down the street with her sister. The boys would be playing baseball in an empty lot, and the Didrikson girls would want to barge into the game.

At first the boys were reluctant. But Millie and her sister soon showed they could swing a bat and throw a ball along with the best of them. Millie hit so many home runs that the boys started calling her "a regular Babe Ruth." When she stepped up to the plate they would yell,

" 'Atta girl, Babe!" Before long she was just Babe. No one ever called her Millie again, not even her parents.

Sometimes the boys called Babe a tomboy, but she didn't mind that. They were glad enough to have her on their teams when they were choosing up sides. When Babe stepped up to the plate in a softball game, she acted as though it were the last game to be played on this earth. Nothing else mattered.

When Babe wasn't competing on a neighborhood team, she was usually competing against herself. She could make an athletic contest out of the simplest errand. Whenever her mother sent her to the grocery store, she would run both ways to see how fast she could make it.

Her mother would say, "Babe, run down to the store and pick up a loaf of bread." Babe would tear out of the house, race down the block, and be yelling for that loaf of bread before she was even in the store. Then she would whirl around and race back to the house, bursting into the kitchen all smiles and out of breath. "What!" her mother would say. "Back already? Why, you only just left." This became a family joke.

Later on, Babe discovered it was more fun to go to the store by hurdling over the hedges that lined each front yard in her block. There was just one problem. One hedge was higher than the others, and it always tripped her. Finally she asked the owner of the hedge if he would mind cutting it down a bit, since it was interfering with her path to the grocery. The neighbor agreed that maybe his hedge did need trimming. He cut it down to size so that Babe could run the full course.

Babe even made athletic contests out of housework. One of her chores was to scrub a big sleeping porch. Her mother expected that porch to shine, and she didn't believe in using a mop. The only way to get a floor clean, she insisted, was on your hands and knees with a scrub brush. Babe got the floor clean, but it always seemed to take her a long time. She would spread a slick coating of soapsuds over the floor, tie a scrub brush to each foot, and then she would run and slide from one end of the porch to the other.

A serious crisis in Babe's life came when she started high school. At least it was a serious crisis as far as Babe was concerned. She was so short that she wasn't permitted to play on the girls' basketball team. Babe couldn't accept a situation like that, so she went to the coach of the boys' team and asked him to help her out. The coach gave her some pointers, and she started practicing after school. She would get out on the court in her bare feet, since she had no rubber-soled shoes, and work on dribbling, pivoting, passing, and shooting baskets. When the boys came out to practice, the coach would tell her to sit on the side lines and watch. "Boys," he said, "know a lot more about basketball than girls."

The following year Babe made her high-school team. Barely topping five feet, she was the shortest girl on the squad. But starting with her first game, she became the team's high scorer. Beaumont High won all its games that year, and Babe's name began to appear in sports items in the newspapers around the state.

That was the beginning.

During the season some of the newspaper articles about Babe came to the attention of Colonel M. J. McCombs, an official of an insurance company in Dallas and director of the firm's ambitious athletic program for women. When he read in the paper about Babe scoring thirty and forty points in her high-school games, he decided to watch her play.

Colonel McCombs drove to Houston one day when Beaumont High was matched against the girls at Houston Heights High School. The Houston Heights girls lived up to the name of their school; they were all tall. They towered over Babe, but she managed to score 26 points in that game. Colonel McCombs was convinced that Babe could help his Golden Cyclones team win the national title.

It was harder to convince Babe's parents that she should be allowed to go away from home to a strange city for a few weeks. The Didrikson family held a conference. Since everyone knew exactly what Babe's opinion was, she was asked to be quiet long enough to give the others a chance to talk. Mr. Didrikson settled matters by deciding to take his vacation and accompany his daughter.

The girls on the Golden Cyclones basketball team all worked in the same office. They were clerks, typists, and secretaries, and they all had outstanding athletic ability. Babe was much younger than any of them. When she was introduced to them, one of the girls took a long, hard look at the newcomer. "Just what position do you think you're going to play?" she asked.

Babe wasn't used to this sort of thing. She didn't quite know what to say. But all the other girls were standing there waiting for her reply, and she rose to the occasion. "What position do *you* play?" murmured Babe.

"I'm the star forward."

"Well, that's what I want to be."

And that's what Babe became—the star forward. She played her first game with the Golden Cyclones the same night she arrived in Dallas, and she was high scorer, scoring five points more than the entire opposing team. A few weeks later she was named on the all-American women's basketball team for that year.

When Babe finished high school, she returned to Dallas to take a regular job with the insurance company and to expand her athletic career. On a softball team she lived up to her nickname by smacking home runs with monotonous regularity. When she wasn't playing basketball or softball, she was participating in swimming meets and high diving.

The sport that was to make Babe a prominent world figure, however, was one she knew practically nothing about when she first went to Dallas. It was track and field. Babe had never seen a track meet until the afternoon Colonel McCombs took her to watch one at a Dallas stadium. From the moment they arrived Babe asked questions. Early in the afternoon she saw some sort of spear lying on the ground and picked it up. "What's this?" she asked.

"That's a javelin," the Colonel told her. "Here, you throw it like this." The javelin throw didn't look difficult. Many other events reminded Babe of the kind of thing she had done as a youngster. The 100-yard dash was about the same as a trip to the grocery store. The high hurdles were just like all that hedge-hopping.

On the drive back to the office Babe asked, "Why don't we organize our own track team?"

"That's just what I thought you'd say," answered the Colonel.

And that is just what they did. The girls gathered in the Colonel's office to decide which events they wanted to train for. Some were interested in running, others liked the broad jump or the high jump, a few thought they would do best in throwing. Babe didn't say a word. Finally she was asked what she would like best.

"I can't make up my mind," answered Babe. "Why can't I train for all of them?"

The other girls laughed, and Babe was embarrassed. But she went ahead and trained for every single track and field event open to women.

When Babe trained, she didn't compromise. She was determined to be a winner, and she had no intention of relying solely on her native ability. Regular practice sessions lasted two hours each afternoon, and afterwards the other girls went home, ate dinner, and relaxed. Not Babe. She rushed through her dinner and then went out to practice some more. She practiced until it grew dark and often for an hour or more afterwards.

No one was surprised when Babe started breaking regional records in track meets all over the South. Then in 1930 and 1931 she started breaking world records.

The following year, 1932, was an Olympic year. The national women's championships in Evanston, Illinois, were to be combined with official tryouts for the Olympic games, slated for Los Angeles later that summer. Babe was looking forward to competing in the Evanston track and field meet, though she couldn't decide which events to enter. She was thinking about this one day when Colonel McCombs said to her, "Babe, you know we're all counting on you to help us win the national championship this year."

"I know," said Babe, "but which events do you think I should enter?"

"I've been studying the records of the top women on the squads competing in Evanston. What conclusion do you think I've reached? I think I'll keep the other girls home. I'd like you to go up to Evanston alone as a one-girl team. I believe you can win the national championship for us all by yourself. That's never been done before."

"All by myself?" asked Babe.

"All by yourself," answered Colonel McCombs.

Shortly after her eighteenth birthday, in 1932, Babe went to enter the National Women's Track and Field Championships as a one-girl team. If she could bring the national championship back to Dallas with her, she could at the same time qualify for the Olympics. It was a big order, and Babe was nervous.

The night before the meet Babe was so keyed up she couldn't sleep. She tossed around in bed for a while, then got up and paced the room. It was near dawn when she fell asleep and close to noon the next day when she awoke. There was barely time to get to the stadium. The opening ceremonies had already started when Babe arrived.

Each team was announced over the loudspeaker, and as the girls ran out on the field, the crowd applauded. Several of the teams had fifteen or more members.

When Babe's turn came, and the one-girl team bounded out on the field, a roar shook the grandstand. Everyone was eager to see how close she would come to winning the national championship single-handedly.

Most of the two hundred women taking part in the meet were entered in only one or, at the most, two or three events. Babe was entered in eight of the ten events being

held, and since she had to compete in both the qualifying
and final rounds, she barely had time to get from one
event to the next.

"For two and a half hours," she said later, "I was
flying all over the place." She high-jumped and broad-
jumped; she ran in the 80-meter hurdles and 100-meter
dash; she put the shot and threw the discus and javelin.

As the spectators realized what was happening down on the field, tension rapidly built up in the stadium. Each time Babe took her place for another event, silence fell over the crowd. When she won, there was an uproar. When she lost, a low moan rose from the grandstand.

When the meet ended, Babe jogged limply off the field. But she had won! She had won the meet all by herself.

A few days later Babe and the other women who had qualified for the Olympics boarded a train for Los Angeles. Most of the lady athletes wanted to spend the trip relaxing. Babe spent most of her time out in the middle of the aisle, exercising. Several times a day she would run the entire length of the train, her arms pumping and her knees flying.

The Olympics opened on August 1, 1932, but Babe didn't really enjoy the opening ceremonies. Her white shoes, issued by the Olympic Committee as part of the United States uniform, hurt her feet. The athletes had to stand on the field for more than an hour while officials and dignitaries made welcoming speeches. It was a hot day, and Babe's shoes got tighter and tighter.

She tried to keep her mind off her shoes. She listened to the speeches, studied the crowd in the stands, and counted the flags flapping in the breeze. Finally she slipped out of her shoes. The girl standing behind Babe noticed this and thought it was a wonderful idea. She slipped off her shoes, too. By the time the speeches ended, nobody in that section had on shoes.

With the ceremonies over, the serious business of the Olympics began. There were only five track and field events open to women that year. No athlete could compete in more than three events. Babe entered the javelin throw, the 80-meter hurdles, and the high jump—the three events in which she had broken world records in Evanston two weeks earlier.

In the javelin throw Babe tore a cartilage in her right shoulder, but she set a new record and won a gold medal.

In the finals of the 80-meter hurdles, held three days later, she jumped the gun, and everyone was called back. Jumping the gun twice meant automatic disqualification, and Babe couldn't afford that. The women knelt at the starting line again. The gun cracked. Babe held herself back until she saw the other runners in front of her. Then she took off. She didn't catch up with them until the fifth hurdle, but she won. She broke the record she herself had set in the qualifying race the day before, and she won another gold medal.

In the high jump the judges ruled that Babe cleared the bar headfirst instead of feetfirst, and her jump was disqualified. She did not contest the ruling. Even without this victory she was the biggest star of the Olympics.

At the end of 1932, Babe was voted the Woman Athlete of the Year in a press poll. This surprised no one. As far as most people were concerned, the eighteen-year-old girl from Texas was the Woman Athlete of any year and all years. Babe Didrikson, and later, when she had married, Babe Zaharias, held a permanent place in the affection and admiration of sports fans all over the world.

Day Dreams

by HARRY BEHN

In some far other time than here
Are forests full of dappled deer

Where wandering minstrel winds awake
Shadows across a misty lake,

Shadowy ripples rippling away
As I dream of a still more distant day

Where gardens greener than my own
Grow round a mossy tower of stone,

Where prancing steeds and knights of old
Wear coats of armour bright with gold,

And children dream, as still they do,
Remembering what they never knew.

LEGENDS, MYTHS, AND OTHER TALES

Sir Gawain and the Green Knight

retold by DOROTHY HEIDERSTADT

Once upon a New Year's Day, the knights of the Round Table gathered in the great hall at Camelot to feast with King Arthur. It was the King's custom never to sit down to dine on that holiday until he had heard some interesting tale, or until some unusual adventure had offered itself.

The cold winter sunlight streamed through the narrow windows onto the rushes strewn on the stone floor for warmth. The knights' shields hung on the walls, each with its own decoration that served to identify its owner when he was dressed in his battle armor. Banners stirred in the wintry drafts, even though a great fire blazed on the hearth. Shivering pages ran about lighting tapers in the silver sconces against the early winter darkness.

Suddenly King Arthur lifted his head sharply, for he heard a horn in the distance. Sir Gawain, his favorite nephew, heard it, too, and stopped his idle, gallant chatter with a lady to listen. Then all the company could hear horns blowing, high-pitched and shrill, and all knew that these were no ordinary horns. The casements shook, and the flames of the candles trembled. As the knights sprang up to seize their swords and shields, the great doors of the hall burst open as if pushed by violent hands, and on a gust of icy wind a strange figure entered.

He was a giant knight on horseback, and he was dressed in green armor from head to toe. Even the plumes and the splendid trappings on his mighty horse were green.

From *Knights and Champions* by Dorothy Heiderstadt. Copyright © 1960, by Dorothy Heiderstadt; published by Thomas Nelson & Sons, New York.

In his right hand the Knight carried a green battle-ax, in his left hand a bough of holly. His eyes gleamed like two emeralds through the visor of his helmet. He leaped from his saddle and stood laughing.

"Knights of the Round Table," he cried, "stand forth! Take up your battle-ax, one of you, and strike at me!"

Arthur's knights looked at one another uneasily. All sorts of visitors came to Camelot, but there had never been one so strange as this man.

"Why should one of us strike at you?" asked the King. "That would be poor hospitality on this festive day. Have you wronged us?"

"I have wronged no one," said the Green Knight. "I was told that here I would find the bravest knights in the world. I come only for adventure's sake."

Everyone could understand that statement, for there was not a man present who did not love adventure for adventure's sake. Sir Gawain, the King's nephew, leaned forward, gazing at the stranger with interest.

"Well," said the Green Knight impatiently, "will no one trade blows with me? Let the bravest among you strike me. Then let him agree to take the same blow from me a year and a day from now. Come, come, is there no one among you venturesome enough?"

At these words King Arthur himself drew his sword and started up. But Gawain cried quickly, "Dear Uncle, let me claim this adventure!" The King hesitated, then smiled and waved his hand in consent.

"I will trade blows with you!" cried Gawain, leaping to his feet and going to stand before the Green Knight.

314

"Good!" cried the Knight. He planted his feet firmly on the floor and removed his helmet to reveal a flowing green beard and a green face. Gawain lifted his sword.

"That paltry thing!" jeered the Knight. "Strike me a real blow with your battle-ax! Or are you afraid of the mighty blow you may expect from me in return?"

Gawain reddened with anger, and thrusting his sword into its scabbard with a clang, he seized his battle-ax. "You will not live to return this blow!" he cried, swinging the battle-ax in both hands above his head.

The Green Knight laughed and dropped to his knees before Gawain, shaking the long green hair from his neck. "Strike!" he said. "Then I will tell you my name and where you can find me a year and a day from now!"

Gawain made no answer, but swinging his ax with all his strength, he cut off the Green Knight's head. Whereupon the stranger picked up his head and set it back on his shoulders.

"I am the Knight of the Green Chapel," he announced, "and that is where you must meet me the day after next New Year's Day, Sir Gawain! There I will return your blow. You will be a coward and shamed before all men if you fail to come."

So saying, the strange Knight mounted his charger and rode out of the hall, leaving Arthur's knights to stare into one another's faces. Once more they heard the wild horns blowing, and then all was still.

"That was no man but a monster," someone breathed. And the others agreed, "It was a monster. No human being can prevail against it. Do not keep the tryst, Gawain."

But Gawain was resolved to go. All that year, as he fought in tournaments and rode forth to right wrongs and rescue maidens in distress, he thought about his meeting with the Green Knight.

When the year had nearly gone and it was Christmastide, Gawain knew that it was time for him to seek out the Green Chapel and receive the deadly blow that was his due. He knew that he could not survive such a blow, for he had not the magic powers of the Green Knight. Yet he had no thought of failing to keep the agreement.

On the morning of his departure he called to his page to fetch his arms. First his men put a doublet of silk upon him and a well-made hood. They set steel shoes on his feet and encased his legs and arms in steel armor. Gloves of metal were placed upon his hands. Then the men enclosed his body in a coat of armor, fixed his spurs to the heels of his shoes, and fastened his sword to his side by a girdle.

Thus arrayed, Gawain went to church and then took leave of King Arthur. His mighty horse, Gringolet, awaited him, encased in armor, too, which glittered like sunlight. Gringolet stood patiently while his master, in his heavy armor, was assisted into the saddle. Sir Gawain then set his helmet upon his head and took up his shield and lance. Bidding farewell to all, he spurred his horse and rode out of the castle courtyard. Not one of those left behind expected to see him alive again.

Gringolet's hoofs, clattering across the wooden drawbridge, were echoed by the hoofbeats of the charger belonging to Gawain's young squire, his only companion.

The squire was taken along to look after Gawain's horse and his armor and to arrange for the burial of his body after his death. It was the custom for knights to be accompanied by their squires, and according to the chivalric code, no squire could be harmed, for he bore no arms. It was probable that even so outlandish a being as the Green Knight would observe the code.

Gawain and his squire heard the drawbridge being pulled up behind them after they crossed over. Sleet was falling, and later there was hail and snow, for it was an uncommonly bitter winter. Into Wales they traveled, over hills and through deep valleys, and across the River Dee. At last, on Christmas night, they came to a castle in the midst of a forest of oak trees. Here they were welcomed by a handsome lord and royally entertained.

Knights and squires led them into the hall and took Gawain's helmet and sword. They helped him remove his armor and brought rich robes for him to wear. A chair was placed for him beside the fireplace, and a table drawn up before it. Gawain sat down to a hearty meal.

"Why do you wander abroad at Christmastide in such bitter weather when most folk are at home?" his host asked curiously. Gawain willingly told his story.

"The Knight of the Green Chapel! I know him well," said the lord of the castle when Gawain had finished. "The Green Chapel is two miles from here, and the name of the Knight is Bernlak de Hautdesert. Some say he is a madman, and some say he is not human but a monster. Whatever he is, it would be better, young sir, to give up your quest and return to King Arthur's Court."

"No, I have given my word," said Gawain. "I will not turn aside from this adventure."

"Stay here, then, until the appointed day," said his host. "On the day after New Year's Day I will send a servant to guide you to the Green Chapel. I would not go there myself for all the gold in the world."

Gawain willingly remained for a week at the fine castle, where he was well entertained. On the appointed day he set out with his squire and the guide for the Green Chapel. Through a wild valley they rode, among great sweeping hills covered with leafless oak trees, white with frost. They saw hazel and hawthorn trees, on whose boughs huddled unhappy birds crying piteously with the cold. Presently the riders came to a roaring stream. Beside it there was a mound overgrown with green moss, with a thorn tree growing before it. They could hear a whining sound, as though an ax were being sharpened. The green mound looked like a cave, for it had great openings at one end and on either side.

"They call this the Green Chapel," said the old servant, reining his horse before the mound. "It is guarded by the Green Knight, who is so cruel and merciless that he kills everyone who passes. Good Sir Gawain, return with me to my lord's castle. I will never tell anyone that you had wisdom enough to let the Green Knight alone!"

Gawain glanced at his squire and observed that the boy was looking at him with confidence. Squire and Knight smiled at one another and exchanged a wordless sentence: This poor, fearful old man has never known adventure for adventure's sake!

319

"No, I thank you," Gawain said courteously to the old servant. "I must fulfill my part of the bargain."

The servant, seeing that it was useless to reason further, bowed his head and rode homeward, leaving Gawain to his fate. Now the two, Knight and squire, dismounted and stood listening to the noise of the ax being sharpened.

Then Gawain saw a great horn hanging on one limb of the thorn tree before him. He set the horn to his lips and blew a mighty blast upon it.

"I am Gawain of King Arthur's Court!" he cried. "I have come to keep tryst with the Knight of the Green Chapel! Sir Knight, come forward, if you are not afraid!"

"Wait!" roared a voice, and there came forth from the mound the Green Knight in his strange armor, ax in hand. "You have been true to your promise," he said. "Are you ready to receive the blow?"

"It is for that I have come," replied Gawain, approaching the Knight and taking off his helmet to bare his head.

"This will be a fatal blow," the Green Knight said, and he whirled the blade around his head, making it sing in the frosty air.

"I am ready," answered Gawain.

Then the Green Knight bent forward and looked at Gawain with narrowed eyes. "You are young to die," he said. "Beg for mercy, and perhaps I will let you go free."

"I have never yet begged for mercy," said Gawain carelessly, and he stood smiling at the Green Knight.

"Then kneel!" thundered his adversary.

Gawain knelt before him and bowed his head. All was still. The birds that had cried so piteously were silent, and even the wind had stopped blowing. Gawain waited, but the expected blow did not fall.

"Arise, Sir Gawain," said the Green Knight gruffly. "I can see that the tales I have heard of King Arthur's knights are, indeed, true; they are the bravest knights in the world. The blow, had I given it, would have finished you; though I tempted you to beg for mercy, you would not. Know you now, had you weakened, you would have died for it. Return to your king, and peace go with you."

The Green Knight threw down his battle-ax and saluted Gawain with his lifted sword. Then Gawain and his young squire rode back to King Arthur's Court.

When they rode into the courtyard at Camelot, trumpets sounded on the battlements of the castle, and banners were unfurled in celebration of Sir Gawain's return. Bells were rung in the highest tower in honor of Gawain, and King Arthur himself came out to greet him. Then the Knight was led into the castle to tell the tale of his adventure at the Green Chapel.

Sir Gawain was ever among the bravest and best of Arthur's knights and was loved all the days of his life.

Saint George and the Dragon

by ALFRED NOYES

Saint George he slew the dragon,
  But he didn't shout hurray.
He dumped it in the wagon
  Just to clear the mess away.

But the wagoner he sold it
  To a showman at the Fair,
And when Saint George was told it,
  He was almost in despair.

For the people crowded round it
  To admire its teeth and claws,
But Saint George he was an Englishman
  And did not like applause.

"The creechah weighed a ton at most,"
  He muttered through his vizahd.
"I do not feel inclined to boast
  About that puny lizahd."

From *Daddy Fell into the Pond and Other Poems* by Alfred Noyes. Copyright 1952 by Sheed & Ward, Inc., New York.

The Legend of the Moor's Legacy

by WASHINGTON IRVING

Many years ago there was a water carrier named Peregil, who came to the well of the Alhambra every day at dawn. He was a short man with bowed legs and a broad back. He filled huge earthen jars with water, strapped them to the back of his little donkey, and trudged through the streets of Granada, crying in a musical voice, "Who wants water, water colder than the snow?" Whenever he served a customer a sparkling glass of water, Peregil always had a pleasant word to say and a smile to give. He was known as the happiest and nicest man in Granada.

But beneath his good humor, Peregil had many cares. He had a large family of ragged children to support, and his wife was no help to him. Before their marriage she had been a village beauty who was very good at dancing and snapping castanets. Now instead of taking care of the house, she slept all day and spent Peregil's hard-earned money on gay clothing. She would even take his donkey to go for outings on *fiestas* and saints' days—which, in Spain, were almost more numerous than days of the week. Besides all this, she was a great gossip and would spend hours in the houses of her talkative neighbors.

Peregil never questioned his wife, and he loved his children very much. He used to work long after sunset just to be able to buy them an extra treat for Sunday.

It was a late hour one summer night, and all the other water carriers had gone home, but there were still customers for water. Like a good father, Peregil thought of his hungry children and said to his donkey, "One more journey to the well to earn a Sunday's treat for my little ones." And he trudged up the steep avenue to the Alhambra, walking beside his donkey, humming a tune.

When he arrived at the well, he found no one there except a stranger in Moorish clothes. Peregil looked at this person with surprise. Moors were considered enemies of Spain and were not often seen in Granada. But the Moor waved to him feebly and said, "I am very sick. Help me return to the city, and I will pay you double what you could earn with your jars of water."

The honest heart of the little water carrier was touched. "God forbid," he said, "that I should ask a reward for helping a fellow human being." So saying, he helped the Moor onto the donkey's back and set off down the road leading back to town. As they walked, Peregil had to hold the Moor upright because the poor man was so weak.

"Where shall I take you?" Peregil asked when they entered the city.

"Alas!" cried the Moor. "I have neither home nor house. I am a stranger to this city. Please let me stay the night beneath your roof and I will repay you a thousandfold."

Peregil was too kind to refuse shelter for the night to a fellow being, so he led the Moor to his own house.

When Peregil's children saw the strange, turbaned Moor, they screamed and hid behind their mother's skirts. She stepped forward, frowned, and declared, "You cannot bring a stranger into our house!"

"Be quiet, Wife," the little water carrier replied. "Here is a poor, sick man without friend or home. We cannot let him die in the streets!"

His wife would still have objected, but Peregil for once was stiff-necked about the matter. He spread a mat on the floor and helped the Moor to lie down upon it.

In a little while it was clear that the Moor would soon die. He called Peregil to him and whispered, "My end is now at hand. If I die, I leave you this box as a reward for your charity." He drew from beneath his cloak a small sandalwood box, but before he could say more concerning it, he fell into a faint and died.

Peregil's wife was now enraged. "This is what comes of doing good to people!" she yelled. "What will happen to us when this corpse is found in our house? We will be sent to prison as murderers, and if we are not beheaded, we will be ruined by the lawyers and judges!"

Poor Peregil was quite frightened. At last a thought came to him. "No one saw the Moor enter our house," he said. "It is not yet day. I can carry his body on the back of my donkey down to the river and bury him in the sands. And no one will know anything at all."

His wife helped him roll the body of the Moor in the mat on which he had died. Then Peregil laid the body across the back of his donkey and took it to the river.

But as bad luck would have it, there lived opposite to Peregil a barber named Pedrillo, one of the nosiest and nastiest gossips alive. He had a face like a weasel, and it was said that he slept with one eye open all the time so as to be sure not to miss anything that happened.

This nosy barber had heard and seen everything that happened at Peregil's house that night. Worse than that, he had followed Peregil and watched him bury the Moor's body. He became so excited that he could not sleep all the rest of the night. At the first light of day he placed his basin beneath his arm and hurried off to his daily customer, the Mayor.

The Mayor had just risen. Pedrillo seated him in a chair, threw a napkin around his neck, put a basin full of hot water beneath his chin, and began to massage his cheek with his fingers.

"Strange doings," Pedrillo said, "strange doings. Robbery and murder and burial, all in one night!"

"Now what's that you say?" the Mayor cried.

"I say," said Pedrillo, brushing lather onto the Mayor's face, "that Peregil, the water carrier, has robbed and murdered a Moor in his house during the night and has buried the body by the riverbank."

"And how do you know all this?" demanded the Mayor immediately.

Pedrillo told the entire story.

Now it so happened that this mayor was one of the most brutal as well as one of the greediest in all of Spain. He set a very high value on justice because he sold it for its weight in gold. He thought, of course, that here was a case of robbery and murder, so there must be a rich booty. How could he get hold of it? Simply to hang a murderer would only be feeding the gallows, but getting hold of the booty would be enriching the judge. He immediately called his sheriff and sent him after Peregil.

The Sheriff was so quick and so thorough that within the space of an hour he had brought Peregil, the donkey, and the sandalwood box before the Mayor.

The Mayor bent over Peregil with a terrible frown. "Listen, culprit!" he roared. "You may as well admit everything. I know all! A gallows is the proper reward for a murderer! But," the Mayor stroked his beard thoughtfully, "the man you killed was a Moor, an enemy of Spain. So if you will give up the spoils of which you robbed him, we'll hush up the entire matter."

The poor water carrier told the entire story truthfully from beginning to end and handed over the sandalwood box as the only thing the Moor had left behind him.

The Sheriff seized the box greedily and gave it to the Mayor, who opened it with trembling hands. But the box contained only a paper scroll, covered with Arabic letters, and the end of a wax candle.

Since there was nothing to be gained by hanging the prisoner, the Mayor decided to set the water carrier free and let him take the sandalwood box. He only seized poor Peregil's donkey to pay the costs of the case.

Now Peregil had to carry water every day without the help of his donkey. He toiled and sweated up the road to the Alhambra, carrying a huge earthen jar on his own shoulders. Besides this, he really missed his friend. "Ah, donkey, donkey of my heart," he would exclaim, "I'll bet you remember your old master. Poor animal!"

And his wife now gave him no peace, but always scolded and yelled at him for ever having helped the Moor in the first place. One day while she was screeching at him, Peregil picked up the sandalwood box and threw it against the mud wall of his house. The box flew open and the paper scroll and candle end fell onto the floor. Peregil stared at them for a long time in silence. Then suddenly he thought that since the Moor guarded this box so well, perhaps there was something important written on the paper. So he picked up the box, the paper scroll, and the candle end, and the very next day he stopped at the trinket shop of a Moor from Tangiers. Peregil showed the Moor the paper.

The old Moor read the scroll carefully, then stroked his beard and smiled. "This writing," he said, "is a spell for the recovery of hidden treasure. The treasure lies buried in enchantment beneath the Tower of the Seven Stories in the Alhambra. And so strong is this spell that the very rock itself will part to admit him who knows its secret."

"Wonderful!" Peregil shouted.

"But wait, water carrier. This spell is of no use unless it is read aloud at midnight by the light of a candle made of strange waxes and perfumes."

"But I have a bit of candle!" Peregil exclaimed. "It was left with the scroll in the sandalwood box." He brought forth the candle end and handed it to the old Moor.

The Moor sniffed the candle thoughtfully. "Here are rare perfumes mixed with the wax," he muttered. "This may be the candle needed—or it may not. If it is, then the strongest walls and the most secret caves will remain open while it burns. But woe to him who lingers within if the candle goes out! He will remain forever spellbound within the rock!"

The Moor and Peregil agreed to try the charm that very night. So at a late hour, when nothing was stirring except bats and owls, they climbed the woody hill behind the Alhambra. They found their way to the tower and stumbled over bushes and stones to the door of a vault beneath its base. Trembling with fear, they climbed down a flight of steps cut into the stone, which led into a dreary chamber, from which another stairway led still deeper beneath the tower. They had climbed down four stories below the rock when, at last, they came to a chamber with a perfectly solid floor of rock. The air was damp and cold in the chamber, but they waited there until they heard the faraway bells of the watchtower strike midnight. Then they lit the candle, and the chamber was immediately filled with the sweet, spicy smell of frankincense and myrrh.

The Moor began to read the scroll in a hurried voice. As he finished, there was a noise as if a thunderstorm had broken out in the earth beneath them. The floor shook and then opened to reveal a long flight of stairs. Shaking with fright, Peregil and the Moor climbed cautiously down the stairs by the light of their lanterns and found themselves in a cave whose walls were covered with Arabic letters. In the center of this cave stood a huge chest covered with mysterious writings and shut up with seven bands of steel. At each end of the chest sat an enchanted Moor in full armor, motionless as a statue. Around the chest were several jars filled with gold and silver and precious stones. From the largest of these jars Peregil and the Moor brought forth armfuls of Moorish gold and bracelets and ornaments of all kinds, while a few necklaces of brilliant rubies and diamonds stuck to their fingers.

They crammed their pockets full to bursting, looking with dread at the two Moorish guards who sat grim and still, staring from enchanted eyes. Then, suddenly frightened at some noise, Peregil and the Moor ran up the staircase, tumbled over one another in their hurry to escape, and knocked over the candle. As soon as the candle was put out, the same thunder from below was heard, and the floor of the chamber closed beneath them.

When they got over their scare, they sat upon the floor of the chamber and divided the money and jewels equally between them. They decided to be content with this amount for the present and to come back to the place another night with donkeys to carry off the main treasure. To make certain of each other, they divided the talisman between them—Peregil kept the paper scroll, and the Moor kept the candle. Then, with full pockets and light hearts, they set off for the city.

As they climbed down the wooded hill beside the Alhambra, the Moor said to Peregil, "My friend, I know you are a wise man and can keep a secret. But if the Mayor should hear of this before we have removed all the treasure, we will be ruined."

"I know it well!" Peregil exclaimed. "Trust me to keep silent."

"I do, I do," the Moor replied, "but you have a wife."

"She shall know nothing of this!"

"Enough," the Moor said. "I depend on you to keep your promise."

Never was a promise more positive or sincere. But when Peregil returned home that night, his wife screamed at him for having been away so long and because the children had nothing to eat. Weary of her voice, Peregil took a golden coin from his pocket and tossed it onto the floor. This was a mistake. No sooner did the woman see that coin than she began wailing and tearing at her hair, saying that Peregil had robbed and murdered some traveler. For how else could a poor water carrier ever come by a gold coin? She was sure that they would all be hanged from the tallest gallows in Granada.

At last, to keep his peace of mind and to stop his wife's tongue, Peregil was forced to tell her the entire story. But he made her promise to keep it a strict secret.

To describe the wife's joy would be impossible. She flung her arms around her husband and almost strangled him with her caresses. "Now, Wife," Peregil said, "what do you say now to the Moor's legacy? Never complain again when I help a fellow creature."

On the following morning the little water carrier took the biggest coin of gold and carried it to a jewelry shop. There he was given only a third of its real value, but Peregil was not a greedy man and was content. He bought clothes for his children and food for a good meal.

Peregil's wife kept her promise of secrecy surprisingly well. For a day and a half she went about the city with a look of mystery. Although surrounded by gossips, she said nothing. Of course, she did talk of buying expensive clothes, getting a new house, taking the children to the country for the summer, and such matters. But her friends simply thought she had lost her wits. At home she could not restrain herself from trying on all the necklaces of diamonds, pearls, and rubies that Peregil had brought back. Wearing them, she would dance before the window of their little house, singing gaily all the while.

As fate would have it, Pedrillo, the barber, saw her. He took one look at those sparkling necklaces and rushed off to the Mayor's house. In a little while the Sheriff was on Peregil's trail, and before the day was over the little water carrier was again dragged before the Mayor.

"How is this, villain?" the Mayor cried in a furious voice. "You told me that the stranger who died in your house left nothing but a sandalwood box. Now I hear your wife is wearing diamonds and rubies and pearls! Prepare, wretch, to give up your riches and to swing on a gallows that is tired of waiting for you!"

The terrified Peregil dropped to his knees and in a trembling voice told the Mayor the entire story of the enchanted treasure. The Sheriff was sent to bring in the Moor who had helped Peregil. The Moslem entered in terror at finding himself before the Mayor, and when he saw Peregil kneeling there he knew what had happened. "Miserable animal," he whispered, "did I not warn you against telling your wife?"

The Mayor now threatened both of them with hanging.

"Softly, good Sir Mayor," the Moor said. By this time he had recovered his usual shrewdness. "Let us not ruin our luck by fighting over it. Nobody knows anything about this except ourselves. Let us keep the secret. There is wealth enough in that cave to make us all rich. Promise a fair division and all shall be brought forth; refuse and the cave shall remain closed forever."

The Mayor and the Sheriff had a whispered talk apart from the prisoners. "Promise anything," muttered the Sheriff, "until we get hold of the treasure. Then we will take it all and have these two burned as sorcerers."

The Mayor agreed. Smoothing his beard and smiling, he turned again to the Moor and said, "Yours is a strange story and must be proved to be believed. This very night you must repeat your spells in my presence. If there really is such a treasure, we will all divide it equally. But if you have fooled me, you shall hang."

Toward midnight the Mayor, the Sheriff, and the nosy barber, all very well armed, took the Moor and Peregil to the Tower of the Seven Stories. The Mayor brought Peregil's donkey along to carry off the treasure and tied it to a fig tree near the door of the tower. Then, without having been seen by anyone, they entered the tower and climbed down the staircase to the lowest chamber.

Here Peregil brought out his scroll, and the Moor brought forth the candle. The spell was repeated, and the floor beneath them opened with a roar, showing the narrow flight of steps. But the Mayor, the Sheriff, and the barber were too frightened to go down into the cave.

So Peregil and the Moor climbed down. There they found everything as they had left it. The two Moorish guards sat exactly as before at either end of the chest.

The partners carried up two of the huge jars filled with gold and precious jewels, staggering and sweating beneath the weight. When these two jars were placed upon the donkey's back, the poor animal could carry no more.

"Let us be content for the present," the Moor said. "Here we have as much treasure as we can carry and enough to make all of us wealthy beyond our dreams."

"Is there more treasure?" the Mayor asked.

"The greatest treasure of all," the Moor answered. "A huge chest bound with bands of steel and, no doubt, filled with pearls and precious stones."

"Let us have this chest, by all means," the Sheriff cried.

"I will go back down no more," the Moor replied. "This is enough for a reasonable man."

"And I," Peregil added, "will not bring up any more burdens to break the back of my poor donkey."

Finding that threats and commands were useless, the Mayor, the Sheriff, and the nosy barber themselves climbed carefully down into the vault to bring up the huge chest.

No sooner were they below ground than the Moor blew out the candle. The floor closed with a sound like thunder, trapping the three greedy men below.

Then the Moor and the water carrier ran up through the tower until they reached the open air, and they rested, gasping for breath, next to the donkey.

"What have you done?" Peregil cried. "The Mayor and the other two are shut up in that cave!"

"It is the will of Allah," the Moor replied devoutly.

"But won't you let them go?" Peregil asked.

"Allah forbid!" the Moor exclaimed, smoothing his beard. "It is written in the Book of Fate that they shall remain enchanted until someone arrives to break the spell.

The will of Allah be done!" So saying, he threw the candle as far away as he could.

Since there was nothing more to be done about it, Peregil, the Moor, and the richly laden donkey made their way back to the city. Peregil could not stop hugging and kissing his little donkey, so pleased he was to have him back. In fact, it would be hard to say whether it was the donkey or the treasure the beast carried that gave the little water carrier more joy.

The two partners divided the treasure equally. Taking care to avoid accidents, they fled Granada. The Moor returned to Tangiers in Africa; and Peregil, his wife, his children, and his faithful donkey made their way to Portugal. There they lived in the greatest of luxury and happiness forever after.

As for the Mayor, the Sheriff, and the barber—they stayed beneath the floor of the great tower and remain there spellbound to the present day. It is said that if there ever comes a day when there are not enough nosy barbers, greedy sheriffs, or corrupt officials in the world, they will be released. But if they have to wait for such a time, they may wait until doomsday.

Stormalong

by ANNE MALCOLMSON

Stormalong died before the last Yankee clipper furled her silver sails, but stories about that good old man are told still wherever old sailors gather. Just where Old Stormalong was born no one knows. He first appeared on a wharf in Boston Harbor. The Captain of the *Lady of the Sea,* the largest clipper ship in the China trade, was signing on men. Stormy gave his full name, Alfred Bullrod Stormalong.

A. B. Stormalong stood five fathoms tall, which is the same as thirty feet. The Captain glanced up at his new man and whistled with surprise. "Whew!" he said. "There's an able-bodied seaman for you, boys."

Someone noticed that the giant's initials stood for just that. From that day to this, sailors have tacked A. B. after their names. This shows that they are able-bodied seamen like Stormy.

Old Stormalong's size and strength helped him a lot on the sea. He didn't have to climb the rigging to furl the topsails. He just reached up from the deck and did it. He could hold the pilot's wheel with his little finger even in the worst weather. In less than a week he'd been promoted from common sailor to bosun.

The cook didn't care much for his company, however, because Stormy made too much work in the galley. He had a weakness for food. He knew a good deal about cooking and wanted everything prepared just so. Besides, he wanted lots of it.

He liked a couple of ostrich eggs fried sunny-side up for breakfast. For lunch he expected a dory full of soup. After his meals he used to lie out on deck in the sun and pick his teeth with an oar.

But Old Stormy was too valuable a man to dismiss because of the cook's grumbling. There were many occasions on which the *Lady of the Sea* would have become the *Lady on the Bottom of the Sea* had it not been for her bosun.

Once, for instance, in the warm waters of the tropical Atlantic, the Captain gave orders to hoist sail and weigh anchor after a morning of deep-sea fishing. The crew heaved and strained at the anchor, but it refused to budge. Something was holding it fast to the bottom. Not even when Stormalong heaved along with the crew would the heavy anchor stir.

So Old Stormy stuck a knife into his belt and dove overboard to have a look-see. Hand over hand he quickly climbed down the anchor chain. Suddenly great waves arose. A commotion began on the ocean floor. The surface frothed and churned. From below came sounds of battle. The crew could see dimly two dark forms struggling in the water's depths. Then the long, black, slimy arm of a giant octopus slapped into the air.

At the sight of it the crew gave up their bosun for lost. No human being could possibly fight single-handed one of those great devils of the sea and come out alive. But before they had a chance to arrange a funeral service for him, Old Stormalong climbed slowly up the chain and pulled himself on deck.

"Whew!" he sighed. "That old squid was a tough one. Had hold of the anchor with fifty arms and grabbed the bottom with the other fifty. He won't trouble us now, though. Tied him tighter than a schoolboy's shoelace. Tied every one of his arms in a double knot."

A year or so after this adventure Old Stormy lost his taste for a sailor's life. He said it was the food. He was tired of hardtack and dried fish and had a hankering for some tender, fresh green vegetables.

His shipmates, however, guessed that the real trouble was lack of space. The *Lady of the Sea* was the biggest clipper afloat, but even so she cramped her bosun. He couldn't sleep stretched out anywhere on board.

After a last voyage around Cape Horn, Stormalong left the wharf at Boston with his pay in his pocket and an eighteen-foot oar over his shoulder. He bade his friends good-by. He said he was going to walk west, due west, and he would stop and settle down as soon as someone asked what the long pole might be. He figured that any county whose inhabitants didn't recognize an oar was far enough from the coast for him.

The *Lady*'s crew heard nothing from their shipmate for several years. Then in the San Francisco gold rush the mate had news. Stormy had bought a township and was one of the best farmers in the whole U.S.A. Stormy a farmer? The mate couldn't believe his ears. But when he was told of Farmer Stormalong's miracles, he knew it was his man, without a doubt!

Stormalong specialized in potatoes. During his first growing season the whole countryside dried up. It didn't rain for six weeks. The little spring that fed the horse trough gave only enough water for the stock. There was not an extra drop with which to irrigate the crops.

Then Old Stormalong went to work. He labored over those drooping, dying plants until the perspiration ran from him in rivers. He sprinkled those potatoes with the sweat of his brow. At the end of the season, when other farmers were moaning over their burnt acres, he drove to market with a bumper crop of the largest, tastiest spuds ever to be mashed with cream and butter.

In spite of this success Stormy wearied of farm life. He was a restless fellow. Often at night when he had milked the cows and locked the henroost, he sat in front of his stove and dreamed about the faraway days on the ocean. At last he couldn't deny to himself that the sea was calling him back.

Word spread through the countryside about a new ship, the *Courser,* that was so huge it couldn't enter Boston Harbor. The inlanders thought this was just another Yankee yarn. They laughed about it as they sat on the front porch of the country store. But to Stormalong the ship was more than a fable. It was a dream come true.

He sold his farm and returned to the East. For several days Stormalong hung around the water front, looking like the ghost of his former self. His ruddy salt-sea color was gone, his eyes had lost their shine, and the shellbacks, or sailors, who had known him in the old days realized that he was a sick man, yearning for the feel of the spray.

They couldn't tell him much about the whereabouts of the big ship he was seeking. It was a real boat, all right. It had anchored outside of Cape Cod some time before with a cargo of elephants for Mr. Barnum's circus. The *Lady of the Sea* had been pressed into service as a tender to bring the freight to shore.

The more the old bosun heard about the *Courser,* the more his mouth watered to see her and join her crew. At last, when a whaler brought word that she was cruising along the Grand Banks off Nova Scotia, Stormy could stand it no longer. He dove off a wharf and swam out to sea.

The next time his old friends saw him he was the captain of the big vessel. The old fire was back in his eyes, his cheeks were brown as mahogany, and his spirit was dancing. For the *Courser* was the only ship in all the world which suited him. He was the only skipper in all the world to do her justice.

She was so long from stem to stern that it took a man on horseback a good twenty-four hours to make the trip. A string of Arab ponies was stabled in front of the forebitts for the use of the officers on duty. The masts were hinged to let the sun and moon go by. The mainsail had been cut and hemmed in the Sahara Desert, the only expanse of land large enough for the operation. When a storm blew up from the horizon, the skipper had to give the order to man the topsails a good week in advance. It took the men that long to climb the rigging.

This last fact had its disadvantages, of course. Until the United States Weather Bureau caught on to the trick of sending out weather reports in advance, the *Courser* was often caught in a hurricane without notice enough to furl her cloth. She was large enough to ride out any storm, even in full sail, without much damage. But there was no way of telling how far off her course she'd be blown.

One time, during a North Atlantic winter gale, the *Courser* was pushed this way and that until she ended up in the North Sea. As you know, the North Sea is just a little sea and not in the same class with an honest-to-goodness ocean. In fact, it is so small and crowded with islands that the *Courser* couldn't turn around.

There to port lay Norway and Denmark. Straight ahead lay the continent of Europe, and to starboard the British Isles. Stormy roared with anguish. He feared lest his clipper, his lovely queen of the five oceans, would have to spend her days with the lowly North Sea fishing fleet for the rest of time.

There was a way out, however. When Stormalong and the mate measured the English Channel, they found that at high tide it was an inch or two wider than the *Courser*. With luck they might squeeze through it and out into the Atlantic again.

So the skipper sent the officers to Holland to buy up all the soap in sight. Then he put his crew to work soaping the sides of the big boat. They slapped the slippery stuff on thick until the *Courser* was as slick as an eel.

Just at the turn of tide, with her full sails set, the *Courser* glided through into the broad Atlantic Ocean. But she had a close call. The headlands on the English coast scraped most of the soap off the starboard side of the vessel. To this day the cliffs at Dover are white.

After this adventure Old Stormy was talked about in every port in the world. No sailor could deny that his highest ambition was to ship under "that good old man."

Great was the mourning from Portsmouth to Hong Kong when news of Stormalong's death finally came. Several reports of it were spread around. One version had it that he was drowned in a storm off Cape Hope. But most of the tales agreed that he died of indigestion. His magnificent appetite had finished him.

His old shipmates gathered for the funeral. They made him a shroud of the finest China silk. They dug his grave with a silver spade. They lowered his coffin into the ground with a silver chain, the color of his sails. And the tears that fell from the eyes of those hard old salts drenched the earth like the rain of a nor'easter.

> Stormy's gone, that good old man,
> To my way, hay, storm along, John!
> Stormy's gone, that good old man,
> To my aye, aye, aye, Mister Stormalong.
>
> Old Stormy has heard an angel call,
> To my way, hay, storm along, John!
> So sing his dirge now, one and all,
> To my aye, aye, aye, Mister Stormalong.

 From the ballad "Stormalong" in *Iron Men and Wooden Ships* by Frank Shay and Edward Wilson.

archy poems
by DON MARQUIS

A newspaperman, Don Marquis, discovered a cockroach using his typewriter. The cockroach's name was archy. "He would cast himself upon a key, head downward," wrote Marquis. "He could not work the capital letters." Recognizing that archy had the soul of a poet, Don Marquis always left paper for him in the typewriter.

book review

boss a new book
has appeared
which should be
read by every one
it is entitled
the cockroach
its life history
it is one of the
best books i ever
tasted i am eating
the binding from
a copy with
a great deal of
relish and
recommend it
to all other
insects yours
truly
        archy

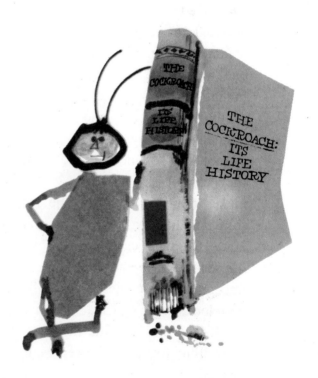

at the zoo

speaking of the aquarium i
was up at the zoo the
other day and when i saw all
the humans staring at
the animals i grew thankful that
i am an insect and
not an animal it must be
very embarrassing to
be looked at all the time by an
assorted lot of human beings and
commented upon as if
one were a freak the animals find the
humans just as strange and silly looking
as the humans find the
animals but they
cannot say so and the fact that
they cannot say so
makes them quite angry the leopard
told me that was one thing that
made the wild cat wild as for
himself he says there is
one gink that comes every day and looks
and looks and looks at him i
think said the leopard he
is waiting to see if i ever really do
change my spots

archy

VERSES

by OGDEN NASH

The Octopus

Tell me, O Octopus, I begs,
Is those things arms, or is they legs?
I marvel at thee, Octopus;
If I were thou, I'd call me Us.

The Porpoise

I kind of like the playful porpoise,
A healthy mind in a healthy corpus.
He and his cousin, the dolphin,
Why they like swimmin like I like golphin.

The Sea-Gull

Hark to the whimper of the sea-gull;
He weeps because he's not an ea-gull.
Suppose you were, you silly sea-gull,
Could you explain it to your she-gull?

Song of the Open Road

I think that I shall never see
A billboard lovely as a tree.
Indeed, unless the billboards fall
I'll never see a tree at all.

VERSES

by EVE MERRIAM

Gazinta

There's a strange sort of bird of a word
That abides near the Great Divide;
A gazinta is this bird absurd.

And here is how it got its name:
Two gazinta four two times,
And four gazinta eight the same.

One, Two, Three — Gough!

To make some bread you must have dough,
Isn't that sough?

If the sky is clear all through,
Is the color of it blough?

When is the time to put your hand to the plough?
Nough!

The handle on the pump near the trough
Nearly fell ough.

Bullies sound rough and tough enough,
But you can often call their blough.

The Tree with Animal Fruit

retold by SOPHIA FAHS and DOROTHY SPOERL

This story is one among several that the Bushmen of Africa tell to explain the beginning of life on the earth. There are only a few thousand Bushmen, and most of them live in the Kalahari Desert in South Africa. They are believed by some to be descendants of ancient cave painters in Spain and southern France. Today they live much as their ancestors did—sleeping in caves or simple huts and hunting with spears and bows and arrows. Like all peoples, they have wondered about man's origin.

Before there were any people or animals *on* the earth, there were people and animals living *under* the earth with Kaang—the Great Master and Lord of All Life. This was a happy place where there was no need of the sun, for it was already light, and no one needed to eat anything, for people were never hungry or sick, and they never died.

From *Beginnings: Earth, Sky, Life, Death*, by Sophia Lyon Fahs and Dorothy T. Spoerl. Reprinted by permission of the Beacon Press, copyright © 1958 Starr King Press.

353

Then in that far-off time, Kaang, the Creator, began to plan for the wonders he would make on the earth and above it. First he made a wondrous tree grow out of the earth. It grew and grew until its branches spread high and wide over the country. Near its roots Kaang dug a hole in the ground. So deep did he make the hole that it reached all the way down to the secret underworld, where the animals and people were then living.

When the hole was finished, Kaang called the first man-of-all-men to climb up the hole beside the great tree to the top of the earth. When this first man-of-all-men came out of the top of the hole, he was very much surprised at what he saw. He looked around this way and that way, before him and behind. He looked up at the blue sky high above and saw the big, bright sun shining on him through the branches of the great tree. Then the first man-of-all-men sat down on the ground under the tree.

Next Kaang sent up the first woman-of-all-women. When she stepped out on top of the earth, she was very much surprised at what she saw. She looked around this way and that way, before her and behind. She looked up at the blue sky and saw the big, bright sun shining on her through the branches of the great tree. Then the first woman-of-all-women sat down under the tree beside the man.

Soon another man stepped out of the big hole, and another woman—then more and more men and women— very many of them. They were all surprised. And they all sat down together under the great tree.

Kaang then began helping the animals climb up the hole and out onto the earth beside the great tree. All sorts of animals came, two by two, then three by three, and then four by four. They came faster and faster and were so eager to reach the top that they pushed and squeezed each other through the hole. Finally, some of them found a way to push themselves up through the inside of the trunk of the tree, and out onto the limbs and to the tips of the branches, from where they tumbled to the ground.

When the last of the animals had finished coming out of the tree, they all gathered around the people sitting on the grass in the shade. The first animals and the first people began talking to one another, for in the beginning of days, animals and men were friends and could understand each other's language.

While they were sitting talking together, Kaang, their Creator and Master, appeared and spoke: "I have brought you out on top of the world together, people and animals, and I want you to live happily with one another. Do as I have taught you and be good to one another. There is but one thing no man nor woman must ever do. You must never build a fire, for on the day you build a fire an evil thing will happen to you."

When Kaang had spoken, he disappeared and hid himself somewhere up in the sky where he could keep watch over his creatures. Some say Kaang comes and goes—sometimes he is above in the sky, sometimes below under the earth. But no one ever sees Kaang.

On the first long day, Kaang decided to make the sun move across the sky and then hide a while under the earth, so that as long as men could see the sun, there would be light, but when the sun went down under the earth, there would be darkness. So it has always been since that day when Kaang brought the first men and women and animals up from under the earth. Night regularly follows day.

But on that first day of all days the first people and the first animals were not expecting the dark to come. As they watched the sun's bright ball move toward the west and slowly drop lower and lower in the sky, they soon found themselves in darkness. The air grew cool. Men and women, not having furry skins like animals', began to shiver. They walked about, trying to keep warm, but the winds chilled them. The darkness became blacker. They could not see one another or the animals sleeping around them. They began to be afraid.

Finally one of the men dared to speak up. "Let us build a fire. Surely it is better to be warm than cold. It is better to have light than to try to live in the dark."

So the first man-of-all-men rubbed two sticks together till they grew hot and a glowing spot appeared. He fed the spot with sticks till flames shot up into the darkness. The men and women were filled with wonder. Soon they felt warm again, and they could see each other's faces. They were very happy.

But the animals were frightened. They rushed off toward the hills, and they never came back to sit again under the big tree with the first men and women or to sleep near them. On that night men lost their ability to understand the language of animals, and animals lost their power to talk to men. When men and animals could no longer understand one another, they began to be afraid of each other and unfriendly. Ever since that night when the first man-of-all-men forgot the command of Kaang, his Creator and Master of Life, and built a fire, animals, except a few such as the dog and the horse, have not been friendly with men.

A Box Full of Troubles

retold by SOPHIA FAHS and DOROTHY SPOERL

This story about the beginning of man's life on earth is one of the myths of ancient Greece. The Greeks were a lively and extremely imaginative people. Centuries ago they created a great civilization that still has an influence on the way we live and think. They believed that man was the most important being on earth and that man could hope to overcome the many troubles of living.

A long time ago there were no animals nor men in the world outside Mount Olympus. Finally Zeus, chief of the gods, called Prometheus and Epimetheus, two of his sons, to come to him. "We need animals and men on the earth," said Zeus. "Go down and create them. When you have made them, give each some special gift." And Zeus handed his sons a box filled with good gifts.

So Prometheus and Epimetheus went down from Mount Olympus to the seashore. As they walked together along the sandy clay and gazed out over the wide ocean, they decided to mold the new creatures from clay and water. Epimetheus set to work at once to make animals, while Prometheus began to model men. Each went about his work in his usual manner. Epimetheus worked without any plan. Because of this habit he had always been called Epimetheus, meaning "afterthought." He thought about things after he had done them. Prometheus, on the other hand, planned what he would do. His name, Prometheus, means "forethought"; that is, he thought before he acted.

 From *Beginnings: Earth, Sky, Life, Death,* by Sophia Lyon Fahs and Dorothy T. Spoerl. Reprinted by permission of the Beacon Press, copyright © 1958 Starr King Press.

As the two brothers worked away, each became so absorbed he did not notice what the other was doing. Epimetheus worked quickly. As soon as he had finished an animal figure, he took something from the box of goodly gifts and gave it to the creature he had made. To the fox Epimetheus gave cunning; to the owl he gave wisdom; the eagle received strength of wing, and the deer swiftness in running. Epimetheus had finished all the animals before he stopped to see what Prometheus was doing.

Now, Prometheus worked slowly and carefully. He was not content with the figure he molded until he had made the very best sort of man he could think of. When finally he had finished, he looked up from his work.

"See, Epimetheus," he cried. "I have finished making the first man. Now I can make more creatures like him, and they can go out into the world to live. What gifts do you have left?"

Epimetheus was startled. Then he was ashamed. He hung his head and whispered, "No gifts are left."

"No gifts for man? It cannot be true! Epimetheus, what have you done?"

"I did not think," said Epimetheus. "While you were working on one man, I made many animals. As each was finished, I gave it a gift. Now all the gifts are gone."

"Man must have some special gift," said Prometheus. "Man is to rule over the animals, so he must be made to have more power than they. Somewhere there must be a gift that is worthy of man. I must find it."

Prometheus walked away down along the shore. As he looked out over the ocean, a great thought came to him.

He turned and swiftly walked back to where Epimetheus was still standing.

"I have decided what man must have," he declared. Then he said defiantly, "It is fire."

"That cannot be," said Epimetheus. "The gods have claimed fire for their own."

"Man must have fire," repeated Prometheus. "I will see that it is secured for this man I have made and for all his kind."

Prometheus walked away again. This time he went straight to the reeds that were growing by the sea. The stalks of the reeds had a hard covering, but inside there was pith, which was soft and damp and would burn slowly. He broke a straight, strong reed from its root, and then he returned to Epimetheus.

"With this reed," said Prometheus, "I will go tonight to the door of heaven and steal fire from the sun. In the morning when Phoebus Apollo, the god of the sun, comes forth in his chariot with flaming wheels, I shall stick my reed into the very center of the flames and bring fire to the earth."

Prometheus climbed quickly up to the very door of heaven. Through all the long hours of the dark and silent night he crouched by the door. Finally dawn brightened in the heavens, and the door swung open.

Then Phoebus Apollo came forth in his chariot with flaming wheels. He looked neither to the right nor to the left, intent upon the course he was to take.

Quickly Prometheus thrust his reed into the center of the flames, holding it there until the chariot had passed.

Then he quickly went back to earth. The man he had made was standing there beside Epimetheus. Fear darkened the man's face.

"I have it!" cried Prometheus.

Gathering dry leaves in a pile on the ground, he peeled off the hard outer stalk of the reed and placed the smoldering pith under the leaves. He fanned them, and he blew upon them. A spark came forth, a wisp of fire curled up, and the leaves blazed. Wonder replaced fear upon the man's face. There was awe in his heart. He had not seen fire on earth before.

As Prometheus molded other men, and women, he taught them how to build fires in front of their caves to keep them warm and to frighten away the wild beasts.

Then Prometheus turned and walked away, knowing that Zeus would soon see what had been done and be angry. Prometheus had saved men by bringing them fire, but from the moment he planned to do it, he knew he would be punished.

Soon things happened as he had known they must. Zeus, looking down from Olympus, saw men handling fire. Great anger welled up in his heart. "Men were not to have fire," said Zeus. "Fire was to be the property of the gods alone. Men will be too powerful with fire. Prometheus is the only one who could have done this thing. He shall be punished for it."

Zeus then sent Mercury, his faithful messenger, to bring Prometheus before his throne. Prometheus stood silently before Zeus. "You shall be sentenced to lie chained forever to a rock on the peak of a high mountain,

362

while vultures from time to time will fly at you and eat your flesh," declared Zeus.

Prometheus looked straight before him. He did not turn his head but followed his captors as they led him forth. In his heart he knew he had done a good thing. He was ready to take his punishment. Men now had fire, and that was enough.

But Zeus was not satisfied to punish only the one who had stolen fire. He called a council of gods.

"Men have the fire which Prometheus has stolen. Men, too, must share the punishment," said Zeus from his throne high on Olympus. "Mercury, bring Vulcan before me." So Mercury brought Vulcan from his forge and led him to Zeus. Vulcan stood silently before the throne, waiting to receive his orders.

"Vulcan," Zeus decreed, "go and fashion a maiden who will have the form of a goddess, and bring her here that each of us may give her some beauty or some charm to attract the men Prometheus has made. When you mix the clay, mix in guile and cunning, a shameless mind, and a deceitful nature. Go!"

When Vulcan had finished his task, he came once more before the throne, leading a maiden by the hand. She was very beautiful, and the gods were pleased with her. Each one gave her a gift. Athene arrayed her in clothes of gleaming beauty. The Hours twined flowers in her hair. Mercury gave her flattering words to say to men, and the Graces put precious jewels upon her. Even Zeus gave her a gift. His was curiosity. And he named the maiden Pandora, meaning "gifted of the gods."

Then Zeus prepared a box and filled it with all kinds of evil things—pain, fear, envy, pride, deceit, hate, sickness, and jealousy. Turning again to Mercury, Zeus said, "Take Pandora down to the earth and give her to Epimetheus. As you leave her to return to Olympus, give her this box and tell her it is a good gift only if she never opens it. The day she looks inside the box, evil will come to her and to all men."

Long weeks and months went by, and Epimetheus and Pandora were happy together. They visited the homes of men, and they walked through the fields. But Pandora became more and more curious about the box and the lovely things that might be in it.

Finally one day when Epimetheus was not at home, Pandora could no longer control her curiosity. "I simply must see what is in the box," she thought. "I will just lift the lid a little bit and peep inside." But the moment

the cover was loosened, all the evil creatures imprisoned inside came forth. Pandora ran away screaming, not knowing which way to turn.

Epimetheus came running home, and he fastened the lid down again. But it was too late. Pain and hate, jealousy and fear, deceit and envy, sickness and pride— all had come forth. Now that they were free, they rushed into every corner of the world.

Late that night Epimetheus and Pandora heard a faint noise coming from the closed box. A voice seemed to cry, "I am Hope. Let me out." For a long time they would not go near the box. But Epimetheus finally said, "It cannot be worse than the things that were freed. Perhaps it really is Hope, as it claims to be."

So they opened the box, and Hope came out. She went forth into the world and put courage into the hearts of men.

So it was that when the world was young, Prometheus gave men the wondrous gift of fire. So it was that all mankind was punished for the gift by the coming of evil things. And so it has been that men have never lost the hope of conquering all these evils.

The Prince and the Pauper

by MARK TWAIN

Adapted for Radio by Deborah Newman

CHARACTERS

TOM CANTY	LORD PROTECTOR
PRINCE	MILES HENDON
JOHN CANTY	GUARD
BET CANTY	HERALD
MRS. CANTY	NARRATOR
KING	HUMPHREY
HERTFORD	LORDS, LADIES, OTHERS

MUSIC. (*Fanfare of trumpets.*)

HERALD. His Most Royal Majesty, King Henry, announces to his loyal subjects the birth of a son, Edward Tudor, Prince of Wales, heir to the throne of England.

SOUND. (*Cheering of crowd.*)

NARRATOR. Yes, all England went nearly mad for joy on that autumn day in the sixteenth century. Everybody took a holiday. There was no talk in all England but of the new baby, who lay wrapped in silks and satins, not knowing that great lords and ladies were tending him—and not caring, either. On this same day another boy was born, unwanted, to a poor family by the name of Canty. And there was no talk at all about this child, Tom Canty, except among the family of paupers he had come to trouble with his presence.

JOHN CANTY (*snarling*). A boy, eh? Another mouth to feed, that's all.

BET. We'll see he's no trouble, Father.

JOHN CANTY. See that you do. Until he's old enough to beg his own way, keep him out of mine.

MRS. CANTY. John Canty, the boy is but a newborn baby. How can you talk of his begging?

JOHN CANTY. How can I talk of his begging? How else do you suppose he's going to earn his keep? I'll teach him to beg and steal; see if I don't.

NARRATOR. John Canty succeeded in making a beggar of the boy but could not make him a thief. For after Tom ventured forth each day to beg a few pitiful coins, he would return to his rickety home and visit his neighbor, Father Andrew, a good old priest.

Father Andrew taught Tom to read and write—and even a little Latin. But best of all, he told Tom charming old tales about giants and castles and gorgeous kings and princes. Tom was delighted. He organized games in which he was prince of a royal court and his special friends were lords and ladies.

One day Tom wandered outside the walls of London, hungry and sore from his father's beatings. He came upon a mighty palace and stared in wonder at the vast building. All at once he caught sight of a spectacle that almost made him shout for joy. Inside the palace gate he could see a boy whose clothing was all of gorgeous satins, shining with jewels. Oh, he was a prince, a living prince, a *real* prince!

GUARD. Get away from that gate, you young beggar!

WOMAN. Look at the little beggar, staring at the Prince like a daft one though the guard strikes him.

PRINCE. Ho, there, guard! How dare you use a poor lad like that? Open the gates and let him in!

CROWD. Long live the Prince of Wales!

NARRATOR. The little Prince of Poverty passed through the gates in his fluttering rags to join hands with the Prince of Limitless Plenty and go with him to a rich apartment. A delicious meal was ordered, and all servants were dismissed when it arrived.

PRINCE. Here, eat, lad. And tell me your name.

TOM. Tom Canty, an' it please you, sir.

PRINCE. 'Tis an odd one. Where do you live?

TOM. In London, please, sir. Offal Court, out of Pudding Lane.

PRINCE. Offal Court! Truly, 'tis another odd one. Have you parents?

TOM. Parents I have, sir, and two sisters. But my father has a wicked heart and beats me.

PRINCE. What? Beatings?

TOM. Oh, indeed, yes, please you, sir.

PRINCE. *Beatings!* And you so frail. Hark ye, your father shall go to the Tower.

TOM. You forget, sir, that the Tower is only for the great.

PRINCE. True indeed. I had not thought of that. How does your mother use you?

TOM. She is good, sir. And my sisters are like her.

PRINCE. Look you, do your sisters forbid their servants to smile?

TOM. Servants! Do you think *they* have servants, sir?

PRINCE. Why not? Who helps them undress at night?

TOM. No one, sir. Would you have them sleep without
their garment?

PRINCE. Their garment? Have they but one?

TOM. Ah, good your Worship, what would they do with
more? Truly, they have not two bodies each.

PRINCE (*laughing*). 'Tis a marvelous thought! Now, tell
me. Have you a pleasant life in Offal Court?

TOM. In truth, yes, so please you, sir—except when we
are hungry. There are Punch-and-Judy shows and
races and fights, and in summer we wade and swim
in the canal and dance and sing about the Maypole in
Cheapside.

PRINCE. Oh, say no more! 'Tis glorious. If I could do
all that just once, I would give up the crown.

TOM. If *I* could wear for only a moment those clothes
you wear——

PRINCE. Would you like to? Then so shall it be! Doff
your rags and don these splendors, lad. It is a brief
happiness, but we will have it while we may and change
back again before anyone comes.

NARRATOR. A few minutes later the Prince of Wales
was clothed with Tom's fluttering odds and ends, and
Tom was tricked out in the plumage of royalty. The
two stood side by side before a mirror, and lo, a miracle—there did not seem to have been any change
made! They stared at each other, then at the glass,
then at each other again.

PRINCE. What do you make of this?

TOM. Ah, good your Worship, do not ask me to answer.
It is not meet that I should utter a thing.

PRINCE. Then I will utter it. You have the same hair, the same eyes, the same voice and manner, the same form and face that I have. Now that I am clothed as you were, it seems I should be able to feel as you did when that brute guard struck—wait! Is that a bruise on your hand?

TOM. Yes, but it is a slight thing, and your Highness knows that the poor guard——

PRINCE. Silence! It was a shameful and cruel thing! If the King, my father—but stir not a step until I come back. It is a command.

NARRATOR. In a moment the Prince had snatched up and put away an article of national importance that lay on the table, and was out the door and flying through the palace grounds in his battered rags.

PRINCE. Open! Unbar the gates!

SOUND. (*Clinking of gates.*)

GUARD. Take that, you little beggar! And that!

SOUND. (*Thud, Prince crying out, crowd laughing.*)

PRINCE. I am the Prince of Wales. My person is sacred. You shall hang for laying your hands on me.

GUARD (*mockingly*). I salute your Gracious Highness. (*Rudely*) Be off, you crazy rubbish!

MUSIC. (*Courtly stringed music, fading away.*)

LADY. Oh, our poor Prince. Did you hear he shut the door on his servants and hid?

SECOND LADY. Mad, that's what the poor lad is!

MUSIC. (*Fanfare of trumpets.*)

HERALD. In the name of the King. Let none listen to this false and foolish matter of the Prince's illness, nor discuss same, nor carry it abroad, upon pain of death.

THIRD LADY. The Prince is coming. How slowly he walks to the apartment of the King.

SOUND. (*Murmuring of crowd.*)

KING. How now, my lord Edward, my Prince? Have you been minded to fool with me, the good King, your father, who loves you?

TOM. You are the *King?* Then I am undone, indeed!

KING. Come to me, my child. You are not well. Do you not know your father?

TOM. You are my dread lord the King.

KING. True, true—that is well. Tremble not so. You are better now. You will not miscall yourself again, as they say you did a little while ago?

TOM. I pray of you, your Grace, believe me, I did but speak the truth. I am the meanest among your subjects, a pauper. 'Tis by a mischance I am here, although I am not to blame. I am young to die, and you can save me with one word. Oh, speak it, sir!

KING. Talk not so, sweet Prince. You will not die.

TOM. God bless you and save you long to bless our land, oh, my King. I am not to die! The King has said it. I may go now?

KING. If you wish. But where would you go?

TOM. But your Highness—I thought I was free to seek the kennel where I was born. I am not used to this splendor. Oh, please, sir, let me go!

KING (*sadly*). Oh, my son, my son. Overstudy has done this. Away with books and teachers! Pleasure my son with sports! He is mad, but he is my son and England's heir, and, sane or mad, he shall reign. He is Prince of Wales, and I, the King, shall confirm it. The papers shall receive the Great Seal immediately. Fetch the Great Seal!

LORD. If it please your Majesty, His Highness, the Prince, has the Great Seal. You gave it to him to keep.

KING. True. My son, where do you keep the Great Seal?

TOM. The Great Seal, my lord? I—I do not understand.

KING. Alas. Let us trouble his poor wits no more. There is time enough for the Great Seal later.

NARRATOR. In the morning the weighty business of dressing the young Prince began. A shirt was taken up by the Chief Equerry in Waiting, who passed it to the First Lord of the Buckhounds, who passed it to the Second Gentleman of the Bedchamber, who passed it to the First Lord of the Bedchamber, who was about to put it on poor Tom when he stopped, aghast, and, pointing to the shirt, passed it back down the horrified line. A hole in the royal shirt! But in good time Tom Canty was in condition to get out of bed and was conducted to his meal in a hall filled with servants.

FIRST LORD. The Prince is eating with his fingers!

SECOND LORD. Sh! Don't let him know we see it.

THIRD LORD. He's filling his pockets with nuts.

TOM. Please, my lords, I crave your indulgence. My nose itches. What is the custom in this emergency?

FIRST LORD. There is no custom, my lord.

TOM. Is there no Hereditary Scratcher?

SECOND LORD. No, my lord.

373

TOM. But what shall I do? (*Pause*) I know! I shall scratch it myself!

THIRD LORD. Oh, that such a thing has come to pass!

FOURTH LORD. I've heard it said among the royal household that the King is not well. This new blow will do his health no good.

FIFTH LORD. An ailing king and a mad prince! What will become of us?

MUSIC. (*Solemn royal march.*)

HERALD. The King is dead. (*Pause*)

CROWD. Long live the King! Long live Edward, King of England!

HERTFORD. If it please your Highness, the royal secretary has some business to present for your approval.

TOM. Yes, my lord.

SECRETARY. Concerning the expense of our late beloved King be it known that during the last six-month period the King's household spent 28,000 pounds; of this, 20,000 pounds is still owed and unpaid. Our coffers are almost empty.

TOM. We are going to the dogs, 'tis plain. 'Tis necessary that we take a smaller house and dismiss the servants. Now, I remember a small house that stands next to the fish market——

HERTFORD. You are tired, my Prince. We shall leave this business for another day. May we go?

TOM. As you wish, my lord. But who are you, lad, kneeling before me? Rise. What would you have?

HUMPHREY. You must remember me, my lord. I am your whipping boy.

374

TOM. My *whipping* boy?

HUMPHREY. The same. I am Humphrey Marlow. Surely your Grace remembers that none may visit the sacred person of the Prince of Wales with blows. Therefore, when he should have a whipping, *I* take the blows. Since you are now King, you will probably no longer vex yourself with dreary studies. My back is my bread. If you stop your studies, my job is gone. You'll need no whipping boy.

TOM. Trouble yourself no longer. Rise now, Humphrey Marlow, Hereditary Grand Whipping Boy to the royal house of England. I'll start to study again and study so badly that they must treble your wages. You may go, Humphrey. Ah, Lord Hertford.

HERTFORD. Your Majesty, I am persuaded that if you will tax your memory a little it will solve the puzzle of the Greal Seal. Will your Grace try?

TOM. The Great Seal? What was it like, my lord?

HERTFORD. Surely your Majesty remembers the Seal?

TOM. No. Describe it to me.

HERTFORD. Alas, his wits are flown again.

NARRATOR. While Tom sits in state, what has become of the real Prince, left to wander the streets of London in beggar's rags? The rain began to fall soon after he was pushed from the palace gates. Then the wind rose, and a raw and gusty night set in, making the houseless Prince more miserable than he had ever imagined he could be. He drifted along into the alleys where the swarming hives of poverty and misery were massed together.

PRINCE. Offal Court, that was the name. If I can find it before I drop, then I am saved. Tom's people will take me back to the palace and prove that I am not their son but the true Prince.

JOHN CANTY (*roughly*). Out at this time of night again, and not a penny on you, I warrant me! If it be so, and I do not break all the bones in your body, then I am not John Canty but some other.

PRINCE (*eagerly*). Oh, then you are his father.

JOHN CANTY. *His* father? I am *your* father, and you shall soon have cause to remember it.

PRINCE. Oh, jest not. Take me to the King, my father, and he will make you rich beyond your wildest dreams. Believe me, man, I am the Prince of Wales.

JOHN CANTY (*amazed*). You've gone stark mad.

PRINCE. Take your hands from me! I tell you I am the Prince of Wales.

JOHN CANTY. Hush your raving. Pah! Here comes that Father Andrew.

PRINCE (*calling out*). Father Andrew, or whoever you are, save me. Save me!

JOHN CANTY. Take your hands off the boy. You'll meddle with me, will you? Take that as your reward.

SOUND. (*Struggle, thud.*)

JOHN CANTY. Hurry, my fine lad, before the mob catches us.

SOUND. (*Footsteps. Door opens, closes.*)

JOHN CANTY. Ho, my family! Fine sport for us this evening! Stand still, lad. Now say your foolery again— if you haven't forgotten it. Who are you?

PRINCE (*indignantly*). I am Edward, Prince of Wales, and no other.

MRS. CANTY. Oh, my poor Tom! Your foolish reading with Father Andrew has taken your wits away.

PRINCE (*gently*). Your son is well and has not lost his wits, good dame. Lead me to the palace where he is, and straightway will the King, my father, restore him to you.

MRS. CANTY. The King, your father? Oh, unsay those words. Shake off this dream. Look upon me. Am I not your mother?

PRINCE. I do not wish to grieve your heart, but truly I have never looked upon your face before.

JOHN CANTY. Let the show go on. Nan! Bet! Upon your knees, you scum, and do him reverence. The show will go on!

NARRATOR. The show did go on, until the poor Prince was sore and bleeding. After the rest of the family slept, the mother lay awake thinking and mourning. What if the boy were really not her son, after all? She must be sure. (*Pause*) A test! Yes, she would try a test.

MRS. CANTY. Since the day when Tom was little and a bit of gunpowder burst in his face, he has never been suddenly startled without casting his hand before his eyes, as he did that day. And he always does this with the palm *outward*. I have seen it a hundred times. I shall shine a candle in the lad's face—thus—and strike his ear, thus! (*Pause*) He did nothing. He barely stirred. And yet—he *must* be my boy!

PRINCE (*sleepily*). Ho, Sir William Herbert! Come and listen to the dream I had. I thought myself changed into a pauper—and—ho, there!

MRS. CANTY (*gently*). Who are you calling, lad?

PRINCE. Who are you?

MRS. CANTY. I—I am your mother, lad.

PRINCE (*fearfully*). It was no dream, then!

SOUND. (*Knocking on door.*)

JOHN CANTY. Who knocks? What do you want?

VOICE. John Canty, do you know what man you laid your cudgel on last night?

JOHN CANTY (*roughly*). I care not.

VOICE. You'll care—if you value your neck. Nothing but flight will save you. Father Andrew is dead.

JOHN CANTY. What? Dead? Up—all of you. You must come with me, mad boy, and speak not our name. We must fly.

NARRATOR. But Canty was stopped by a group of watermen at London Bridge who insisted that he drink the health of the Prince of Wales with them, and while he was doing so, the Prince slipped out of his grasp, dived into a forest of legs, and disappeared. He had but one course to pursue—to find his way to the palace, make himself known, and denounce the impostor. He made up his mind that Tom should be hanged according to the law in cases of high treason.

PRINCE. Open the gates! I tell you I am the Prince of Wales. I will not be driven from my ground!

SOUND. (*Jeering of crowd.*)

HENDON. Though you are a prince or no prince, it's all

the same. You are a brave lad and not friendless. Here, come with me. Come, lad, for your own good. You must not say you are the Prince of Wales.

PRINCE. And why not? I *am* the Prince of Wales!

HENDON. England has no Prince of Wales. The King is dead.

PRINCE (*wonderingly*). Then—I am king—king of England!

HENDON. Come along, lad. I'll take care of you and watch over you. Here we are, now.

SOUND. (*Door opens, closes.*)

PRINCE. You are good to me, and I shall not forget it.

HENDON (*cheerfully*). Now, then, we'll have a bite to eat. I'll get the chops from the stove and join you——

PRINCE. Would you sit in the presence of the King? You did save me from injury and shame—perhaps you did save my life, and so my crown. Such service demands a rich reward. Name your desire, and it is yours.

HENDON. Your Majesty no doubt knows of the story of the great lord who received as a reward the privilege of wearing a hat before the kings of England.

PRINCE. I do.

HENDON. Then I beseech the King to grant me but one privilege: that I and my heirs forever may *sit* in the presence of the king of England.

PRINCE. Rise, Sir Miles Hendon, Knight. Rise and seat yourself. Your petition is granted.

HENDON. Thank you, your Majesty. (*In an undertone*) 'Twas a clever thought I had. Else I might have had to stand for weeks until the poor lad's wits were cured.

PRINCE. And now I have a plan that shall right things. I will write a paper in three languages—Latin, Greek, and English—and you will take it to the palace tomorrow. Then they will know me. I shall start it first in Greek.

SOUND. (*Scratching of pen on paper.*)

NARRATOR. While the Prince was preparing his message, Tom was causing a stir throughout England——

WOMAN. God preserve His Most Sacred Majesty, King Edward. A dear little urchin he is, too! His praises are on all men's lips.

SECOND WOMAN. He saved the Duke of Norfolk's life.

THIRD WOMAN. He pardoned the witches.

FOURTH WOMAN. Now he is bent on destroying the cruel laws that oppress the people.

NARRATOR. Yes. Tom was making quite a stir—but the rightful Prince heard none of it. For he soon fell again into the clutches of John Canty, who took him to live with a band of outlaws. The Prince resisted all attempts to make him beg and steal—as well as he could. He escaped from the outlaws, but finally he and his good protector, Miles Hendon, landed in prison. Cold, hungry, miserable, and afraid, the King of England learned about his people and his country as no king before him had ever done.

PRINCE. No one believes me. But no matter. Soon all these wronged prisoners will be free. The laws that put them in prison shall be swept from the books. The world is made wrong. Kings should have to live by their own laws at times, and so learn mercy.

MUSIC. (*A dignified march.*)

WOMAN. Here comes the King!

CROWD. God save His Majesty!

NARRATOR. Yes, it was the King in procession—or so the people of London thought. All the gorgeous ceremony, the splendid trappings—all for Tom Canty, on his way to be crowned king of England. Tom's cheeks were flushed with excitement. He was about to throw a huge handful of coins into the crowd when suddenly he caught sight of a pale, astounded face. He recognized his mother! Up flew his hand, palm outward, before his eyes—that old gesture born of a forgotten episode. In an instant Mrs. Canty was tearing her way out of the crowd to Tom's side.

MRS. CANTY. Tom! Tom, my son, what have you done?

TOM (*coldly*). I do not know you, woman.

GUARD. Here, woman, away from the King.

MRS. CANTY. But I tell you he is my son.

TOM. I do not know that woman.

NARRATOR. But even as Tom Canty spoke these words, a shame fell upon him that turned his pride to ashes and withered his stolen royalty.

LORD PROTECTOR. My lord, it is an ill time for dreaming. Lift up your face and smile upon the people.

TOM. I cannot.

LORD PROTECTOR. It was that crazy pauper who disturbed your Highness.

TOM. She—she is my mother.

LORD PROTECTOR (*fearfully*). God save England. The King has gone mad again.

NARRATOR. The procession continued. The booming of the artillery announced the arrival of the King at Westminster Abbey. Tom was robed and prepared for the ceremony and entered the Abbey clothed in a long robe of gold. The ancient ceremonies went on and on. At last the final act was at hand. The crown was lifted from its cushion and held over the head of the trembling mock king. At this moment a bare-headed boy dressed in rags appeared in the great aisle of the Abbey. He raised his hand solemnly.

PRINCE. I forbid you to set the crown of England upon that forfeited head. *I* am the King!

SOUND. (*Crowd murmuring: Who is he? What is he?*)

TOM. Loose him and stop. He *is* the King!

LORD PROTECTOR. Mind not his Majesty. His illness is upon him again. Seize the vagabond!

TOM. On your peril, touch him not. He *is* the King. Oh, my lord, let poor Tom Canty be first to swear loyalty to you and say, "Put on your crown and enter into your own again."

WOMAN. Look—now that they are together—what a strange resemblance.

MAN. They are like twins. My Lord Protector, do you notice this?

LORD PROTECTOR. By your favor, sir, I desire to ask you certain questions.

PRINCE. I will answer them, my lord.

NARRATOR. The Lord Protector asked many questions about the court, the late King, the Prince, the Princesses, and the boy answered them all correctly and without hesitation. It was strange; yes, it was unaccountable. All who heard it said so.

LORD PROTECTOR. It is most wonderful—but it is no more than the King likewise can do. These are not *proofs*. Arrest this—no, hold! Where is the Great Seal? Do you know that, boy? It is passing strange that so bulky a thing as the Seal of England—a huge golden disk—can vanish away, and no man be able to get track of it.

TOM (*excitedly*). A huge golden disk? Was it round and thick with letters upon it? Yes? Oh, now I know what this Great Seal is that there's been such a worry about. If you'd described it to me, you could have had it three weeks ago. I know where it is—but I did not put it there—first.

LORD PROTECTOR. Who then, my lord?

TOM. He that stands there—the rightful king of England. He shall tell you himself where it is. Remember, my Prince, how we exchanged garments for a jest? Then you noticed my hand had been hurt. At this your Highness sprang up, vowing vengeance, and as you ran toward the door, you passed a table. That thing you call the Seal lay on that table. You snatched it up and looked about for a place to hide it. Your eye caught sight of——

PRINCE. Hold! That's enough. In an arm piece of the armor that hangs on the wall in the palace, the Great Seal will be found.

TOM (*triumphantly*). Right, my King, right. *Now* the scepter of England is yours.

NARRATOR. The whole assemblage was on its feet now and well nigh out of its mind with excitement. At last a messenger appeared again upon the platform—and in his hand he held aloft the Great Seal!

CROWD. Long live the true King! Long live Edward, king of England!

NARRATOR. For five minutes the air quaked with shouts, and through it all a ragged boy stood flushed, happy, and proud.

TOM. Now, oh, my King, take these royal garments back and give poor Tom, your servant, his shreds again.

LORD PROTECTOR. Let the beggar be stripped and flung into the Tower.

PRINCE. I will not have it so. But for him, I would not have my crown again. (*Curiously*) Tell me, my friend, how did you remember where I hid the Seal? I myself had forgotten.

TOM. Ah, my King, that was easy. I used it many times.

PRINCE. How did you use the Great Seal of England?

TOM. To—to crack nuts with!

NARRATOR. But the multitude had come to see a coronation, and now at last they saw one. The King ruled worthily, and more than once, when a great advisor argued that a law caused no suffering, Edward would say to him——

KING EDWARD. What do you know of suffering and oppression? I and my people know, but not you!

MUSIC. (*Royal theme.*)

Five Hundred to One

by WILLIAM PÈNE DU BOIS

When Peter Graves was fourteen years old he had a marvelous adventure. He met a retired but extremely active inventor, whose name was Houghton Furlong. One of Houghton's most interesting inventions was an antigravity metal called Furloy. With just the right amounts of Furloy tied to various parts of a specially designed harness, Peter was able to overcome the pull of gravity. He could suspend himself in the air or fly through it.

Peter and Houghton formed a partnership and set out to make money from the stunts Peter could perform with the aid of Furloy.

Houghton and Peter decided to go before large audiences and to offer big rewards or money-back guarantees to anyone who could figure out how the stunts were done. They arranged an exhibition that was to take place at Princeton University at a great international pre-Olympic track meet in which the United States team was challenging an all-star European squad. In his letter to the director of athletics at Princeton, Houghton described Peter as a young lad, nearly fifteen, who promised to beat the times established in all the running events during the afternoon and the heights and distances covered in all the jumping contests. The letter also stated:

> I further offer five thousand dollars to anyone in the audience who can guess how he does these extraordinary feats, and I shall accept no pay from you if he does not outrun and outjump any of the afternoon's track men. If, on the other hand, young Peter's performance passes undetected and is in every way successful, I shall be only too pleased to accept as payment 10 per cent of the afternoon's profits.

The reply was simple: Bring him along.

To publicize the attraction, the director of athletics simply sent copies of Houghton's letter to the major news services, and most of the newspapers in the world seemed to take great pleasure in printing it without comment. The stadium was sold out a week in advance.

What Houghton and Peter didn't find out until later was that one man had bought five hundred seats, scattered throughout the stadium, and was personally offering another five thousand dollars to any of his five hundred guests who could somehow catch Peter Graves and bring him to him. This fellow was a wealthy industrialist, and he had bought the five hundred tickets for the employees of his factory and given them all the day off. His name was Llewelyn Pierpont Boopfaddle. He was intensely interested in Peter's stunting and had told a newspaper that he would pay five thousand dollars to learn the secret of it. Peter and Houghton had laughed at the offer when they read about it.

The two friends didn't watch the track meet at the stadium. They were in the privacy of a small dressing room in the field house, which Houghton managed to get for them so that Peter could put on his harness, with its concealed balls of Furloy, unobserved. At Peter's insistence, they had come two hours before he was to perform so that he'd have "plenty of time to dress carefully." He was dressed carefully in just five minutes and spent the rest of the time asking Houghton at three-minute intervals what time it was. He suffered a little from that empty feeling in the stomach which bothers athletes before they swing into action. He had practiced track events a few days before in a big, lonely field, but although he had jogged with Furloy some thirty or forty miles, there were a few kinks in his stride, and his footwork made him nervous. The limited size of the Princeton stadium was quite unsuited to his giant strides. Like trying to play tennis on a Ping-pong table, he thought, or motorboat racing in a swimming pool.

To hide the harness he wore a sweat suit. He had a nice one made to order, with gray pants trimmed with broad red stripes down the sides and a flaming-red sweat shirt on which was written PETER GRAVES. He was tickled with the idea of this sweat suit. He thought it great fun to break records without bothering to warm up in his suit.

The buzzer rang in the dressing room. Houghton undid the belt that strapped Peter to a bench and kept him from rising to the ceiling of the room on the slightest movement. Peter jumped up.

"Here you go," said Houghton. "You'll be wonderful. Just keep an eye open for the monster Boopfaddle." He walked Peter carefully out into the warm sunshine in the arena of the stadium. The day was perfect, without a trace of wind. A public-address system blasted forth this introduction:

"Attention, ladies and gentlemen, attention, please! At this time, as you all know, we have been promised some miraculous feats by a young boy named Peter Graves. This is the first performance in any stadium by this young man, and we cannot therefore accept any responsibility for the quality or sincerity of the performer. Peter Graves is now standing at the far end of the straightaway. He's wearing a bright-red sweat shirt. The stadium is yours, Peter Graves!"

There was a hush in the audience, and all eyes were on Peter. Houghton let go of him, patted him on the back. "Underplay it if possible," he advised, "and good luck!"

Peter jogged up to the edge of the football field and in two giant strides covered its entire length. The crowd rose to its feet and applauded. There was also much laughter in the crowd, due, no doubt, to the incredible nature of the performance so far and the comparison of Peter's brief and sensational dash to the more common feats just put on by the world's greatest athletes.

The crowd was with Peter, and now it was just a simple matter for him to amaze them further by doing whatever his imagination suggested on the spur of the moment. Hearing the great burst of applause, the American and European Olympic athletes left their dressing rooms and hastened back to the track to see Peter.

Peter took a few mincing steps up to the pole-vaulting pit. The bar was set at a little over fourteen feet. Peter squatted down on one foot and hopped over the bar, clearing it lavishly with about thirty feet to spare. Then, seeing the United States Olympic team lined up on the edge of the track, cheering him wildly with broad grins on their faces, he was suddenly filled with emotion.

Here were the faces he knew well from seeing them in newspapers and magazines, great heroes of his, all applauding him—it was just a bit too ridiculous. He did a standing broad jump across the football field, landing directly in front of the American team. He looked over all of the familiar faces. "It's all a trick," he stammered earnestly. "Of course it's all a trick!" He turned around and broad jumped to the other side of the field and repeated this youthful explanation to the Europeans. This was translated, for the benefit of the foreigners, into Swedish, French, Finnish, Italian, German, and Hungarian, each translation being greeted with sympathetic laughter and applause. The crowd couldn't have been more delighted. The cheers rocked the stadium.

"Peter Graves!" barked the public-address system. "The official timers would like to clock you in a hundred-yard dash. How about it?"

Peter nodded his head to indicate he was willing.

His first attempt was a flop because on his third step, instead of breaking the tape at the end of the stretch, he cleared it by fifteen feet. He tried again. This time he measured the course so that he broke the tape but didn't go quite so fast as in his first attempt. His time was 2⅞ seconds. On his third try he put on a much greater burst of speed, but he was going so fast at the finish that he wasn't able to stop short. Seeing that he was about to plummet into the audience, he thought fast and tried to clear the stadium with a tremendous leap. He nearly did it, too, but, missing slightly, he landed in the top two rows. The people in that section of the audience shrieked.

They quickly made room for Peter. He landed in a shower of sparks and a great burst of apologies as his spikes struck the concrete seats.

He had turned around, blushing slightly but inwardly most pleased with the commotion, when he noticed three rather plump ladies pushing their way toward him and reaching out in a rather obvious attempt to grab him. Peter didn't know it, of course, but these were three shipping clerks from Boopfaddle, Inc., reaching for that five-thousand-dollar prize package, Peter Graves. He jumped back over rows of ducking heads to the field to take an acrobat's bow.

"Peter, are you tired?"

Peter shook his head at the loud speaker to indicate that he wasn't.

"The official timers are curious about how fast you can run a mile. Would you please try running one?"

Peter answered with a nod.

A mile at Princeton is four times around the track. Peter started out at a good clip. One good thing about running a Furloy mile is that it can be run as if it were a sprint, that is, wide open all the way. Peter took two steps, then realized that he'd have to cut corners because his stride was so long. The stadium was definitely too tiny for a Furloy mile at top speed. He rounded the corner in sloppy fashion; then, miscalculating the length of his stride, he again left the track and found himself on his way to land in the audience. There were the same terrified shrieks and shower of sparks. Peter excused himself, faced the loud speaker, and shrugged his shoulders to indicate that he didn't find the mile too suitable an event for his capabilities.

Another group of respectable-looking people descended on him. This time Peter didn't notice them until a boy his age shouted, "Hey! Look out, Peter!" Peter jumped back on the field at the last possible moment.

Peter turned around when he reached the field and noticed a nice little squabble brewing in the stands he had just left. "Why don't you leave the kid alone!" "Why don't you mind your own business!" And so on. Peter scratched his head. He couldn't figure out this behavior. He thought that maybe his superhuman jumps, made possible by Furloy, had aroused such curiosity that some people just had to grab him and take him apart to see how he worked. Actually he had just slipped through the agile fingers of Boopfaddle's filing department. He walked, loping like an antelope, back to the starting line for another mile attempt.

Houghton was standing at the edge of the field with the Princeton University director of athletics and the United States Olympic track team.

"Has he picked a college yet?" asked the director. "He'd make a nice little football player. What does he train on? He looks in great shape."

"He likes Mexican jumping beans a lot, with a side order of spinach and a nice tall glass of rusty water. It's the iron in his diet. He can't swim, but he'd make an awfully nice anchor."

"Seriously though, what's the trick?" asked the director.

"Ha, ha," laughed Houghton. "That information would cost you about twenty thousand dollars at this point."

"I'm afraid it's just a little steep," the director said.

Peter, in the meantime, had made another stab at the mile and had again slipped and flown up into the audience. This time he had to evade a pair of outstretched arms. Peter sprang back to the field and trotted over to Houghton.

"Say, what's up? The audience seems out to get me."

"So I've noticed." Houghton turned to the athletics director. "What do you make of it?"

"I don't know. I can assure you this sort of thing is new to me, but, then, so is Peter. Most athletes here stay in the field. Wait a minute," he added. "One fellow did buy five hundred seats to be spread throughout the stadium. That might possibly be some sort of clue. Have you got any enemies?"

"Boopfaddle!" Houghton groaned. "I'll bet anything. He's been wanting to find out what makes these stunts work. We've got to get out of here fast. Do one more stunt while I get to the car, Peter. I'll meet you at the car. Get there as fast as you can; don't stop to change your clothes." Houghton ran off.

"What would you like to do?" asked the director. "By the way, I'm the fellow who has been speaking on the public-address system. I'll announce anything you want."

"Just say that I'm going to make another mile attempt. I don't want them to think I'm leaving yet. I'm going to jump over the closed end of the stadium and get to the car as fast as I can."

Palmer Stadium is shaped like a horseshoe, with an open end. Peter noticed that quite a few people had left their seats and lined up along the open end, apparently to try to prevent him from getting away. Houghton's car was parked on a street that ran parallel to the closed end of the stadium.

Peter jogged around the track carefully once, then put on a burst of speed and leaped over the audience in the

closed end of the stadium. He didn't quite clear it, but
with another kick from the top row, he jumped to the roof
of the field house, and then to the roof of the Cap and
Gown Club, looking for Houghton's car. He saw it and
jumped, hoping to land in it or at least near it. He mis-
judged the trees and, to his disgust, found himself tightly
wedged in the overhanging branches between two trees.

Houghton parked his car directly underneath Peter.

"Come down out of there! Just drop!" Houghton
ordered.

The crowd could be seen racing up the hill from the stadium.

"I can't! I'm stuck fast. I can't even move!" Peter was shaking his arms and legs but showed no signs of losing altitude.

"Good heavens!" Houghton yelled. "You'll have to unload some of the Furloy. Make it snappy!"

Peter yanked one of the small leather-covered balls from his harness. It shot through the branches and disappeared in the sky. He still didn't move. He tore off another, and another, and crashed into the seat of Houghton's car. Houghton stepped on the gas, and the old car roared away.

"Are you badly hurt?"

"I guess not," said Peter disgustedly. "Everything was going perfectly. We could have done that act in every stadium in the United States. *That Boopfaddle!*" He shook his fists and trembled all over.

"How many Furloys have we left?"

"Two!"

"Well, never mind! We'll think of something great to do with them."

A substance like Furloy had almost endless possibilities, as one can see from Peter's marvelous performance in the stadium at Princeton. The whole story of how Peter and Houghton learned to manage Furloy and to astound the public with what it could do is told in the book entitled Peter Graves, *by William Pène du Bois.*

Armstrong Sperry was born and brought up in the rocky hills of Connecticut. One of his earliest recollections is of hearing his great-grandfather tell of hair-raising adventures with pirates in the China Sea, of cannibals and whales and lagoon islands, rich with pearls.

As a boy, Armstrong Sperry was always drawing pictures and scribbling stories. His teachers shook their heads in gloomy doubt, certain that no good could come to any boy who preferred drawing cannibals to solving problems of algebra, or who would rather invent a yarn of his own than read Latin.

As a young man, Mr. Sperry worked as a commercial artist, drawing pictures of vacuum cleaners, canned soup, and beautiful young ladies. He began to wonder if being an artist was as exciting as he had always supposed it must be; and always at his elbow there lurked the friendly ghost of old Captain Armstrong, his great-grandfather, saying, "You don't think this city of concrete and steel and asphalt is all there is to life, do you? Why, there's an island down in the South Seas. Prettiest little island I ever did see...."

And that was why, one fine day, Armstrong Sperry turned his back forever on vacuum cleaners and canned soups and followed the sun to the South Pacific.

The two years he spent wandering through the South Seas were the most determining years of his life. He knew finally what he wanted to do: He wanted to tell stories in words and in pictures. And who was the logical audience for such stories? Boys and girls, of course.

 From *The Horn Book* Magazine, July-August 1941. Reprinted by permission of The Horn Book, Inc., Boston.

THE RAIN FOREST

Written and illustrated by

ARMSTRONG SPERRY

400

Chad Makes a Promise

In the lofty reception room of Government House, Chad Powell squirmed nervously on the chair's edge, his sun helmet gripped in both hands. For half an hour the boy had been waiting in response to a summons from Sir Hubert Murray, Lieutenant Governor of Papua. And the uncertainty which had beset Chad that morning, when his father failed to meet him at the steamer, quickened to anxiety. What could have happened to Dad? Their reunion had been arranged weeks before by cable. Surely Sir Hubert had sent for Chad to clear up the mystery. But the feeling of anxiety persisted, for in a country as unpredictable as New Guinea anything could happen.

The boy mopped his face with a wilted handkerchief. Suddenly he felt forlorn and alone and no older than his fourteen years. After weeks of travel by train and boat he could hardly believe that he had arrived that afternoon in Port Moresby, capital of Papua. For months he had been reading and dreaming about this great, mysterious island, with its extremes of heat and cold, its deltas and grassy lands, its waterless regions, its teeming Rain Forest, its mountain ranges that lifted sixteen thousand feet into the sky. Already the cities he had left behind—New York, Chicago, San Francisco, Sydney—seemed incredibly remote and unreal.

But there was nothing unreal about that tropical downpour blotting out the red-roofed bungalows of the little harbor town: solid sheets of water whipped by the wind. Was it true that New Guinea enjoyed nine months of rain and three of "wet season"? Only a few minutes ago the sun had been blazing! Yes, anything could happen in this strange place.

It didn't occur to Chad, sitting there so uneasily, that he had completed a journey unusual for a boy of his age to embark upon alone. For in the years since Chad's mother died, he had become accustomed to joining his father during vacations. The elder Powell was an ornithologist whose work had taken him to such out-of-the-way places as Dutch Guiana, Lanai, and the upper Orinoco. Now New Guinea! For the past five months Chad's father had been encamped in the mysterious Rain Forest, seeking rare specimens of the bird of paradise. And there Chad was supposed to join him during an extended winter vacation. But Dad had failed to meet the steamer. What was the next move now?

A shadow fell across the doorway, and the boy glanced up expectantly, half rising. But he saw only a stalwart native dressed in the regulation blue loincloth and shirt of the Armed Constabulary force. The chocolate-brown face was amiable and reassuring.

"Me Sergeant Jigori," the constable introduced himself. "What name you, *taubada?*"

Taubada—that word meant "master," the native salutation of New Guinea.

The boy smiled back at the friendly Papuan, feeling somehow less forlorn. "I'm Chad Powell," he answered. "Will His Excellency be able to see me soon?"

"*Io, taubada*—yes, master. He coming now!" And Sergeant Jigori snapped to rigid attention.

Chad rose hastily as two men entered the room. The boy's first impression of them both was of size and energy. The older man he recognized instantly from photographs he'd seen of Sir Hubert Murray. The younger man was lean and deeply tanned, with a snub-nosed Irish face; he wore bleached khaki shorts and shirt of a cut that suggested the Patrol Officer of Papua.

"Sorry to keep you waiting, young man," His Excellency boomed, half crushing the boy's hand in a powerful grip. "Blame it on O'Malley, here! He's been giving me a report of a raid in the upper Lakemanu district."

Chad liked the Lieutenant Governor instantly, but it was the Patrol Officer who caught and fixed the boy's attention.

O'Malley's glance was bright and blue and fearless. "The upper Lakemanu's the district where your father has established his base camp," he said quietly.

Chad stammered, "But I expected Dad to meet me at the steamer! Has anything happened?"

"I have bad news for you, son," the Lieutenant Governor said then. "That's why I sent for you."

The boy's breath caught. "What's the matter, sir?" he faltered. "What has happened to my dad?"

"Nothing at all!" the man amended hastily. "I should have said disappointing news. Stupid of me. But sit down, sit down! Jigori, fetch some lemonade for the young *taubada*. Lots of ice in it. Americans like ice."

Chad relaxed in his chair, vastly relieved. Nothing had happened to Dad after all. That was the only thing in the world that mattered.

He heard Sir Hubert saying, "I remember when I was in America every waiter in every hotel filled my water glass with ice. Beastly stuff!"

Chad asked, "What's gone wrong, sir?"

"It's your father's plane," His Excellency explained. "He had planned to have you fly inland tomorrow to join him. The plane's been taking in supplies once a month. But on the return flight last week it was forced to make an emergency landing in Hall Sound. Broke a propeller, among other things. There are no replacements at Lae. So we've got to send to Sydney for them."

The boy's heart sank. He thought of the beautiful silver Fairchild-Amphibian . . . Dad had sent him pictures of it. And he thought of the precious time that would be lost waiting for repairs, stranded here in Port Moresby instead of being with Dad in the heart of the Rain Forest.

Chad's voice was tight as he asked, "Will it take long to patch up the plane, sir?"

"Perhaps one month. More likely two."

"Two months?" the boy echoed weakly. He had to be back at school by March, and here was December half gone.

Sir Hubert's tone was quizzical as he replied, "One of the first words that you'll learn in New Guinea, Chad, is *dahori*."

"I know what that means," came the rueful answer. "It's like *mañana*. It means presently or tomorrow or by-and-by."

"That's right. New Guinea is the land of *dahori*. No need for hurry: there's always tomorrow."

O'Malley, with a note of astonishment, put in, "I didn't know American schools taught the Motuan dialect!"

Chad grinned at the surprise in the man's face. "I tried to learn a little Motuan as soon as Dad promised I could join him during vacation. It's a lot easier to learn than the Portuguese I tried, or Hawaiian that time at Lanai."

"You've been around, I'd say," the Patrol Officer remarked with a smile.

"Yes, sir."

"Don't call me 'sir'! I'm just O'Malley."

At that moment Sergeant Jigori reappeared with a tall, frosted glass, and Chad Powell knew that never had he tasted lemonade on a hot day that went so directly to the right spot. Between gulps he demanded, "Has Dad found the birds he wanted?"

"That's another thing," His Excellency replied. "Your father's last note said he'd captured every known variety of paradise bird except the very one he'd come to New Guinea to find."

"The King of Saxony?"

The man nodded. "It's extremely rare. I've never heard of a specimen being taken out alive."

Everything, Chad thought, seemed to be going wrong on this trip. He knew how bitter would be his father's disappointment in crossing half the world to find a certain specimen, only to fail. And now the plane had cracked up. Chad set down an empty glass, and his face was glum as he looked at the two men opposite him, finding no words.

But Sir Hubert said, "Come, cheer up, young man! Things are never so bad as they seem. There's always *dahori,* you know. And there's another way for you to join your father except by plane."

Instantly the boy straightened. His spirits went bounding. "How is that, sir?"

The big man chuckled. "You've come to New Guinea at an exciting moment, my lad. A raid has just been carried out at Ambush Creek, in the very district where your father is camped. A band of unknown savages looted the supply depot of an old miner named McKay. Two of his boys were murdered."

Chad felt a prickle along his spine. "But—but what's that got to do with me, sir?"

"O'Malley is leaving for Lakemanu tomorrow to track down the culprits—a mission that will take him near your father's camp," His Excellency explained. "You may accompany him. Unless, of course, you'd prefer to wait until the plane is repaired?"

"Oh, no!" The denial came so readily that both men laughed. Eagerly Chad leaned forward. "I'd like nothing better than to go with Mr. O'Malley," he cried. "I can be ready any time. When do we start, sir?"

"Not so fast! Not so fast!" The Patrol Officer's keen blue eyes seemed to weigh the boy who faced him. What the man saw seemed to reassure him. "It'll be a hard trip," he warned. "Ground you'd cover in a few hours by plane will take us days, even weeks. Dangerous, too. The Kukukukus are bad customers, with no respect for human life. They've never been brought under government control."

"Kuku-kukus?" Chad echoed. What a ridiculous name for a band of warlike savages!

"They're the fiends who, *I* believe, raided McKay's depot. There are several different tribes of Kuku-kukus. Some are pgymies. The footprints left behind at Ambush Creek were those of little people, so I've a pretty good hunch whom I'm looking for."

The Patrol Officer sounded as casual as if he were passing the time of day. From his tone an outsider would have thought it child's play for a single white man, accompanied by only half a dozen native Armed Constables, to enter hostile territory and capture alive a band of unidentified cannibals.

Sir Hubert's face mirrored the pride he felt in his Armed Constabulary—the force he had labored so long to build and develop. "My Patrol Officers are as justly famous as the Canadian Northwest Mounted Police," he stated. "Like them, they always get their man!"

"*Almost* always, sir," O'Malley corrected his superior respectfully. "We have been known to fail."

"Not often, not often!"

"Are the Kuku-kukus really cannibals?" Chad broke in excitedly.

"Indeed they are," O'Malley asserted. "Even in this year of 1940 little is known about them except their reputation. The pygmies are particularly cunning fighters and hard to track down. Sometimes they live in tree-house villages, but many of them are nomads roaming the Rain Forest."

"And you think you can actually run down the band that raided Ambush Creek?" Chad said incredulously.

"That is my mission," came the modest reply.

"You see"—His Excellency took up the explanation— "to let such an offense go unpunished lessens the prestige of the Government. We always try to capture the culprits and bring them to justice in Port Moresby. The back-country savages live in the Stone Age, Chad. To them any stranger is a potential enemy to be robbed or killed on sight. We are trying to teach them that they must live in peace with their neighbors and respect the property and lives of others." The man's face clouded momentarily as he sighed, "But I am afraid it will be a long time before they realize that the Government is their friend, not their enemy."

"And Dad's camp is in that wild territory?" the boy faltered.

"In the very heart of it! But your father is an old hand in the bush. He knows how to look out for himself."

O'Malley's blue eyes twinkled. "Getting cold feet, Chad? Perhaps you'd rather back out——"

"Of course not!" the boy retorted. "When do we start?"

"The *Elevala* is loading my gear," the Patrol Officer returned. "Tomorrow morning she'll sail us up the coast to Kukupi, where we start inland. Can you be ready by six?"

"I'll be there!"

Sir Hubert rose, terminating the interview. "Then it's all settled. I couldn't place you in safer hands, young man, than Pat O'Malley's." The big man crushed Chad's hand. "Good luck to you, and my respects to your father. If there's anything you need——"

"I have everything, sir."

As the boy turned away, he discovered that O'Malley was exchanging a few hurried words in Motuan with Sergeant Jigori.

"I'll have a surprise for you in the morning, Chad," the Patrol Officer announced, while a glance of secret amusement passed between him and the native constable.

Jigori, with the air of a friendly conspirator, grinned and nodded his bushy mop. "A fine surprise, *taubada*," he chuckled.

Completely mystified, Chad looked from one to the other, but O'Malley offered no further explanation. "Tomorrow at six sharp. Don't dare to be late!"

"You can count on me, sir."

"The name's O'Malley," the man reminded him.

"All right, O'Malley," the boy laughed. He liked the big Irishman standing there so foursquare and solid.

Here was a friend who would be ready and fearless in any emergency, who would never let him down. "Good-by, Sir Hubert," Chad stammered. "My thanks for everything, sir."

"God bless you, lad. Tell your father I'll send in the plane with supplies at the first possible moment."

Back in his room at the hotel, Chad whistled furiously as he packed his duffel bag.

"Boy, am I lucky!" he thought happily, and his heart was full to bursting.

Everything that had seemed to be going so wrong suddenly was righted. New Guinea was a wonderful place! This journey to the Rain Forest would be the most exciting adventure anyone could have.

Perhaps if, in that moment, Chad Powell could have had some inkling of what was to befall him in the Rain Forest, a measure of his eagerness might have dwindled.

As it was, he laughed exultantly and cried aloud, "I'm on my way, Dad! I'll be with you before you know it. And I may even find that King of Saxony bird for you! You'll see!"

These words, so lightly spoken, seemed to fall upon the air with a solemn, fateful ring, like a promise. Moving toward the open window, Chad caught a glimpse of lights winking on in the little harbor town. Somewhere a flock of purple, glossy starlings chattered as they feasted in a wild fig tree, and the boy detected the clear whistle of the pied butcher bird even before he caught the black-and-white flash of its plumage.

Off to the north the mighty ramparts of the Victor Emmanuel range loomed shadowy and mysterious: mountain fastnesses which, after three and a half centuries, still guarded their secrets from inquisitive eyes. Far up on those timbered slopes, in the region known as the Rain Forest, the Kuku-kukus roamed unchallenged, and there a single white man sought the rare bird of paradise. And tomorrow morning at six o'clock young Chad Powell of New York City would be leaving to join that beloved white man in the most thrilling adventure of his life.

As he closed the door of his room and went down to supper, Chad remembered the surprise which O'Malley and Sergeant Jigori had cooked up between them. What could it possibly be?

The boy shook his head in complete bewilderment. After all, New Guinea was a land of surprises!

O'Malley's Surprise

The government ketch *Elevala* lay tied up to the wharf, her sides gleaming white in the early morning sun; from her peak a blue ensign whipped smartly in the wind. As Chad Powell jumped out of the car, the hands of his wrist watch pointed squarely to the hour of six.

Everywhere there was a bedlam of noise and activity. An impatient toot from the *Elevala*'s whistle jogged the pace of the heavily laden stevedores, who went aboard by one gangplank and descended by another. The hold of the little ketch was being filled with all the equipment and supplies that O'Malley would need over a period of many weeks.

Captain Ritchie, a bluff and hearty sea dog, greeted Chad with a broad imitation of the manner in which he believed all Americans talked. "How be you, Yank? I reckon we-all air mighty glad to make yore acquaintance. I swan!"

Chad came back at him with the lingo he'd picked up in Australia. "I'm bonza, sir. Strike me pink if I'm not!"

The Captain howled. "I wouldn't mind bein' fourteen again myself, not if I could have a trip like the one in store for you. Gets pretty dull just cruisin' up and down the coast, not seein' anything fiercer than a dugong, when all the time those mountains are as full of cannibals as a Papuan *dubu* is full of fleas!" The Captain turned his head to shout, "Hey, O'Malley, here's your charge!"

At that moment the Patrol Officer himself popped out of the cabin. He glanced at his watch. "Right on the beam, I see."

"How about that surprise you promised?" Chad asked.

"Jigori's just gone to fetch it," the man answered with a grin. "Come aboard and see for yourself."

As Chad stepped on deck, the cabin door opened, and Jigori emerged, followed by a boy: a Papuan boy about Chad's own age. Chad took in many things at a glance: the flash of amusement that passed between the Sergeant and the Patrol Officer; the fact that the Papuan boy had a quick, intelligent face and a mop of bushy hair, that he was dressed only in the blue cotton waist cloth of New Guinea and a greenstone amulet suspended about his neck.

O'Malley was chuckling, "Here's your surprise, Chad. I thought you might like a companion of your own age

414

on this trip. This fine lad is Jigori's only son. His name is Natua."

"Fine boy, my Natua," beamed the Sergeant, shoving his son a step forward.

The two boys, races apart, eyed each other uncertainly. "What's he like?" Chad was wondering. "How'll I ever talk to him?" Then, seeing the puzzled intentness of the Papuan boy's look, he knew that these same questions were racing through Natua's head.

Chad smiled and held out his hand. It was caught instantly in a firm grip.

"How are you, Natua?" In that moment Chad could not think of a single word of Motuan.

"*Taubada*," the other murmured, his voice low.

That word *master* again! Quickly Chad corrected him. "Not *taubada*. Friend!"

Natua's smile flashed as he understood the American boy's meaning. With glowing eyes he repeated, "Fren'."

And from that first moment of their association Natua's name for Chad Powell was Fren'.

O'Malley was delighted with the way the two boys seemed to be hitting it off. "You'll find Natua speaks a bit of English," he said, "and he'll brush up your Motuan." And the man turned away, relieved. With half a glance O'Malley could see that the two boys were going to become firm friends.

"Chad, stow your duffel aboard!" Captain Ritchie barked. "Natua, take those cameras to O'Malley's cabin. Look alive, you two! There's work to be done. You can get acquainted later."

There seemed to be no end to the supplies that were being loaded aboard the little *Elevala*. Ammunition in sealed cases. Twist tobacco for trade, packed in far-off Virginia. Boxes of salt: the currency of mountain Papua. Medicine. Kerosene. Rice in waterproofed bags. Once the party left the ship, there would be no way to replenish supplies until the Fairchild-Amphibian could be repaired.

O'Malley was everywhere present, checking off lists, issuing orders in that cool, unruffled tone which later Chad was to know so well.

Sensing something of the boy's bewilderment, the Patrol Officer took time out to explain, "Every last thing we need has to be packed on someone's back. Forty pounds is the legal limit per man, and one carrier within a month consumes the load of rice he starts out with. Inland travel has its headaches, lad."

Sergeant Jigori, meanwhile, was lining up the twenty Armed Constables who were to accompany the party. There was no nonsense about Jigori now: here was a task-master who demanded the best of the men who stood rigidly at attention. Each constable (or A.C. as a man was always referred to) was equipped with a Lee-Enfield carbine and twenty rounds of .303 ammunition. Barefooted, bushy-headed, dark faces solemn with the responsibility of their position, they stared straight ahead as Sergeant Jigori stalked stiffly up and down the line. These men were seasoned veterans of the bush, proud of the high tradition of their service.

Even O'Malley paused for a second to glance with affection at the A.C.'s. Most of them had gone along with him on other patrols and had proved themselves in the face of danger.

"Look at 'em!" the Patrol Officer gloated, to no one in particular. "Where will you find a finer bunch of men?"

It was obvious to Chad that the A.C.'s held Sergeant Jigori in healthy awe, while they idolized O'Malley. One Papuan stood apart from the others, a big black fellow with a broken nose; he was dressed in a clean though tattered singlet and *rami*. Perched jauntily on his pate was the crown of an American straw hat from which the rim had been cut away.

O'Malley beckoned this fellow over for Chad to meet. "This is Jokuri, our cooky-boy," the man explained. "I call him Joe Currey. He's the *worst* cook on earth! Isn't that so, Joe Currey?"

The broken-nosed Papuan giggled like a schoolgirl and hung his chin on his massive chest. *"Io, taubada,* that is true."

Three shrill blasts from the *Elevala*'s whistle produced a magical effect upon drowsy Port Moresby, for this was the signal. of departure. Men, women, and children came hurrying toward the wharf, drawn like magnetized bits of metal—running, walking, a few on bicycles or driving horse-drawn vehicles. The arrival or departure of any ship was the biggest event in the little harbor town's uneventful days.

In the stern, surrounded by duffel bags and cases of gear, Chad and Natua watched the hawsers being cast free and hauled aboard.

"We're off, Natua!"

"Io, Fren'," the other answered, and in hesitant English added, "We are off."

The two boys looked at each other and smiled.

"Gee," Chad thought, "he's a swell egg. We're going to get along fine."

From across a widening strip of water cries of good luck and safe return were shouted in several languages, while flowers pelted the little ketch like confetti.

"Good-by! Good-by!" Chad heard himself shouting, to no one in particular. The deck had begun to lift and quiver beneath his feet, filling him with excitement.

As the sturdy ketch swept out to sea, the voices from the land came fainter and fainter, while the figures on the dock dwindled in size. Off to the north the red ramparts of the Victor Emmanuel range beckoned. and the *Elevala,* eager as any greyhound, seemed to be racing toward them.

O'Malley pointed out Mount Yule. "That block of stone is ten thousand feet high and marks the eastern boundary of the Kuku-kuku country," he explained. "You'll be seeing a lot of Mount Yule, at closer range. Your dad's up there somewhere."

"I wish he could know that I am here," the boy returned. "He won't know about the accident to the plane, and he'll be terribly worried. How long before we reach his camp?"

"A week or ten days, with good luck."

A week or ten days! Days of traveling twelve to fourteen hours, up the Lakemanu as far as it was navigable, then inland to the supply depot that had been raided by the Kuku-kukus. Then on into the Rain Forest: home of the fabulous birds of paradise, and of naked brown men who moved like shadows through the jungle. To himself Chad murmured, "It won't be long now, Dad."

Thirty miles east of Kerema, the *Elevala* dropped anchor off the delta formed by the mouths of the Tauri and Lakemanu rivers. Here, at the village called Kukupi, canoes were found ready and waiting for the government party: splendid dugouts of native construction, narrow of beam and sixty feet long.

Within an hour the canoes were loaded almost to the gunwales with O'Malley's gear and equipment. Then, with Chad and Natua and the Patrol Officer in the leading canoe, and four A.C.'s for paddlers, the journey upriver began.

"Tungom's the next stop," exclaimed O'Malley.

"How far is that?" Chad demanded.

"Fifty miles."

"As the crow flies?"

"As the crocodile swims!" And out of sheer high spirits and joy in hitting the trail again, O'Malley flung back his head and sang.

The boys made themselves as comfortable as possible on a pile of duffel, sheltered from the sun's fierce glare by a thatch of *nipa*. The A.C.'s proved to be powerful paddlers, and each thrust of their long-handled blades left Kukupi farther and farther behind.

All that day, as one hour merged into another, no actual land could be seen nearer than the distant ranges— only vast areas of cane-covered swamp, broken here and there by the mouths of small streams which were outlets of lagoons behind the main river. In some places thousands of untidy sago palms could be seen, and black-trunked mangroves, whose exposed roots writhed like sea serpents above the surface of the river.

By midafternoon O'Malley pointed out a native village. "That's Moviavi. Two thousand people live there on half-submerged islands."

Through the binoculars Chad could make out bamboo dwellings perched on stilts high above the water. They appeared to be connected with runways like boardwalks.

"How do people live with no land for gardens?" the boy asked, bewildered.

"Compared to the inland tribes the Moviavis live high," O'Malley told him. "They spear fish and turtle and crocodile and hunt all sorts of waterfowl with their arrows.

Then they have lotus root, crustaceans, and sago. Not a bad diet for anyone."

Suddenly the glasses in Chad's hands trembled a little. "I think I see a fleet of canoes putting out toward us," he cried.

"You can bet you do! In the old days this would have been a ticklish moment for any explorer. But all these people want now is to trade."

The Moviavi canoes came racing across the water. As they drew nearer, Chad discovered that they had no outriggers and the paddlers stood upright to achieve tremendous speed with little apparent effort.

O'Malley chuckled. "The Papuan savage in his native habitat. Probably you think they're after your scalp, but they're not."

These were reassuring words, for the advancing savages looked wild enough to chill the stoutest heart. The Patrol Officer signaled his A.C.'s to halt. Like water beetles the Moviavis closed in and circled round, shouting at the top of their lungs the peace-word of all Papua, *"Sambio! Sambio!"* These naked black men had the powerful shoulders and long arms of canoe tribes. Their black hair, bleached with lime, bushed wildly over their skulls: cassowary quills had been thrust through holes pierced in their hawklike noses. Necklets of crocodile teeth gleamed against their skin. The Moviavis were an awesome sight.

"Sambio! Sambio!" Chad and Natua shouted back, eager enough to be friends with this wild band.

Gorgeous plumes of the bird of paradise were being offered by the savages for barter. But these O'Malley refused, since the Government forbids the white man to trade for these plumes. Instead, tobacco and coveted empty meat tins were exchanged for packages of sago.

The trade was quickly concluded. Then with a chorus of *Sambio*'s the Moviavis swung in a wide circle and raced for their distant village, eager to display their trophies. And with their departure Chad experienced a sensation of breathlessness, as if he himself had been racing at top speed.

"A great people," O'Malley remarked, watching the canoes sweep away. "Papua forces her men to live the way she wants them to. In swamps or on the beach or walled up in those mountains."

"Is that the reason there are so many different languages in New Guinea?" Chad wondered.

"That's right. The country itself has kept its various tribes from getting together. Why, within a radius of two miles you can find as many as three totally different languages. I don't know how we Patrol Officers would get along without the Motuan lingo. But it's useless in the mountains. That's where sign language becomes a fine art."

"I'm glad I learned a little Motuan," Chad said. "Natua and I will get along better."

"With his help you'll be spouting it like a native before you know it," the man promised. "And it's surprising how quickly Papuan kids learn English."

Natua seized every opportunity to instruct his new friend, pointing out the legions of black and white geese, the gray cranes and pelicans that rested on the water hyacinths, the beautiful white egret standing in solitude.

In each case the Papuan boy used the Motuan words, while Chad carefully repeated them, filing them away in his memory. It became a sort of game, which had no beginning and no end.

All that afternoon the river twisted and turned, sinuous as a python whose back was burnished brass. Moviavi and its wild people had been swallowed in the swamps. Now there were no people to be seen anywhere, no sign of human habitation.

"Must have been a lot of rain in the mountains," O'Malley was grumbling. "The current is picking up.

But we've got to expect that. This is the season that is called *fidi*."

Imperceptibly the river was becoming a swift-flowing stream against which the burdened dugouts made labored progress. Stumps of trees, washed down in the flood and half submerged, became treacherous snags; unseen rocks were indicated only by swirling, sucking whirlpools. Chad began to wonder where and in what manner he and his companions would pass the night.

Suddenly Natua gripped Chad's arm. "See, Fren'!" the Papuan boy cried excitedly. "There is the *puk-puk!* See?"

He pointed to a low sandbank that was dotted with stumps of driftwood.

"Puk-puk?" Chad parroted, mystified.

"He's trying to tell you that those stumps are really crocodiles," O'Malley laughed.

Sure enough, Chad could then distinguish that the bleached and mottled logs were indeed crocodiles, and he felt a prickle of goose flesh.

"Perhaps it's really driftwood," he suggested hopefully.

"That driftwood could come to life mighty fast if you took hold of its tail," the Patrol Officer retorted. "Sometimes a canoe gets stuck on a shoal. And do you know what I do then?"

"What?" the boy demanded.

"I blow my nose—good and hard. The noise makes all the crocs dive into the drink. That raises the water so my canoe can float. Simple, what?"

"And do you expect me to believe that?" Chad said.

"After thirty years in New Guinea, my lad, I've learned never to believe or disbelieve any story. You'd be surprised how often the impossible can happen in this country. And that's a fact!"

Throughout the day there had been few mosquitoes on the river, but as afternoon waned they materialized out of the swamps in savage, hungry legions. With each breath it seemed to Chad that he inhaled a cloud of insects, while his arms grew weary with flailing the air. O'Malley puffed furiously at his pipe, creating a small area of immunity about his head. Natua and the half-naked A.C.'s endured the pests with stoic indifference.

It was fortunate that just before dusk a high bank of red earth loomed out of the reeds. O'Malley directed the paddlers to steer for it.

"Here's where we tie up for the night," the man said, with a note of relief. "I'd begun to think we'd have to anchor in midstream. But now we can have Joe Currey cook one of his inimitable dinners. There's no end to Joe's ingenuity. Tonight we'll have rice and bully beef. Tomorrow night we'll have bully beef and rice. The next night rice and—but why go on and on? The menu's always the same."

Sergeant Jigori's canoe swung alongside. The brown face was alive with excitement. "Excuse, *taubada*," the Papuan cried, "but Orai has seen a grandfather *puk-puk* in the shallows. A good dinner it would be for us all. He would like your permission to kill it."

O'Malley hesitated. "Don't know as I care to lose a good A.C. to get a poor supper," he grumbled.

"Orai very clever," Jigori promised eagerly. "He catch *puk-puk* kill 'im dead-finish quick. *Puk-puk* no catch Orai."

The Patrol Officer capitulated. "But tell Orai," he added darkly, "if he gets eaten I'll flay him alive." And to Chad the man added, "Now you'll see some fun. Orai's an old hand at this game, or I wouldn't let him tackle it. Come on, we'll go ashore with the A.C.'s."

Orai, a sinewy fellow who might have been any age from thirty to fifty, produced a length of cane looped at one end. Climbing the slippery bank of red earth, he peered intently into the water. The other A.C.'s deployed along the bank, holding one end of the cane, while O'Malley stood ready with his rifle. Chad and Natua peered down into the yellowish water, where they made out the dim form of a great crocodile lying motionless on the sandy bottom. At a signal from Orai the other A.C.'s burst into a terrific din of shouting and yelling.

"What are they making that noise for?" Chad wondered. "They'll scare the croc away."

"Noise confuses the *puk-puk*," Natua answered. "You will see."

Abruptly the commotion stopped. Orai slid into the water. The boys could see him swimming downward with slow, easy strokes, the cane trailing behind. Entirely unhurried, the A.C. went about his dangerous game as if it were part of an ordinary day's work.

The crocodile had made no movement. Through the gathering gloom Chad caught the orange glow of the monster's eyes, and he knew a frightening tension of suspense. Scarcely daring to draw breath, he bent his gaze upon the water. Now Orai was swimming toward the crocodile from behind, the noose of cane reaching cautiously forward. Then, with a motion so quick as to confuse the eye, the noose slipped over the long snout. Orai shot toward the surface. One hand yanked the cane taut.

Then things began to happen! The water was lashed to foam. The monster rose to the surface to fight for its life. But the strong arms of the A.C.'s were hauling on the cane lasso, and the noose grew tighter with every movement of the thrashing body. Shouting with victory, the Papuans hauled their victim up the bank, keeping out of

428

reach of that punishing tail. A well-placed bullet put an end to the crocodile's struggles. Then the jubilant A.C.'s fell upon their prey with bush knives while Joe Currey built a roaring fire and rattled his pots and pans.

Someday when he returned to America, Chad would like to tell his schoolmates that he'd eaten crocodile This was the only reason why, later, he consented to try a morsel. He found it tough and rank.

O'Malley refused to touch it. "I've never been hungry enough yet to come to it," he said. "But look at those A.C.'s! You'd think that stuff was tenderloin steak. Ah, here comes Joe Currey with our rice and bully beef! What did I tell you?"

Natua was as happy as the Constables in making a meal of the tough flesh.

"Funny thing about these crocs," O'Malley observed between mouthfuls of bully beef and hot tea. "In some rivers they're small and harmless, while in others they're large and extremely ferocious. There seem to be two different kinds of 'em. The bad kind—*crocodilus porosus,* I believe the scientific boys call 'em—have been known to attack and take a man right out of a canoe. I remember once, at the mouth of the Purari, the prow of my whaleboat struck the snout of a half-submerged croc, and that beast came openmouthed right after us. It took half a dozen bullets to polish him off."

"It seems strange that a salt-water creature can live in fresh water, too," Chad observed.

"They're equally at home in either. I've found their eggs a hundred and fifty miles inland. And wherever the crocs go, they earn a bad name. When we reach Tungom, old Chief Samarai will tell you how I once got rid of a particularly nasty one that had been terrorizing the whole community."

"*You* tell me about it," Chad begged. "Old Samarai might forget, and I couldn't understand him, anyway."

O'Malley was an easy talker, who enjoyed his youthful audience. Sitting there on the high red bank of the Lakemanu River, with a smudge to discourage the mosquitoes and the A.C.'s still busily gorging their fill, the Patrol Officer told Chad Powell the incident concerning the crocodile that terrorized the village called Tungom.

"No one had ever caught sight of the beast," the man said. "But children and pigs were disappearing with unpleasant frequency at night. In the morning nothing could be seen but a trail in the mud leading to the river. I happened to be passing through Tungom on routine patrol, and Samarai asked my help."

"What did you do?" Chad demanded as Natua, having eaten to repletion, joined him to hear the story.

"Well, I told Samarai to kill the biggest, fattest pig he owned. This was a blow to the old Chief, for a pig means more to a Papuan than his wife and children! But finally he gave in, and I told him he had to let the meat spoil. When it was good and ripe, I planted a pound of dynamite inside the carcass, with a yard of fuse attached. Then I dropped it into the pool to which the croc's trail always led. I'd fixed a five-minute fuse to give the beast time to discover the bait. Well, sir, there came one terrific explosion! And, believe me or not, that old brute crawled out on shore as alive as you please. But not for long. He just rolled over on his back and gave up the ghost. You'll meet Samarai soon," O'Malley concluded. "He's a wily old rascal, but we're great buddies."

While this tale was being told, Sergeant Jigori was supervising the setting up of a tent fly. Two cots were placed beneath the canvas and rigged with protective coverings of mosquito net. Jigori's orders were obeyed with alacrity, and Chad was filled with admiration for the quick, intelligent way in which the A.C.'s pitched camp for the night. This was an old story to them.

"Where will Natua sleep?" Chad asked.

"He can spread his blanket roll under the tent fly," O'Malley answered.

"On the ground?"

"Of course! Natua has never slept in a bed in his life. For that matter, I doubt if he's ever sat on a chair."

The Papuan boy, who had been following the conversation as best he could, smiled happily and went to fetch his blanket roll.

"Natua's a grand lad," O'Malley said then, his voice warming. "Someday he'll make a great A.C., just like his father."

"It's funny," Chad answered. "Even though Natua and I can't talk much yet, we don't have trouble understanding each other. And Sergeant Jigori seems like someone I've known all my life!"

The man nodded approvingly. "Good boy! You'll get along with these people. It will be an experience you'll never forget." He stretched and yawned, rose to his feet.

"Time to turn in. One thing about this country—you get to bed early. It's the only way to outwit these blood-thirsty mosquitoes."

Natua appeared with his blanket roll and spread it on the ground between the two cots. As Chad, weary with the events of this long day, crawled under the mosquito net, he heard the carefree chatter of the A.C.'s rolling up in their blankets by the smoldering cookfire. Almost immediately O'Malley's deep breathing rose on the air. It was followed by that of Natua, who had fallen instantly asleep.

But, tired though he was, Chad could not get to sleep. He pulled the blanket close, against the chill mist that rose from the river; saw the giant constellations go wheeling up the southern sky. Somewhere a chorus of frogs set up a hoarse croaking, while the unremitting hum of millions of mosquitoes, trying vainly to penetrate the net, seemed like the background music of all other night sounds. Yet somehow a sense of the solitude of this savage land made itself felt as a slow invasion of Chad's being. He could not have put into words what it was he felt. But it was as if vast, elemental forces were close at hand, waiting to overwhelm him, and already his blood was aware of their nearness.

"Something surely is going to happen to me," he thought drowsily. "Something important. . . . I wonder what it will be. . . ." His eyelids drooped, lifted, drooped again. "I wonder. . . ."

Tungom

The land rose gradually as the region of naked, drowned trees and sago swamps was left behind. Timber appeared, stunted at first but growing taller with the miles. The flowering D'Albertis creeper formed a wall of crimson along the riverbanks. Named after the intrepid Italian explorer who had been first to navigate New Guinea's unknown rivers, this barbaric creeper hung in loops on the outer foliage of the jungle, its massed blooms suspended like bunches of bananas, while the red-and-green lories that fed upon its blossoms were scarcely less brilliant than the flowers themselves.

As the snakelike line of canoes twisted endlessly up-river against the current, Chad Powell had the feeling that this was a journey which had no beginning and led nowhere. The heat of midday burned into him like an inescapable eye, consuming energy, lulling thought.

Thus it was a welcome sound when, two days after passing Moviavi, O'Malley proclaimed, "Just around the next bend you'll see Tungom! I'll wager old Samarai will kill the fatted pig for us."

Chad's interest quickened. "Will we stay there long?"

"Just overnight, while we recruit carriers. Samarai knows we're coming. He'll have the boys rounded up."

"But suppose he doesn't——" Chad suggested.

"It's a punishable offense to refuse to carry for the Government," came the man's brief reply. "You can wager that hours ago everybody in Tungom knew just when we'd be arriving."

"How do they do it?" the boy marveled.

"Don't ask me! It's as if the earth itself could talk or the river carry messages. Sometimes I swear it's positively creepy the way news travels in Papua."

At that moment a shout burst from the A.C.'s— "Tungom! Tungom!"—and the canoes headed eagerly in for shore where, at the base of a steep bank, a mob of shouting and gesticulating natives had gathered on a landing stage.

Chad Powell eyed that clamoring crowd uneasily, for they seemed to him like a flock of vultures. And suddenly he recalled a joke made by a schoolmate when Chad first announced that he was going to New Guinea: "How about being eaten by cannibals?" He had scoffed at the idea, retorting that he didn't expect to end up in the soup kettle. He didn't—then. But, eying those bushy-headed, naked savages who were awaiting him on shore, he began to wonder.

Seen by the sun's hot glare, the mob on the landing stage was a confused mass of muscular bodies that were a shining red: an effect combined of coconut oil and coloring matter. Their headdresses were intricate arrangements of dogs' teeth and feathers. At closer range there was a sort of magnificence about the men with their bold decorations. But the women were indescribably ugly with their close-cropped heads, their lack of all adornment. Was O'Malley handing him over to a band of cutthroats and cannibals?

"Stand by to land!" O'Malley called out, as the leading canoe slid up alongside the landing stage.

436

Instantly dark hands grasped the gunwale. Chad and Natua and the Patrol Officer were half carried, half dragged up on the platform. But the faces pressed so close were grinning in friendly fashion, and after the first shock of alarm and surprise Chad caught his breath with relief. He heard O'Malley saying, "Here comes old Samarai," and saw an enormously fat figure of a man waddling down the steep bank.

"Samarai, you old scoundrel!" O'Malley shouted. "You're fatter than ever. Why don't you *roll* down the bank?"

There was superb dignity in the Chief's carriage as he lumbered to meet his guests. Only the twinkle in his black eyes indicated that Samarai took no offense at the levity of the Patrol Officer's words.

When O'Malley led Chad forward to be presented, the Chief bent an astonished gaze upon what was the first white boy he had ever seen. Samarai plucked at a strand of Chad's blond hair as if he could not believe it. He shook his head in amazement.

Posting a guard over the canoes to make sure that nothing would be stolen, the Patrol Officer led the way up the steep bank to the village, while the whole population trailed after him. The village itself proved to be only a double row of houses facing each other across a strip of ground that was hard packed by generations of bare feet. A great *dubu* house, or men's clubhouse, dominated all others in size and elevation. Toward this dwelling Samarai led his guests, and at their approach the *dubu* boys themselves came swarming out to meet the visitors.

These "boys" ranged in age from fifteen to twenty-five, and it was from their ranks that the carriers would be recruited. They were elaborately decorated and streaked with red ocher, their waists drawn in to wasplike dimensions by the tight leather belts which were their insignia. Chad remembered reading about them somewhere; remembered that as soon as a Papuan boy reaches the age of fourteen he enters the Men's House, where he lives in company with other boys until he grows up and marries. Women are forbidden, on pain of death, ever to enter the *dubu*.

A sense of unreality fixed itself upon Chad Powell as he and Natua climbed the notched log that was the stairway into the great *dubu*. Sorcery charms hung above the door, swaying in the wind: bones and tufts of hair. Here were all the things he'd ever read or heard about a Papuan village: the lofty structure built entirely of bamboo, an amazing piece of architecture executed by the crudest of implements; and the *dubu* boys themselves with their barbaric decorations and their tireless hubbub of banter and comment.

"There's not one nail in this whole construction," O'Malley pointed out, enjoying Chad's astonishment. "Each joint is lashed with rattan. I'd like to see the house an American would build with no material but a clump of bamboo and a stone ax!"

The interior was dim and cool, the floor soft with layers of many mats; but there was no furniture of any sort. Samarai clapped his hands to summon food and drink and sent the *dubu* boys scuttling; then the Chief folded his great bulk on the mats with the ease of long practice and motioned his guests to be seated.

Chad and Natua sank down beside O'Malley. But suddenly the Papuan boy sprang to his feet, an exclamation bursting from him.

"Taubada!" he cried, clutching the Patrol Officer's arm and pointing upward toward the rafters. "Look there!"

All eyes followed the direction of the boy's finger. Chad's blood froze. For directly under the peak of the roof, on a crossbeam, an enormous snake was uncoiling itself, preparing to descend.

"It's—it's a python," Chad stammered. "O'Malley, do you see?"

The man flung back his head and laughed. "Keep your shirts on, boys! That's only Samarai's pet rat-catcher. He's too well fed to bother you. There are more rats here in Tungom than in all the sinking ships of the world. Sit down, sit down! The snake just wants to make friends. He likes to have his head scratched!"

But the boys' eyes remained fixed uneasily upon the monstrous serpent that came slithering down one of the uprights. At Samarai's low whistle the python undulated across the mats, and Chad could have sworn that it was at least twenty feet long and thicker than his leg. The spadelike head rose and shot toward the old Chief, who promptly scratched the scaly hide with a forked stick reserved for that purpose.

"I wish he'd get on with his rat-catching," Chad murmured uncertainly. "I like him better up in the rafters than in my lap."

But the snake, forming a single loop over Samarai's forearm, settled down contentedly in apparent sleep. The *dubu* boys appeared, bearing calabashes of some dubious-looking food. Chad was vastly relieved when O'Malley, with a great show of politeness, refused to rob his host, stating that the *taubadas* had brought their own food. Whether the Chief was deceived Chad could not tell. But he saw that O'Malley and Samarai were friends.

The Chief beamed with delight when O'Malley said to the boy, "Samarai's a regular scoundrel—a combination chief, sorcerer, and general villain."

"How old is he, anyway?"

"About as old as Mount Yule, I'd say. But in spite of being a humbug he's got a lot of sound knowledge."

Samarai nodded in complete agreement, though Chad knew the Chief understood not a word being spoken.

"Knowledge of what?" the boy asked.

"All sorts of things. He knows, for example, exactly which vegetables should be grown in different soils, and the proper time of year for planting. He knows when to cut away the sprouts and where to get the seeds. He can tell exactly when the different fish will run in the rivers.

441

You may be sure he knows all about native poisons! To look at him you'd think he was just a genial old man, but I'd hate to guess how many enemies he's liquidated."

Samarai interrupted this statement with a few sentences of gibberish, after which his paunch shook with mirth.

"He's asking me if I remember how he saved my life," O'Malley chuckled.

"Did he?"

"More or less," the other admitted. "Three years ago it was, when I was on patrol here. I'd been marching all day in wet clothes and sleeping at night in wet blankets when an attack of lumbago and malaria knocked me out." O'Malley grinned reminiscently. "Samarai ordered Jigori to set up the tin bathtub that was part of my equipment and fill it with cold spring water. Then he ordered his men to ease me into it! I was burning up with fever, and that water felt like ice, and I yelled at them to get me out of that tub. But Samarai defied me! He took hot stones from the cookfire and dropped them sizzling into my bath. The water got hotter and hotter, and I stewed in a cloud of steam. Jigori was mad as a bandicoot. He held his knife at Samarai's ribs, showing him the exact spot he'd drive it through if anything happened to me. But that didn't scare Samarai. When he thought I'd boiled long enough, he hauled me out of the tub, laid me flat on my face, and plastered me all over with scalding wet clay. I really thought I was being killed, and I yelled at him to take off that plaster! Jigori came within an ace of killing the old scoundrel then and there."

"But the lumbago?" Chad suggested.

442

O'Malley laughed and fetched the old Chief a clap on the back. "Next morning I could have tipped over the world! Walked fifteen miles through the bush and ended up fresh as a yearling. Yes, sir, Samarai's a smart old scoundrel."

Leaving O'Malley in conference with the Chief, Chad suggested to Natua that they look over the village.

"Keep a weather eye out for snakes," O'Malley called after them. "Tungom's got more than any other place in New Guinea. They come in all sizes."

And Chad noticed later that a boy climbing a coconut tree beat at the branches with a stick before thrusting in his hand.

"The death adder . . . is very poisonous," Natua explained in his halting mixture of Motuan and English. "Sometimes it hides in a tree among the coconuts or in a bunch of bananas."

But here in Tungom there were too many strange things demanding Chad's attention to worry overmuch about snakes. Every impression, each detail, seemed new and amazing to him. He noticed, for example, that many of the older women in the village lacked the little finger of the right hand.

"They are widows," Natua informed him. "It is the custom to cut off that finger."

Involuntarily Chad winced, but the Papuan boy assured him, "Not painful! I show you how they do—like this!" And Natua struck his funny bone a sharp blow, indicating that before the operation the sensation of pain was deadened in this manner.

It was here, too, that Chad first beheld the mysterious dog of Papua—the animal whose origin was untraceable. Sharp-muzzled, with pricked-up ears and bushy tail, it suggested the wild dingo of Australia. But there was this difference: the Papuan dog never barked!

"Tonight you will see," Natua laughed. "This dog has no voice to bark. But he howls! Ah, he howls!"

A circuit of the village brought the two boys back to the place where Joe Currey was setting up his pots and pans to prepare the evening meal.

"What are we having for supper, Joe?" Chad asked.

"Rice and bully beef, *taubada*."

"But we had rice and bully beef last night!"

"Not so, *taubada*," Joe Currey reproached. "We had bully beef and rice."

Joe maintained an attitude of studied indifference to the naked audience, which ranged from old age to infancy and which hung upon his every action. Was Joe Currey not cooky-boy for the visiting *taubadas?* How could these unclothed savages of Tungom understand the mysteries of preparing bully beef? The awe-stricken spectators clucked with amazement at the shining saucepans, the copper tea-kettle. Their own food being always roasted on hot stones, any sort of cooking utensil was unknown to them.

When Jigori had rigged the portable dining table and adjusted the canvas stools, Chad and Natua and O'Malley sat down to their evening meal. Samarai joined them, squatting on the ground beside the table. He disdained the bully beef but fell upon a calabash of rice and sweet potatoes that had been placed before him. An ecstatic light came into his eyes as he popped sticky handfuls into his mouth. He ate without speaking, glancing up from time to time with a wink and a nod of complete enjoyment.

"Look at the old rascal," O'Malley chuckled. "Even if you didn't know he was the village sorcerer, you could tell it by his size. They're always better fed than their fellows. They get the best of the garden produce, the fattest wallabies, the choicest bits of flesh at the feasts."

"What happens if they *don't* get them?" Chad demanded.

"Puri-puri! Black magic!" came the ready answer. "These sorcerers know secrets that have been guarded for generations. They know that the gall of a particular fish will rob a man of his senses. They know that invisible slivers of bamboo, placed in a man's food, will pierce his intestines and kill him."

Beyond the small circle of the dinner table half the population of Tungom stood grouped in respectful silence, watching their chief dine with the *taubadas*. Samarai rolled his eyes importantly, patted his full paunch. Somewhere in the shadow of the *dubu* house, drums had begun to beat; and the dusk was filled with their heavy throbbing.

"Plague take them," O'Malley sighed, shoving his empty plate aside and rising. "The boys will dance all night long, and we won't get a wink of sleep."

"Can't Samarai command them to stop?" Chad asked.

"Ho! He'll be in the center of the dancers. A hundred *dubu* boys have volunteered to carry for us. Their departure must be celebrated."

The fires blazed higher as night stood on, and the drums sent out a blood-chilling tattoo. And, as O'Malley had predicted, when the first dancers began to perform, there was Samarai in the very center, stamping his feet to the rhythm like a gigantic heathen idol come to life.

"The worst of it is," O'Malley grumbled, "our A.C.'s will get into it, too, and be as groggy as the rest of 'em tomorrow when the canoes have to be loaded."

For a long time Chad lay awake under the mosquito net, hearing the thud of bare feet striking rhythmically against the earth. The shadowy *dubu* house was filled with unexplained rustlings and murmurs. High up in the rafters a terrified squeal snapped off abruptly as Samarai's pet python snatched its evening meal. . . .

As it turned out, nature broke up the revelry with a thunderstorm of uncommon violence—a blinding electrical explosion followed by a downpour that extinguished the fires in clouds of steam and sent the dancers scuttling for shelter.

After that there was only the drumming of rain on the *nipa* thatch and the eerie, mournful howling of Papua's strange dogs. And Chad's last thought before falling asleep was: "Tomorrow I'll be on my way again. . . . One day closer to the Rain Forest . . . to Dad."

The Renegade

A shrill blast from a police whistle roused the sleeping village at break of day. The *dubu* boys came straggling out of their shelters, rubbing sleep from their eyes. Few of them wanted to serve as carriers for the *taubadas;* too well they knew the hard and dangerous inland trail. But they were aware that if they should run away and take refuge in the bush Samarai would make *puri-puri* on them and their families. So they contented themselves with the tobacco and rice issued by the Government and pocketed their wage of fifteen shillings a month.

With noisy authority and backed by a rifle butt, Sergeant Jigori prodded the sluggards. "Get along there, you!"

447

he shouted. "Whose sons are you? You think to lie sleeping all day like a *taubada?* What you think the Government pays you for? Get along, now!"

Out of all the hundred *dubus* lined up for inspection, there was one who stood apart from his fellows both in size and in demeanor. This man, tall and powerfully built, slouched at sullen ease, chin lowered, eyes truculent.

"Who is that fellow?" O'Malley demanded of the Chief.

"He is Kaiva. He has the strength of two men," Samarai replied. "But a devil dwells within him. I would not choose Kaiva, *taubada.* He will cause trouble on the trail."

Reluctant to relinquish so powerful a carrier, the Patrol Officer asked, "What do you mean—there is a devil in him?"

"Always he makes mischief among the people," came the answer. "Only by *puri-puri* can Kaiva be controlled. Otherwise he would have been driven out of the village or killed."

"A renegade, eh? I'll take a chance on him," O'Malley decided. "He's too strong to pass up."

Upon which decision Jigori shouted, "You, Kaiva! In line there. Quick time!"

After a second's indecision, when it seemed that the big *dubu* would defy the command, Kaiva slunk into line. But the look he cast at Sergeant Jigori was dark with anger.

The carriers now chosen and inspected, a scene followed which, later, Chad was to see repeated almost daily: a commotion that became a riot as each carrier fought to seize what he believed to be the lightest load. Actually each of the loads weighed the forty-pound limit set by law.

But the *dubu* boys imagined that a small box of ammunition or medicine must surely weigh less than a large blanket roll! And it called for Jigori, laying about him with the rifle butt, to bring order and accomplish loading the fleet of canoes.

The departure at hand, Samarai rubbed his flat nose against O'Malley's after the fashion of Tungom farewells. "You will report to me any *dubu* who does not obey," the old Chief said, and added anxiously, "and you will watch Kaiva, *taubada?* You will remember?"

"I'll remember," the Patrol Officer promised. "And as for you, you old rascal, you'd better go on a diet or you'll surprise yourself by popping like a balloon." These last words were spoken in English, incomprehensible to Samarai; but they left the old Chief cackling with delight.

Chad extended a hand to say good-by; but Samarai was too quick for him, and the boy felt his nose being rubbed violently against the old Chief's.

"Sambio! Sambio!" Relatives and friends of the carriers were weeping bitterly as the *dubus* climbed into the canoes and shoved away from the landing stage. They knew that they would be gone for many weeks and that some of them might never return. Voices rose in a loud wailing: *"Aé-éé-éé."*

The canoes stretched out along the river like a mile-long serpent, those holding the carriers and equipment being placed in the center of the line, the head and tail being guarded by the A.C.'s. The party was now moving closer and closer toward hostile territory, and the dense growth that covered the riverbanks formed a natural ambush.

This realization was brought home to Chad Powell when O'Malley handed him a revolver and cartridge belt. "Buckle this on, lad," the man said. "Just in case you want to pop off a cassowary." But a note of seriousness lurked in O'Malley's banter, and the boy's fingers shook a little as he buckled the belt about his waist.

The silent jungle, looming so close at hand, seemed suddenly sinister and filled with nameless dangers. Natua, in the bow of the canoe, was engaged in honing his bush knife with the stone kept for that purpose, and from time to time he cast a dark glance at the fringing trees.

Already the river was awakening from the spell of night. Cockatoos and hornbills rose with raucous cries from their sleeping places in the jungle. The air was alive with the rustle of wings, the flash of brilliant plumage, while the forest re-echoed to a medley of bird song. Early morning was the time of magic in New Guinea: mists rising from the river, every branch and leaf asparkle with dew, the sun bringing comfort after the bitter cold of night.

As the birds darted overhead or flitted through the jungle, Natua asked Chad to name them in Motuan.

"Maybe you think you're getting a vacation from school," O'Malley chuckled.

Chad laughed and retorted, "Natua's got the makings of a good sergeant!"

But secretly the boy was pleased with his rapid progress in the native tongue. It seemed as if every day he could see a fresh advance. He and Natua were getting along famously now, shifting from one language to another as necessity demanded.

Long before noon the sun had ceased to be a friend. It burned with cruel violence while Chad and his companions sweltered under the thatch of *nipa*. The cloudburst of the night before had set the river at flood, with a strong current against which the canoes made slow going. The carriers chattered as they paddled, calling from one canoe to another, often going off into explosions of mirth.

Chad would have given much to understand their conversation. When he questioned O'Malley, the man answered, "It's just nonsense. Papuans are born storytellers. I suppose that's true of all people who have no written language. The history of the tribe is handed down by word of mouth from generation to generation. Here no story is too tall to tell! Storytelling is really barefaced lying raised to a fine art."

Occasionally there were halts as a python was discovered hanging from a limb above the water, waiting to gorge on the flying foxes that nested in thousands along the shore, or when an A.C. went ashore to dig turtles' eggs in a sandbank, these eggs being highly prized as food.

But the first real excitement was provided indirectly by Sergeant Jigori. His canoe had been at the end of the long line, but by noon he came racing up against the current to pull alongside O'Malley's craft. The Sergeant's face was contorted with anger.

"What's the trouble?" the Patrol Officer demanded.

"That Kaiva, *taubada!* He is up to tricks."

"Already? What's he done?" And the man's voice sharpened.

For answer Jigori extended one hand; in his palm lay a steel jackknife of fine design.

"Why, that's my knife!" O'Malley exclaimed. "I hadn't even missed it."

"Kaiva had it, *taubada.*"

O'Malley was incredulous. "But how——"

"He showed it to me himself," the Papuan stated. "He said he had stolen it from your pocket."

The Officer's face was grim. After a second he said, "It's easy to see what Kaiva's up to. He stole the knife and showed it to you, knowing you'd tell me. He expects to be sent back home for such a deed. That's what he wants. Well, he's guessed wrong!"

"You will keep him, *taubada?*"

"He is a strong carrier," the man grudged. "Watch him sharply in the future."

"*Io, taubada.* Kaiva is of the family of bush dogs." And the Sergeant spat wrathfully.

O'Malley made no further comment, but it was obvious that he was angry and disturbed. Jigori's eyes were dangerous, and Natua, watching his father covertly, held silence.

Lunch was consumed without going ashore: packages of brick-hard sago for the A.C.'s and carriers, the inevitable bully beef for the *taubadas.*

Natua refused to sample Chad's share. "New Guinea food, that is good," the Papuan boy smiled as he gnawed at his cake of sago. "Sweet potatoes, taro, bananas— *ai*, these are good! But food closed up in a tin? No!" And he shook his bushy mop vigorously.

"Stick to your sago if you like it," Chad retorted. "I'd as soon eat a slice of cement, myself."

To which O'Malley put in, "You may be eating sago and liking it before you get back to New York City."

That afternoon they came upon a suspension bridge, the first indication that human beings dwelt in this part of jungle and river. The bridge consisted of two ropes of twisted cane, one about four feet above the other, laced together at short intervals by vines.

"Surely no one but the Human Fly could walk across that!" Chad exclaimed.

"No one but a Papuan, you mean," O'Malley retorted. "Beastly things, those suspension bridges. Your feet slide every which way. I never cross one but I'm blue with funk."

They passed slowly under the bridge, speculating as to what savages might have built it and where they might now be. Sharper watch was kept, and the canoes held warily to the center of the river.

The sun dropped rapidly at dusk; and with its passing the thermometer dropped, also, while a cold mist rose from the water to set the naked paddlers ashiver. In the middle of the river stood a densely wooded island, and O'Malley gave orders to tie up there for the night. The *dubus* were instructed to unload and carry the supplies to the highest elevation of ground. Waterproofed tarpaulins gave further protection. But the carriers had scarcely set about their task when Sergeant Jigori's voice could be heard, loud with anger. O'Malley whipped about, seeking the cause of trouble.

On the edge of the shore Kaiva was standing with arms stubbornly folded across his chest. He stared stonily ahead, gazing past the irate Jigori.

"What's going on, Sergeant?" O'Malley called out.

"This bush dog refuses to carry, *taubada*."

"Don't let him get away with that," the Patrol Officer snapped.

Jigori needed no further support. He signaled to Joe Currey and Orai, and the three flung themselves upon Kaiva and threw him flat on his face. And in spite of his

454

struggles the three A.C.'s managed to bind a forty-pound sack to the *dubu's* back. Then they yanked Kaiva to his feet.

"You will carry now, bush dog!" Jigori ground out. "It will go worse with you next time."

Somewhat chastened, the renegade Kaiva carried his load to high ground, dumped it, and returned to the canoe for another. But Chad, standing beside O'Malley, saw the look which the *dubu* cast in their direction. In that dark and sullen glance burned an inextinguishable hatred.

"It looks as if Kaiva's determined to make trouble," the boy said in a low tone.

"A few days on the trail will take the bombast out of him," came the Patrol Officer's grim promise. "Go tell Joe Currey to get busy, lad. I could eat a raw cassowary!"

Before the tent fly could be rigged and the dining table set up, rain began to fall heavily. Dinner was hurried through, to the accompaniment of a torrential drumming on the canvas—a cloudburst of such violence that the rising river droned above the beat of rain.

O'Malley knocked out the ashes of his pipe. "Worse than usual," he muttered. "This whole island may be under water by daybreak." He came to his feet impatiently, peering into the gathering darkness. "There's nothing we can do about it. Might as well get some sleep while we can."

Without removing their damp clothing Chad and O'Malley turned in to snatch a few hours of rest.

But it was still dark when Jigori routed them out with a startled warning. *"Taubada!* The water comes!"

By the aid of a hurricane lamp it could be seen that already the flood was within a foot of the bank of the island. Orders were barked right and left. Within seconds the sleeping camp was a beehive of activity. By the cross rays of two lamps, carriers and A.C.'s cut timber and dragged it to an elevation near the tent fly. Cane "rope" was gathered while a platform was constructed ten feet above the ground, with living trees for supports. Here the precious stores were placed and covered with tarpaulins: slow, heartbreaking work carried out in rain and darkness. Before the last of the supplies were hoisted to safety, dawn was breaking above the roof of the jungle; and, with its appearance, the rain ceased. But the swollen river was still rapidly rising, reaching up over the banks of the island. Camp was struck. Personal equipment was stowed in the restless canoes.

O'Malley said, "Jigori, choose two men to remain with you on the platform and guard the stores. The rest of us will start upriver. As soon as we make camp, I'll send back for you."

"*Io, taubada.* No bush dogs will steal the rice while Jigori breathes."

As the straggling line of canoes pulled away against the current, Chad glanced back and, in the half light of dawn, discovered that almost the entire island was now under water. The tarpaulin-covered platform with its three occupants floated above the river on living stilts.

456

Ambush Creek

Not until the following afternoon was O'Malley able to send back for Jigori and his two companions. Natua's relief at his father's safe arrival brought to Chad a realization of the deep, quiet bond which existed between the Papuan constable and his son.

At this point the river had so shallowed that further progress against the rapids was impossible. Here the camp was made from which the party would start on foot into the Rain Forest. And it was in the vicinity of this camp that Jigori discovered faint hunting tracks.

"The country of the Kuku-kukus at last," O'Malley said. "From now on, keep your eye peeled!"

Chad was thrilled by the man's words. Here he was, actually on the edge of the great Rain Forest! "You believe those tracks were really made by the Kuku-kukus?" he demanded, and his heart skipped a beat.

The man nodded. "And don't forget—they are people who know how to shoot arrows very quickly. And they're clever at ambush or spear pit or tethered snake."

"Tethered snake?"

"One of their favorite tricks," O'Malley declared. "They tie a cord to a death adder's tail and stake it beside the path. The snake, which ordinarily would run away, becomes so enraged that it attacks the first man who comes along. Oh, you have to keep your eyes open and your wits about you in the Rain Forest, all right!"

In order to discourage any carriers who might be tempted to desert at this point and return to their village downriver, the Patrol Officer ordered all the canoes to be destroyed.

Chad was astounded. "But how are we going to get back again?" he wanted to know.

"We'll build rafts. It's great fun rafting down these rivers when the current's with you."

It seemed to the boy that he could hardly wait to get started into the Rain Forest. He knew that the next objective was McKay's camp at Ambush Creek, raided by the Kuku-kukus. And after that, the last stage of the journey: Dad's camp at the headwaters of the Lakemanu. A few more days, a week at most, would find Chad reunited with his father. Small wonder that the boy counted the hours. He and Natua lent a hand wherever they could to

458

speed preparations for departure. Gear and equipment were being made up into lots weighing eighty pounds. These, lashed to bamboo poles, would be a load for two carriers: the tried and approved method of transportation through very dense jungle. No detail escaped O'Malley's notice, and Chad was filled with admiration for the way in which the Patrol Officer handled his men. He possessed an uncanny ability to forestall all the laggards and to detect those who pretended illness or injury. Scrupulously just, he was never bad-tempered without cause. With the single exception of Kaiva the men gladly would have laid down their lives for the *taubada*.

It was a great moment when camp finally was struck. The party moved into the Rain Forest and abruptly entered another world, where the broiling rays of the sun were cut off and the green gloom dripped with moisture. Two A.C.'s went in front with bush knives, cutting a track on a compass course at O'Malley's direction. Chad and Natua trailed the Patrol Officer and Jigori, while the line of carriers lengthened behind like a giant python.

Track-cutting to permit the *dubus'* passage was slow, and it did not take Chad Powell long to discover that walking in New Guinea demanded a technique all its own. At every step the boy slipped or slid into slimy mud, sometimes knee-deep; or else he was crawling over a maze of enormous twisting roots. The carriers' bare toes, used as fingers, were better than hobnailed boots. More than once Natua's strong grip saved Chad from sprawling headlong. Spikelike thorns ripped through clothing and flesh. Everywhere there were punishing lawyer vine and razor grass.

460

Here, too, Chad made his first acquaintance with the leeches: repulsive, threadlike worms which, eating their fill, became as round and resistant as rubber balls. They seemed to be everywhere, inescapable and voracious, attaching themselves through two layers of cotton clothing, even managing to work through the eyelets of Chad's boots. The naked carriers suffered greatly from these pests, the leeches often fastening themselves tightly between the men's bare toes.

But to O'Malley they were an old story. "Cheer up, young fellow," he scoffed. "The higher you climb, the thicker the leeches! Oh, it's a bonza country, New Guinea."

Chad did his best to keep pace with the leaders; but as one hour merged into another, this came to seem like the longest day of his life. He quickly discovered that a native carrier never stopped while climbing a hill; obviously the *taubada* could not pause too often, either, without losing caste in the eyes of the *dubus.*

When at noon the party halted for a brief rest, Natua surprised O'Malley by saying, "On the trail, *taubada,* I noticed the man Kaiva doing strange things."

"What sort of things?" the man demanded.

The Papuan boy hesitated, choosing his words. "I saw him kick at the grass on each side of the trail; he searched the ground as if seeking something he could not find."

"Perhaps he was looking for beetles or grubs," the man suggested.

But Natua shook his head, and his tone was uneasy as he answered, "More likely Kaiva seeks something to make *puri-puri.*"

O'Malley's laugh dismissed the subject. "Kaiva's *puri-puri* may scare people in his own village, but it won't hold water here."

Chad could see, however, that the Papuan boy was genuinely disturbed; and he remembered then how deeply the fear of sorcery was ingrained in every Papuan, haunting him from childhood to the grave. Corroboration of this fact came within an hour, when the party, emerging into a clearing, stumbled upon a store of food cached by some tribe which seemed to have vanished from the earth. The cache was protected by sorcery symbols consisting of bunches of human hair and a broken skull. Warily every Papuan in the party circled the cache.

"Look at 'em," O'Malley chuckled, with a kind of fond indulgence in his tone. "Most of these A.C.'s were born in Port Moresby, but they're Papuan clear through: they never fail to dodge a sorcery mark. That smashed skull is more effective than the strongest padlock. If these men were starving, nothing could tempt them to rob that cache!"

"What do you suppose happened to the savages who made the cache?" Chad wanted to know.

"No telling. They may have us under observation right at this moment."

Late that afternoon they came to a mountain torrent which could be crossed only by means of a slippery foot log. Natua's bare feet seemed scarcely to touch it as he darted across. The carriers, likewise, heavy-laden though they were, took it on the run. But, as he slithered cautiously across, Chad dared not look down lest he lose his balance and plunge into the rushing stream.

463

Gaining the far bank, the A.C.'s set up the tent fly for the night; the *dubus* gratefully dumped their loads; Joe Currey built his fires and set the "billy" to boil. Making camp, eating, sleeping, taking to the trail: these were now parts of a familiar pattern which seemed unchangeable.

The evening count of the carriers disclosed the startling fact that one man had disappeared. That man was Kaiva. No one remembered seeing him drop out of line.

O'Malley muttered wrathfully, but Jigori suggested, "Maybe Kuku-kuku kill 'im dead-finish, make soup."

To which Orai added, "No good kind, that soup!"

But further discovery was more serious: Kaiva, when last seen, had been carrying the tin dispatch box containing maps and writing materials.

"Jigori, take two men and go after him," O'Malley snapped. "Unless I miss my guess, his object is to follow closely at the rear of our party, enjoying its protection without having to carry a load. Kaiva would never dare try to get back to Tungom alone."

After Jigori's departure a strong guard was posted over the camp. Those not on duty fell into a light sleep.

Toward dawn Chad was startled by the sound of voices and the glare of a flashlight. Instantly awake, the boy sat up in his blankets to see Jigori handing the tin dispatch box to O'Malley.

"We found the bush dog a few miles back," the Sergeant explained. "He was cooking some rice he had stolen. He started back with us, quiet as a baby. But at the mountain river he broke away and ran. We could not find him again in the darkness. So we brought the *taubada's* box."

"I'd rather have the box than that scoundrel Kaiva," the Patrol Officer muttered.

By the time the party again took up the trail, it had begun to rain dismally. The forest oozed and steamed at every pore, and long before noon the humidity was almost unbearable. Chad's clothing, taken off wet the night before, was mildewed; the leather covering of his camera was peeling. But there were compensations. For this was the day when Chad heard his first bird of paradise: a clear-pitched *ka-ka-ka,* so characteristic of the sounds in New Guinea's uplands. It went ringing through the jungle, transfixing the boy on the spot. The call rose again in crescendo, and at that moment across the dark background of forest there flashed the bird itself—a brief vision of golden head and blood-red plumes.

"A *Raggiana,*" Chad breathed. "Natua, did you see? Oh, what a beauty!"

Through hearing his father talk so much about his work, the boy had come to recognize all the known specimens: the gorgeous *Raggiana,* the *Magnificent,* the *Gorget,* the *Empress,* and the *Blue.* But how thrillingly different to see one flying through its native jungle! It made up for all the hardships and discomforts, for the rain and the leeches, for the interminable bully beef!

He resumed the trail fired by new enthusiasm. But the stingless bees soon brought him down to earth. This new pest, little larger than a common housefly, made the ensuing hours a nightmare. They crawled into Chad's eyes and ears and mouth, got inside his clothing, clustered over his food. They clung like a living blanket to the bodies of the carriers, setting nerves and tempers on edge. And here at this altitude, where the aneroid showed six thousand feet, the number of snakes seemed suddenly to be legion. They were everywhere, of the death-adder variety: short and brownish-colored, with a broad head tapering away to the body. It seemed miraculous that the barefooted carriers should escape unscathed.

With a sensation of vast relief the boy heard O'Malley saying, "We're almost at McKay's depot. And I don't mind admitting I could use a day's rest."

The man had hardly finished speaking when, crossing the crest of a razor-backed ridge, they saw a muddy stream below. The A.C.'s gave a shout of joy.

"That's it! Ambush Creek," O'Malley said. "We're practically in civilization, lad. Tonight you'll sleep in a

regular bed and get a dinner fit for a king. Old McKay's got the best cooky-boy in all Papua."

The straggling column emerged from the jungle into a garden rich with maize and sweet potatoes and sugar cane. Beyond the garden a group of houses could be seen—built native-fashion of bamboo and *nipa,* yet with an undeniably European air about them. From somewhere came the blare of a radio in full blast.

Then from the porch of one of the houses an elderly white man emerged—a white-bearded man of heroic proportions, dwarfing the natives grouped around him. In a loud voice he called, "Welcome, strangers!"

O'Malley hurried across the compound to grip McKay by the hand; these two were old comrades of the bush. Introductions were effected, and everyone seemed to feel

welcome at once. The weary carriers dumped their loads and sought their quarters, while Jigori posted a guard over the stacked rifles.

The old miner's home proved to be a curious blend of civilization and savage Papua. Native trophies lined the walls: spears and bone implements and dancing masks. Chairs and tables were piled with magazines and newspapers, months outdated. A radio was blaring headline news from an Australian station, and the old man moved to turn it off.

O'Malley settled himself comfortably with a tall glass that had been thrust into his hand. "What's the gold situation? I'll wager you're richer than Croesus."

The old miner's face lighted; his eyes, so blue against the weathered copper of his skin, sparkled. "Gold?" And his voice warmed. "Why, it's richer here than the Klondike ever was—or such is my belief. Not yet, perhaps, but soon. One of these days a man with a good box will take out more than fifty ounces a day."

"You've been claiming that as long as I can remember," the Patrol Officer chaffed.

Somewhat nettled, the old man replied testily, "One of these days, O'Malley, you'll look back and remember that if you'd staked out a claim as McKay told you to, it'd be a lot more profitable than running cannibals to earth."

"But what luck have *you* had?" Chad asked eagerly.

"Not bad, son; not bad at all. But not good enough yet." Affectionately the old miner tapped the chamois money belt he wore about his waist, and the boy saw that it sagged with weight.

468

McKay poured some gold dust into his hand and offered it to Chad. It ranged from tiny yellow flecks to rough bits the size of a match head.

To the boy's surprise, when he handed it back, the miner said, "Keep it, son. Plenty more where that came from— or such is my belief."

The boy protested, "But this is worth a lot of money!"

"Tush! Just a memento of Papua to show your great-grandchildren!"

To Chad it seemed incredible that this indomitable old man should be content to live in such a remote wilderness, alone except for a handful of native workers, beset by fever and the constant threat of savage tribes. But the belief that someday he would strike it rich burned like a flame at the back of McKay's blue eyes, blinding him to danger and privation.

Tea was served in tin mugs; and there were crispy sweet potatoes, baked in their jackets, and jam tarts that made the boy's mouth water. McKay's cooky-boy was certainly tops! While his guests ate, the old miner filled in details about the raid on his supply depot.

"I'd been prospecting upriver for a week," McKay explained. "Four boys went with me, and two were left to guard camp. A bout of fever delayed my return. But when I get back here, what do I find——"

Chad was sitting on the edge of his chair. "What?" he breathed.

The old man's eyes clouded. "This place had been ransacked. Turned inside out. Knives stolen, pickaxes, shovels, prospecting pans—everything. Those fiends even tore off the red-and-blue labels from a box of flashlight batteries. Guess they liked the color and wanted it for decoration."

"And the two boys you'd left as guards?" O'Malley interrupted.

"Don't hurry me," McKay returned crossly. "I'm comin' to them." He shook his head. "They must o' put up a good fight. Plenty signs of a bloody tussle. But, judgin' by the footprints, the poor lads must o' been outnumbered twenty to one. Didn't have a chance. Good boys, too. Been with me nigh onto twelve years."

"Were they carried off?" Chad demanded.

"Aye. There wasn't hide nor hair of 'em. Carried off. And eaten, you can wager."

"Was there any clue as to which tribe of Kuku-kukus this one might be?" O'Malley questioned.

"There was," came the ready answer. "The footprints in the mud weren't no bigger than the spread o' my palm. A pygmy's foot is the biggest part of him. This was the work of those sneaky little Kiapou ringtails. Maybe they don't stand taller than a cassowary's wishbone, but they're straight poison."

The gleam in O'Malley's eye hardened; his jaw clamped. "I'll round up the ringleaders," he promised quietly.

"I don't figger you'll find 'em hangin' round here waitin' for you," came the dry rejoinder.

"I'll find 'em, never fear."

McKay's eyes lighted. "I'd admire to see 'em all swingin' from the gibbet in Port Moresby."

470

O'Malley laughed. "Maybe I'll send you an invitation to the necktie party." But behind the banter of his words lay unswerving purpose.

The prestige of the Service must be upheld by the roundup of the culprits. This offense could not be allowed to go unpunished.

Chad could not rid his mind of the picture painted by the old miner: two loyal Papuan boys, not much older than Chad himself, carried off by the Kuku-kukus to a horrible fate. . . . Who would believe that, within two months' traveling time from New York City, men still slew their enemies from ambush and carried out dark and terrible rites at their feasting places? Yet these things did take place in the secret heart of the Rain Forest, for the notebooks of Papua's Patrol Officers were filled with substantiating testimony. And in that second, New Guinea seemed a sinister and forbidding place, with the Rain Forest closing in to forge an unbreakable circle.

The night proved bitterly cold. Chad slept in underclothes, trousers, flannel pajamas, socks, a sweater, and two pairs of blankets. But even with a lighted lantern placed under his cot he shivered as with an ague. He didn't realize then that this was the forerunner of his first attack of malarial fever—the penalty exacted of all who dwell for long in New Guinea. But his fever began to climb, and racking chills and nausea alternated with a blazing inferno of heat.

Weakly Chad called for assistance. His cot was carried close to the fire, where O'Malley plied him with a whacking dose of quinine and forced him to swallow pints of scalding tea. From a vast distance the boy seemed to hear the man's voice saying, "You'll learn to take fever in your stride, lad. . . . No one in New Guinea escapes it for long." . . . And, weaving through a blur of delirium, the native carriers seemed to advance and recede like figures out of a nightmare, while Natua's concerned face swam and dimmed. . . .

But by dawn Chad was on his feet again! He felt weak as a string, but clear-headed, and the fever had burned itself out. Ravenous with hunger, he ate a monstrous breakfast and felt his strength returning with each mouthful. By the time he had buckled on his holster and made ready to hit the trail, he felt as if he could have tipped over a mountain.

McKay was reluctant to see his visitors depart. Not often did he have a chance to carry on a conversation with his own countrymen.

To Chad and Natua the old miner said, "Take care o' yourselves. You both got good heads of hair, so don't be gettin' scalped for it!"

The carriers shouldered their loads. The A.C.'s, all vigilant now, took their appointed places, their Lee-Enfields held ready for use. Once more the column got under way; but before the Rain Forest opened to swallow them whole, Chad glanced back to wave a salute to the intrepid old miner. Then he faced ahead, where a glimpse of fortresslike Mount Yule could be seen through a rift in the trees—the constant beacon by which O'Malley laid his course.

The Patrol Officer glanced down at the boy, and a smile lighted his face. He flung an arm across Chad's shoulders.

"You'll be with your dad now before you know it," the man promised.

Attack

Late that afternoon they crossed one of the numerous small tributaries of the Lakemanu River.

Sergeant Jigori, who had been sent ahead to scout, came back in a state of great excitement. "Much footprint show in the mud!" he exclaimed. "There is also *puri-puri*." With which, Jigori swept aside a curtain of brush and pointed ahead.

Chad caught his breath. For, directly in the path, a cleft stick had been driven deeply into the ground; and within the cleft a broken human bone had been tied, together with a scrap of freshly cooked pork that swarmed with ants.

The boy glanced wide-eyed at O'Malley. "What does it mean?" he quavered.

"That there's a village ahead whose natives want nothing to do with us. If we persist, they suggest that we may be killed and eaten."

For a second Chad's knees turned to water. "But— what'll we do? We have to go ahead, don't we?"

For answer the man replied, "You'd never get far in this country if you turned back at every warning." He gave the command which again set the party in motion.

But the carriers shied away from the sorcery sign, passed it in a wide curve, while the A.C.'s, visibly uneasy, held their carbines ready.

However, there was no further challenge to advance, though Chad had the scary feeling that the trees were filled with concealed figures, that eyes were watching his every movement. The imprint of naked feet in the muddy trail indicated that many savages had passed this way quite recently. Inching forward, O'Malley and Jigori led the way with utmost caution.

They came presently to a clearing where great trees had been felled by stone axes, and a garden well planted with sugar cane and taro. Suddenly Jigori drew up short, motioned the column to halt. For a second it seemed that the Papuan was undecided whether to advance or to retreat. Chad and Natua peered over his shoulder. A grisly sight met their eyes.

"What is it?" Chad whispered.

O'Malley whispered back, "The Papuan way of burying the dead."

A bamboo cage, roofed with thatch and raised some six feet above the ground, stood at the side of the trail. Within the cage, half doubled over, was the mummified body of a warrior. A broken bow and some arrows lay across his arms. On the ground below, a supply of food that was still fresh had been placed in a calabash.

In a low tone Chad asked, "Why the food?"

"For the dead warrior," Natua whispered back.

"But the dead can't eat."

Natua shook his head at such incomprehension. "There is a spirit in man. There is also a spirit in food. When the man-spirit goes up to the sky, the food-spirit must go, too—to nourish him."

O'Malley put an end to this discussion by giving the order to advance. Warily the column moved forward, every man on the alert. They came quite unexpectedly upon the native village. It stood on a rocky spur, protected by a stockade of rough-hewn logs so tall that they almost hid from view the peaked thatch of many dwellings. The stockade loomed boldly against the glow of a fire-red sunset, and to Chad Powell there was something indescribably forbidding about the scene. Mountain barriers stretched to east and north; dark, rain-filled clouds were being driven by the wind across the conflagration of the sky. And as far as the eye could reach, a thousand square miles of wild and lonely splendor enclosed this silent, sinister village.

Nervously Jigori muttered, *"Taubada,* these be a strange people. We will not be able to talk with them, I think. Observe these trees!" And he pointed to enormous stumps which bore the marks of stone axes. *"Ruma momo,* many houses!" he exclaimed, counting on his fingers. "Two, three, five, nine, thirty!" These were the only numerals Jigori knew, and he displayed them with proud extravagance whenever possible.

They discovered that the stockade could be entered by a single small opening—a slit just wide enough to permit the passage of a man's body. The eyes of the carriers were wide with alarm. One by one the *dubus* came straggling up, waiting to take their orders.

"Shall I enter the village, *taubada?"* Jigori asked bravely.

For a second O'Malley paused, irresolute; and Chad knew exactly what was passing through the man's mind. Was the village as empty as its deep silence indicated?

Or were savages hiding on the other side of that doorway, waiting to smash the skull of the first man who ventured through? If Jigori went first, he might immediately be killed. But if O'Malley went first and were slain, it would leave the entire party stranded without a leader in the Rain Forest, as helpless as a ship without a rudder.

479

A moment of silence stretched to eternity. Within the stockade were no wailing babies, no howling dogs. Was this only a lure to deceive the unwary? O'Malley gave the brief signal that Jigori was awaiting. The Papuan dropped flat on his stomach, rifle in one hand, knife in his teeth. Through the mud he wriggled toward the opening in the wall. Behind him O'Malley prepared to follow. Chad's heart was pounding, his throat dry. Natua clutched him by the arm; the two boys stood as motionless as if a spell had been cast upon them. Their gaze never left that slitlike opening.

Jigori had disappeared. It was a breathless moment. Then, in utmost relief, they heard the Sergeant shout, "No one here! The bush dogs have fled!"

The carriers, who had been caught at the edge of panic and ready to bolt, now felt very brave indeed. At the top of their lungs they shouted into the jungle, "Sons of bush dogs! You fear to show your faces. Come eat the food you have left in your fires. This is not food for men. We know true food and we know pig food." Thus they boldly berated their unseen enemies.

Their taunts passed unchallenged.

But as Chad quickly slipped through the stockade at O'Malley's heels he heard the man saying, "Don't imagine we're not under observation! I'll wager they've got lookouts in every treetop, reporting just what they see."

The empty, silent houses, high-peaked and forbidding, filled the boy with awe. Their black doorways seemed to stare like accusing eyes. Potatoes were baking in the smoldering cookfires; on very short notice an entire

population had vanished into the jungle like marionettes yanked on unseen wires. Even the dogs had fled, and the pigs had been carried to safety.

"We'll put up at the *dubu* for the night," O'Malley decided, and gave orders for a heavy guard to be posted.

The *dubu* house dominated the village. An immense dwelling, it was perhaps a hundred feet long, with a roof that rose as sharply as the prow of a ship. Above the doorway sorcery charms swayed in the wind. The shadowy interior was partitioned into cubicles; along the walls were weapons, sleeping capes, bird-of-paradise plumes—all left behind in their owners' panicky flight.

A sharp exclamation broke from O'Malley. "What have we here?" he said.

Half buried under a pile of mats, an ancient savage cowered—an emaciated cripple who had been abandoned to his fate. Clawlike hands covered the shriveled old face; the man was whimpering incoherently. O'Malley ordered food to be placed beside the old savage, who refused to touch any of it, burying his head in ostrichlike desperation.

"We'll let the old fellow have the *dubu* to himself and pitch our tents outside," the Patrol Officer decided. "He'll have the fleas for company. Tonight we sleep in our clothes, my lad, and hold our rifles handy!"

At that moment a sound like an eerie yodeling could be heard. It seemed to come from the ridge to the east of the village.

"Papuan telegraph!" O'Malley muttered, facing toward the sound. "The blighters are signaling to other members of the tribe. You'd be surprised how many miles that sound carries in these mountains."

Chad found himself shivering. "What do you suppose they're saying?" Instinctively he dropped his voice, as if those on the distant hilltop might overhear his words.

"Just as well we don't know!" the man retorted. "But, after all, who can blame 'em? We're strangers. And in Papua all strangers are possible enemies."

"You—you think they might attack us tonight?" There was a cold feeling around Chad's heart.

Natua, too, seemed strangely silent; his eyes were round and black.

"They won't attack before dawn in any case," the Patrol Officer stated. "That's their favorite hour."

"Why should they hold off till then?"

"Because the savage knows that men sleep heaviest at that hour. And also it gives the attacker enough light to pursue anyone who might otherwise escape."

But, although the yodeling continued without letup, the night proved uneventful. There was little sleep, however, for those within the stockade. Long before dawn Joe Currey had breakfast ready, and Jigori was bullying the carriers into action. Chad knew that he would not be sorry to shake the dust of this hostile village. Within the *dubu* the ancient savage still cowered under his pile of mats; he had not touched a mouthful of the food at his side. As evidence of good will and to pay for the taro taken from the gardens, O'Malley placed a bag of salt, two steel hatchets, and a bolt of red calico in the doorway of the *dubu*.

The moment the security of the stockade was left behind, everyone knew that attack from ambush could be
expected. Since the carriers must be protected at all costs,

Armed Constables guarded the head, the middle, and the tail of the column. O'Malley himself, with Chad and Natua at his side, walked just behind Orai and Jigori. Tension passed like an electric current along the men.

Cautiously they moved forward to a belt of *kunai* grass—a natural ambush that grew shoulder-high. Everywhere there was only silence. Even the cockatoos, sentinels of the jungle, seemed to have vanished. Chad could feel his heart pounding in slow, heavy strokes. The tall *kunai* grass closed in upon him, half suffocating him with a sensation of helplessness.

The belt of grass ended suddenly, and they emerged from it upon a muddy track indented by the fresh footprints of many men. Here a great tree had fallen across the path.

Instantly O'Malley rapped out, "Examine each end of that tree, Jigori. See if it fell of its own accord. And watch out for spear pit or tethered snake!"

Chad held his breath till he heard the Sergeant report, "The bush dogs did not fell this tree, *taubada*. It was struck by lightning."

"Under way, then, Sergeant. Keep your eye peeled."

"I know the tricks of these people," the Papuan replied confidently. "They cannot fool Jigori."

"Sergeant, do your crowing when we're out of the woods," said O'Malley.

"Io, taubada."

O'Malley shot a quick glance at Chad and grinned. "Scared?"

Chad gulped. "You bet!" But somehow the question, so casually put, filled him with reassurance.

Who could be scared for long in the company of a man like O'Malley? Bravery is as infectious as panic. Danger was routine to the Patrol Officer, and he strode toward it.

Suddenly at the rear of the column pandemonium broke loose. Screams. Shouts. Two shots were fired in rapid succession.

O'Malley whipped about and raced toward the rear of the straggling line. Chad could hear him shouting, "What's happened? Anyone hurt?"

By the time the two boys reached the rear, they saw a carrier named Maipa stretched on the ground in a pool of blood. A deep-driven arrow quivered in one thigh. Another was buried in his shoulder. A dozen arrows bristled from the ground where they had fallen like quills of a porcupine.

"Ambush, *taubada!*" Orai panted, the rifle still smoking in his hands. "Maipa is wounded."

"I'll attend to him," O'Malley cried. "Jigori, calm down those carriers. Chad, fetch the first-aid kit."

As the boy raced to carry out the order, a wild chattering and screeching could be heard in the jungle—a bloodcurdling shrill of yodeling cries.

Infuriated, the A.C.'s poured a volley of blind shot into the trees, calling out, "Whose sons are you? Bush dogs! Come out and fight like men!"

But the unseen enemy maintained safe distance, yelling the louder. The attack, so suddenly launched, resulted in the wounding of only Maipa. With the attack at such close range, it seemed incredible there should be but a single casualty.

O'Malley knelt beside the fallen carrier. His hands were quick and sure. Without glancing up he demanded of Orai, "Just how did it happen?"

"Three bush dogs were hiding behind one tree," the A.C. stammered. "I saw their bows drawn on Maipa. I killed one of them, but his companions were able to drag him away."

Standing by with iodine and gauze, Chad watched O'Malley extract a bamboo-bladed arrow an inch wide, buried deep in the carrier's thigh. The second arrow, firmly wedged into the shoulder bone, was removed only after great difficulty. The wounded Maipa clamped his jaws stoically and did not cry out. The wounds were washed with a solution of permanganate, then flooded with iodine.

"You never know whether these arrows are poisoned or not," O'Malley was muttering. A padding of gauze soaked in castor oil completed the operation. "Maipa will have to be carried, Jigori. Have a litter made for him."

"*Io, taubada.*"

A solemnity had fixed itself upon the entire party. The wounding of Maipa had brought home, as nothing else could, the ever present actuality of peril. Death could dart from ambush with the speed of light. What had happened to Maipa could overtake any one of them. Gently the wounded carrier was lifted by his fellows and slung between two poles in a crude hammock. Inveterate chatterers on the march, the *dubus* were now quiet as again the column got under way.

The yodeling of the unseen enemy was more distant, but it seemed to have been taken up by many more voices. It could be heard echoing from valley to valley: interrogation and reply, statement and decision.

Grimly O'Malley said, "Every village within a hundred miles will know about this attack. I don't like the sound of it! Some of the other tribes may have a try at it."

"If Kaiva's still trailing after us, maybe they'll be satisfied with him," Chad suggested.

"Shouldn't wonder. He'd make quite an addition to the soup kettle."

Here there was no discernible track, and Jigori slashed the way on a compass course. Limestone walls thickly studded with trees raised barriers on every hand. Sometimes the Sergeant's trail was almost straight up; the others clambered after him as best they could, clinging to roots and to the trunks of trees, clutching at ledges of rock. Sometimes Chad found himself hanging on by his hands alone as his feet fumbled for a niche. In some places the perpendicular walls leaned toward each other, and the boy felt like a fly crawling across a ceiling. Once, gasping for breath, he saw Natua laughing at him; the Papuan boy seemed as unflurried as if scaling walls were a daily assignment.

Natua nodded his head to indicate a group of needle-like peaks which loomed close at hand. "The god-spirits in battle use mountains as clubs," he said.

And Chad panted back, "Sometime I'll tell you about Rip Van Winkle! That's a good story."

But without the Papuan boy's assistance Chad would have been hard put to make the steep ascent. Natua's grip was always steady if his friend stumbled. Chad had climbed the Green Mountains of Vermont, the White Mountains of New Hampshire, and the lava slopes of

Haleakala. But he knew now that those were only bumps compared to this geological upheaval. This was like an obstacle race all the way. Only the realization that each hour was bringing him closer and closer to his father gave him the strength to keep on climbing.

His spirits bounded when, from somewhere up ahead, O'Malley called back, "There it is, lad—the Olipai River. Just the other side of that we'll climb a hill and come on your dad's camp."

Chad's legs went suddenly weak. He straddled the trunk of a tree, gripped it with his knees, and hung on. With one hand he mopped his sweaty face. "Are we really that close?" he demanded, scarcely daring to believe.

"Two hours and we'll be there."

It was at this moment that Natua discovered he had lost his *tiki*, the good-luck amulet which had been given him at birth. Somewhere along the trail the cord that held it about his throat had broken.

The boy's discovery of the loss upset him profoundly. There was something like foreboding in his voice as he said, in a low tone, "This can only bring ill fortune. One should never part with a *tiki*—except as a gift. To lose it, the god-spirits do not forgive."

Nothing Chad could say consoled the other. To the American boy it seemed foolish to make such a fuss about a little greenstone figure.

Natua shook his head solemnly. "I have been careless of the god-spirits' favor. They will not forgive."

But Chad was too excited at the prospect of meeting his father to be concerned for long with a lost *tiki*. As the

490

boy tagged at Jigori's heels, new energy seemed to power his muscles. All fatigue had vanished; he knew only the impulse to forge ahead.

Jigori urged him to greater caution. "This is not Port Moresby, *taubada*," the Sergeant reminded him dryly. "This is the country of the Kuku-kuku!"

But they came at last without mishap to an immense clearing, where a sort of rude landing field had been constructed in hard-baked clay.

A cry broke from the boy. "That's where Dad's plane lands! Golly Moses!" And he let out a whoop of joy. "O'Malley, we're really here! Come on, Natua! Let's go!"

But for the space of a breath Chad's legs defied him, because out of one of the shelters a man—a white man— came on the run.

Chad found his voice, but it sounded funny in his own ears. "Dad!" he shouted. "Dad—I'm here at last!"

Chad has many exciting adventures before he and Natua find a King of Saxony for Chad's father. You can read about the rest of their adventures in the book, The Rain Forest, *by Armstrong Sperry.*

Glossary

Full Pronunciation Key

The pronunciation of each word is shown just after the word, in this way: **ab bre vi ate** (ə brē′vē āt). The letters and signs used are pronounced as in the words below. The mark ′ is placed after a syllable with primary or strong accent, as in the example above. The mark ′ after a syllable shows a secondary or lighter accent, as in **ab bre vi a tion** (ə brē′vē ā′shən).

Some words, taken from foreign languages, are spoken with sounds that otherwise do not occur in English. Symbols for these sounds are given at the bottom of the page as "Foreign Sounds."

a	hat, cap	j	jam, enjoy			u	cup, butter
ā	age, face	k	kind, seek			u̇	full, put
ã	care, air	l	land, coal			ü	rule, move
ä	father, far	m	me, am			ū	use, music
		n	no, in				
		ng	long, bring				
b	bad, rob						
ch	child, much						
d	did, red						
		o	hot, rock			v	very, save
		ō	open, go			w	will, woman
		ô	order, all			y	young, yet
e	let, best	oi	oil, voice			z	zero, breeze
ē	equal, see	ou	house, out			zh	measure, seizure
ėr	term, learn						
f	fat, if	p	paper, cup			ə represents:	
g	go, bag	r	run, try			a in about	
h	he, how	s	say, yes			e in taken	
		sh	she, rush			i in April	
		t	tell, it			o in lemon	
i	it, pin	th	thin, both			u in circus	
ī	ice, five	ᵺ	then, smooth				

---

foreign sounds

Y as in French *du*. Pronounce ē with the lips rounded as for English ü in **rule**.

œ as in French *peu*. Pronounce ā with the lips rounded as for ō.

N as in French *bon*. The N is not pronounced, but shows that the vowel before it is nasal.

H as in German *ach*. Pronounce k without closing the breath passage.

This pronunciation key is from the *Thorndike-Barnhart Advanced Junior Dictionary.* Special acknowledgment is made to Clarence L. Barnhart, editor of the Thorndike-Barnhart Dictionaries, for his assistance in the preparation of this glossary.

492

abacus   ardent

ab a cus (ab′ə kəs), frame with rows of counters or beads that slide back and forth in grooves or on wires, used in calculating. *n.*, *pl.* **ab a cus es, ab a ci** (-sī).

abode (ə bōd′), place to live in; dwelling; residence. *n.*

1 3 5 2 0 6 4 7 0 8

Abacus. Beads above bar: 5 each when lowered. Beads below bar: 1 each when raised. Numbers are shown below each wire for setting of 1,352,064,708.

abort handle (ə bôrt′), handle or switch which is used to remove the capsule from an improperly functioning rocket.

Abra ham (ā′brə ham), the ancestor of the Hebrews. *n.*

ado be (ə dō′bē), **1.** sun-dried clay or mud. **2.** a brick or bricklike piece of such material, used in building. **3.** built or made of sun-dried bricks. Many people in southwestern United States and in Mexico live in ado-be houses. 1, 2 *n.*, 3 *adj.*

Adobe house

ad ver sary (ad′-vər ser′ē), **1.** person opposing or resisting another person; enemy. **2.** person or group on the other side in a contest. *n.*, *pl.* **ad ver sar ies.**

ae on (ē′ən), a very long period of time; many thousands of years: *Aeons passed before life existed on the earth. n.* Also, **eon.**

-age, suffix meaning:
1. act of: *Breakage = act of breaking.*
2. collection of; group of: *Baggage = a group of bags.*
3. condition of; rank of: *Peerage = rank of peers.*
4. cost of: *Postage = cost of posting.*
5. home of: *Orphanage = home of orphans.*
Words made with *-age* often acquire special meanings.

ag gran dize ment (ə gran′diz mənt), increase in power, wealth, rank, etc.; making greater. *n.*

ag ile (aj′əl), moving quickly and easily; active; lively; nimble. *adj.*

ague (ā′gū), **1.** a malarial fever with chills and sweating that occur at regular intervals. **2.** a fit of shivering; chill. *n.*

Ah Chow (ä′ chou′), *Chinese.*

alac ri ty (ə lak′rə tē), brisk and eager action; liveliness: *Although the man was very old, he still moved with alacrity. n.*

Al ham bra (al ham′brə), palace of the Moorish kings at Granada, Spain. *n.*

al ien (āl′yən), foreigner; stranger. *n.*

Al lah (al′ə or ä′lə), the Moslem name of the one Supreme Being, or God. *n.*

al ma nac (ôl′mə nak), a calendar or table showing the days, weeks, and months. Many almanacs give information about the weather, sun, moon, stars, tides, church days, and other facts. *n.*

Al sace (al′sās), region in northeastern France. *n.*

am me ter (am′mē′tər), instrument for measuring the strength of an electric current in amperes. *n.*

amp., ampere.

am pere (am′pir or am pir′), unit for measuring the strength of an electric current. Ordinary light bulbs take from ¼ to ½ ampere. *n.*

Am roo (äm′rü), *Berber. n.*

am u let (am′yə lit), some object worn as a magic charm against evil. *n.*

An dros Island (an′dros or an′drəs), an island between Florida and Cuba. *n.*

an er oid   or   **an er oid ba rom e ter** (an′ər oid or ban rom′ə tər), an instrument for measuring air pressure and determining the height above sea level.

an ten na can is ter (an ten′ə kan′is-tər), a container for holding the antenna, located on top of a space capsule.

aq ua lung (ak′wə lung′), a diving device consisting of cylinders of compressed air strapped to the diver's back and a glass mask placed over the eyes and nose. The supply of air to the diver is regulated automatically by a valve. *n.*

aq ue duct (ak′-wə dukt), **1.** an artificial channel or large pipe for bringing water from a distance. **2.** structure that supports such a channel or pipe. *n.*

Aqueduct

ar chae ol o gist (är′kē ol′ə jist), expert in archaeology. *n.* Also, **archeologist.**

ar chae ol o gy (är′kē ol′ə jē), study of the people, customs, and life of ancient times. Students of archaeology dig up, classify, and study the remains of ancient cities, tools, monuments, or any other records that remain. *n.* Also, **archeology.**

ar dent (ärd′nt), full of zeal; very enthusiastic; eager. *adj.*

---

hat, āge, cãre, fär; let, bē, tėrm; it, īce; hot, gō, ôrder; oil, out; cup, pùt, rüle, ūse; ch, child; ng, long; th, thin; ŦH, then; zh, measure; ə represents *a* in about, *e* in taken, *i* in April, *o* in lemon, *u* in circus.

ar ray (ə rā′), dress in fine clothes; adorn: *Elsie was arrayed like a queen. v.*

art ful (ärt′fəl), skillful; clever. *adj.*

ar ti san (är′tə zn), workman skilled in some industry or trade; craftsman. Carpenters, masons, plumbers, and electricians are artisans. *n.*

-ary, suffix meaning:
1. place for—, as in *infirmary.*
2. collection of—, as in *statuary.*
3. person or thing that is, does, belongs to, etc., —, as in *adversary, commentary.*
4. of or having to do with —, as in *legendary.*
5. being; having the nature of —, as in *secondary, supplementary.*
6. characterized by—, as in *customary.*

as phalt (as′fôlt), 1. a dark-colored substance, much like tar, that is found in various parts of the world or obtained from petroleum. 2. a smooth hard mixture of this substance with crushed rock, used for pavements, roofs, etc. *n.*

as sem blage (ə sem′blij), group of persons gathered together; assembly. *n.*

as ter oid (as′tər oid), any of the many very small planets revolving about the sun between the orbit of Mars and the orbit of Jupiter. *n.*

Athe na (ə thē′nə), the Greek goddess of wisdom, arts, industries, and warfare, identified with the Roman goddess Minerva. *n.*

Athe ne (ə thē′nē), Athena. *n.*

-ation, suffix often added to a verb to form a noun:
1. act or state of —ing: *Admiration = act or state of admiring.*
2. condition or state of being —ed: *Cancellation = condition or state of being canceled.*
3. result of —ing: *Civilization = result of civilizing.*

-ative, suffix meaning:
1. tending to —: *Talkative = tending to talk.*
2. having to do with —: *Qualitative = having to do with quality.*

At-mun (ät′mun′), *African. n.*

At-mun-shi (ät′mun′shē′), an African tribe. *n.*

auc tion (ôk′shən), a public sale in which each thing is sold to the person who offers the most money for it. *n.*

auc tion eer (ôk′shən ir′), man whose business is conducting auctions. *n.*

au to mat ic pilot (ô′tə mat′ik), a device for automatically steering an airplane or space craft.

azul (ä sül′), *Spanish.* blue. *adj.*

Ba la (bä′lä), *Zulu. n.*

bal lis tic path (bə lis′tik), in rocketry, a missile flight path that follows a curved path similar to that of a bullet.

ban di coot (ban′də küt), a small ratlike animal of Australia that carries its young in a pouch on its abdomen. *n.*

Australian bandicoot (about 2½ ft. long)

ban ter (ban′tər), playful teasing; joking. *n.*

barb (bärb), point projecting backward from the main point. *n.*

bar bar i an (bär bãr′ē ən), 1. person who is not civilized. 2. not civilized; cruel and coarse; almost savage. 3. foreigner differing from the speaker or writer in language and customs. 4. differing from the speaker or writer in language and customs. 1, 3 *n.*, 2, 4 *adj.*

bar bar ic (bär bar′ik), crudely rich or splendid. *adj.*

barge (bärj), 1. a large, flat-bottomed boat for carrying freight: *a grain barge.* 2. *Informal.* push oneself rudely: *Don't barge in where you're not wanted.* 1 *n.*, 2 *v.*

barque (bärk), a kind of ship with three masts. *n.*

Bar ri nish (bar′i-nish′), island off the coast of Connemara. *n.*

bar ter (bär′tər), 1. trade by exchanging one kind of goods for other goods without using money. 2. act of bartering. 1 *v.*, 2 *n.*

Bar thol di (bär tōl dē′), **Au guste** (ō gyst′), 1834-1904, French sculptor. *n.*

Ba sho (bä′shō′), Japanese poet. *n.*

bat tle ment (bat′l mənt), wall for defense at the top of a tower or wall, with indentations through which soldiers could shoot. *n.*

be-, prefix meaning:
1. thoroughly; all around: *Bespatter = spatter thoroughly or all around.*
2. at; on; to; for; about; against: *Bewail = wail about.*
3. make; cause to seem: *Belittle = cause to seem little.*
4. provide with: *Bespangle = provide with spangles.*

be head (bi hed′), cut off the head of. *v.*

be nev o lent (bə nev′ə lənt), kindly; charitable. *adj.*

be rate (bi rāt′), scold sharply. *v.*, **be-rat ed, be rat ing.**

Ber ber (bėr′bər), 1. member of a race

living in northern Africa, west of Egypt. **2.** their language. *n.*

Ber gen (bėr'gən), seaport in southwestern Norway. *n.*

Bern lak de Haut des ert (bėrn'lak də hôt'di zėrt').

bide (bīd), continue; wait. *v.*, **bode** or **bid ed, bid ed, bid ing.**

bide one's time, wait for a good chance.

bil ly (bil'ē), *Australian slang.* a tin kettle or pot used for outdoor cooking. *n.*

Bi mi ni (bi mē'nē), one of the Biminis, a group of islands north of Andros Island. *n.*

bird of paradise, bird of New Guinea noted for its magnificent plumage.

black smith (blak'smith'), man who works with iron. Blacksmiths mend tools and shoe horses. *n.*

blight (blīt), any disease that causes plants to wither or decay. *n.*

blight er (blīt'ər), *British slang.* **1.** rascal. **2.** fellow; chap. *n.*

blitz krieg (blits'krēg'), warfare in which the offensive is extremely rapid, violent, and hard to resist. *n.*

block house (blok'hous'), a building, usually of reinforced concrete, near a missile-launching pad. It houses the control systems for the launching of a missile and is designed for protection from blast, heat, and radiation hazard. *n.*

bob stay (bob'stā'), rope or chain to hold a bowsprit down. See picture under **bowsprit.** *n.*

bond (bond), anything that ties, binds, or unites: *a bond of affection between sisters.* *n.* **bonds,** chains; shackles.

bon za (bon'zə), *Australian slang.* first-rate; excellent. *adj.*

boost er (büs'tər), a missile's first stage, supplying the initial thrust needed for launching. *n.*

boo ty (bü'tē), plunder; things taken by robbery. *n., pl.* **boo ties.**

bo sun (bō'sn), a ship's officer in charge of the anchors, ropes, rigging, etc. He directs some of the work of the crew. *n.* Also, **boatswain.**

Bou lan ger (bü län zhā'), *French. n.*

bow sprit (bou'sprit), pole or spar projecting forward from the bow of a ship. Ropes from it help to steady sails and masts. *n.*

bran dish (bran'dish), wave or shake threateningly. *v.*

BOWSPRIT

BOBSTAY

bra zen (brā'zn), **1.** made of brass. **2.** like brass in color or strength. *adj.*

Bres lau (brez'lou or bres'lou), German name of **Wroclaw** (vrôts'läf), a city in southwestern Poland, formerly part of Germany. *n.*

brig (brig), a square-rigged ship with two masts. *n.*

Bud dha (bud'ə or bü'də), 563?-483? B.C., great religious teacher of Asia, founder of Buddhism. *n.*

bue no (bwā'nō), *Spanish.* good!

bul ly beef (bul'ē), canned or pickled beef.

Bu se la pi (bü'sə lä'pē), *Zulu. n.*

bush (bush), **1.** a woody plant smaller than a tree, often with many separate branches starting from or near the ground. **2.** spread out like a bush; grow thickly. **3.** open forest; wild land. **1, 3** *n.*, **2** *v.*

Bush man (bush'mən), member of a South African tribe of roving hunters. *n., pl.* **Bush men.**

butcher bird, bird that kills more prey than it can eat and hangs this on thorns.

cabin boy, boy whose work is waiting on the officers and passengers in a ship.

cache (kash), **1.** a hiding place to store food or supplies. **2.** a hidden store of food or supplies. **3.** put in a cache; hide. **1, 2** *n.*, **3** *v.*, **cached, cach ing.**

cais son (kā'sn or kā'son), a watertight box or chamber in which men can work under water. *n.*

cal a bash (kal'ə-bash), **1.** gourd whose dried shell is used to make bottles, bowls, drums, rattles, etc. **2.** bottle, bowl, etc., made from such a dried shell. *n.*

Ca nav er al (kə nav'-ər əl), **Cape,** a station in Florida for testing rockets and missiles and for launching satellites and space probes. Now called **Cape Kennedy.**

Can ton (kan ton'), city in southern China. *n.*

ca pit u late (kə pich'ə lāt), surrender on

WATER

MUD

ROCK

Caisson. The weight of the masonry on the bottom of the caisson forces it into the sand and mud at the bottom of the water. Air under pressure is then forced into the caisson, driving out the water and permitting workmen to enter through air locks.

---

hat, āge, cãre, fär; let, bē, tèrm; it, īce; hot, gō, ôrder; oil, out; cup, pút, rüle, ūse; ch, child; ng, long; th, thin; ℸH, then; zh, measure; ə represents *a* in about, *e* in taken, *i* in April, *o* in lemon, *u* in circus.

certain terms or conditions. *v.*, **ca pit u-**
lat ed, ca pit u lat ing.

cap sule (kap′sl), part of a rocket containing instruments, a man, etc. In flight
the capsule separates from the motors and
goes into orbit or is recovered at a later
time. *n.*

cap tive (kap′tiv), 1. prisoner. 2. held as
a prisoner; made a prisoner. 1 *n.*, 2 *adj.*

cap tor (kap′tər), person who takes or
holds a prisoner. *n.*

car bine (kär′bin), a short rifle or musket. *n.*

car ti lage (kär′tl ij), the tough, elastic
substance forming parts of the skeleton of
animals with a backbone; gristle. *n.*

cas so wary (kas′ə wer′ē), a large bird
of Australia and New Guinea, like an ostrich,
but smaller. Cassowaries
run swiftly, but cannot
fly. *n.*, *pl.* **cas so war-**
ies.

caste (kast), 1. a Hindu social class. By tradition, a Hindu is born into
the caste of his father
and cannot rise from it.
2. a social system having
class distinctions based
on rank, wealth, posi-
tion, etc. *n.*

Cassowary
(5 ft. tall)

lose caste, lose social rank or position.

cas u al (kazh′ù əl), 1. without plan or
method; careless: *a casual answer.* 2. uncer-
tain; indefinite; indifferent; vague. *adj.*
—**cas′u al ly,** *adv.*

cas u al ty (kazh′ù əl tē), person killed or
wounded as a result of enemy action. *n.*, *pl.*
cas u al ties.

cav al cade (kav′l kād′ or kav′l kād),
1. a procession of persons riding on horses
or in carriages. 2. a dramatic sequence or
procession; a parade. *n.*

ce les tial (sə les′chəl), of the sky; having
to do with the heavens: *The sun, moon,*
planets, and stars are celestial bodies. *adj.*

Celt (selt or kelt), a member of a people
to which the Irish, the Scots, and the Welsh
belong. *n.* Also, **Kelt.**

Celt ic (sel′tik or kel′tik), 1. of the Celts
or their languages. 2. the languages spoken
by the Celts. 1 *adj.*, 2 *n.* Also, **Keltic.**

cen tri fuge (sen′trə fūj), machine for
separating cream from milk, bacteria from
a fluid, etc., by means of centrifugal force. *n.*

Cha ka (chä′kä), *Zulu.* *n.*

cham ois (sham′ē), a soft leather made
from the skin of sheep, goats, deer, etc.
n., *pl.* **cham ois** (sham′ēz).

char ac ter is tic (kar′ik tər is′tik), a
special quality or feature; whatever distin-

guishes one person or thing from others:
Cheerfulness is a characteristic that we admire
in people. *n.*

chas ten (chās′n), restrain from excess or
crudeness. *v.*

Chi co (chē′kō), *Spanish.* *n.*

chiv al ric code (shiv′l rik or shə val′-
rik), the code of chivalry.

chiv al ry (shiv′l rē), 1. the qualities of an
ideal knight in the Middle Ages. Chivalry
included bravery, honor, courtesy, respect
for women, protection of the weak, gener-
osity, and fairness to enemies. 2. rules and
customs of knights in the Middle Ages. *n.*

ci ca da (sə kā′də or
sə kä′də), a large in-
sect with transparent
wings. The male makes
a shrill sound in hot,
dry weather. *n.*, *pl.* **ci-**
ca das, ci ca dae (-dē).

Cicada (about
⅔ life size)

Cleng Peer son (kleng per′sôn), *Nor-*
wegian.

clip per (klip′ər), a sailing ship built and
rigged for speed. *n.*

Clu an na Marbh (klü än′ nə märv′),
Irish.

co-, prefix meaning:
1. with; together: *Coöperate = act with or*
together.
2. joint; fellow: *Coauthor = joint or fellow*
author.
3. equally: *Coextensive = equally extensive.*

cock a too (kok′ə tü′ or kok′ə tü), a
large, brightly colored parrot
of Australia, the East Indies,
etc. *n.*, *pl.* **cock a toos.**

cof fer (kôf′ər or kof′ər), a
box, chest, or trunk, especially
one used to hold money or
other valuable things. *n.*

col league (kol′ēg), an associate; fellow worker: *His*
colleagues taught his classes
while he was ill. *n.*

Cockatoo
(about
18 in. long)

co los sal (kə los′l), huge;
gigantic; vast: *a colossal*
statue, explosion, etc. *adj.*

co los sus (kə los′əs), a huge statue. The
Colossus of Rhodes was a statue of Apollo
at Rhodes, made about 280 B.C. It was one
of the Seven Wonders of the World. *n.*, *pl.*
co los si (-los′ī) or **co los sus es.**

Co lum bia University (kə lum′bē ə), a
university in New York City.

com po si tion (kom′pə zish′ən), the
make-up of anything; what is in it: *The com-*
position of this candy includes sugar, chocolate,
and milk. *n.*

com pound (kom′pound), an enclosed
yard with buildings in it. *n.*

con cord (kon′kôrd or kong′kôrd), agreement; peace; harmony: *concord between friends. n.*

con dens er (kən den′sər), device for receiving and holding a charge of electricity. *n.*

con form i ty (kən fôr′mə tē), fitting oneself and one's actions to the ideas of others; compliance. *n., pl.* **con form i ties.**

Con ne mara (kon′ə mä′rə), a wild, mountainous region on the west coast of Ireland. *n.*

con stab u lary (kən stab′yə ler′ē), constables of a district; policemen. *n., pl.* **con stab u lar ies.**

con tig u ous (kən tig′yü əs), **1.** in actual contact; touching: *A fence showed where the two farms were contiguous.* **2.** adjoining; near. *adj.*

con vey (kən vā′), **1.** carry; transport: *A bus conveys passengers.* **2.** express; make known; communicate: *His words convey no meaning to me. v.*

con vey er belt (kən vā′ər), a moving belt that carries things from one place to another.

coo lie (kü′lē), an unskilled, native laborer in China, India, etc. *n.*

cor mo rant (kôr′mə rənt), a very large, greedy sea bird that has a pouch under the beak for holding fish. *n.*

cor po ral (kôr′pə rəl), the lowest noncommissioned army officer, next below a sergeant. He usually commands a squad. *n.*

corporal's guard, a small group of soldiers commanded by a corporal.

cor pus (kôr′pəs), a body. *n., pl.* **cor po ra** (-pə rə).

cor rob o ra tion (kə rob′ə rā′shən), additional proof: *Tom's sticky face was corroboration of his mother's suspicion that he had been eating jam. n.*

cor ro sive (kə rō′siv), eating away gradually; tending to eat away gradually. Most acids are corrosive. *adj.*

counter-, word element meaning:
1. against; in opposition to: *Counteract = act against.*
2. in return: *Counterattack = attack in return.*
3. so as to correspond: *Counterpart = part that corresponds.*

cov ert (kuv′ərt), secret; hidden; disguised: *covert glances. adj.* **—cov′ert ly,** *adv.*

cre scen do (krə shen′dō), a gradual increase in force or loudness. *n., pl.* **cre scen dos.**

crest (krest), **1.** decoration at the top of a coat of arms. A family crest is sometimes put on silverware, dishes, letter paper, etc. **2.** the top part; top of a hill, wave, etc.; ridge; peak; summit. **3.** reach the crest or top part of (a hill, wave, etc.). 1, 2 *n.,* 3 *v.*

crib bing (krib′ing), framework of logs or timbers used in building. *n.*

Croe sus (krē′səs), a very rich king in Asia Minor from 560 to 546 B.C. *n.*

cru cial (krü′shəl), very important; critical; decisive. *adj.*

crus ta cean (krus tā′shən), any of a group of water animals with hard shells, jointed bodies and appendages, and gills for breathing. Crabs, lobsters, shrimps, etc., are crustaceans. *n.*

cu bi cle (kū′bə kl), a very small room or compartment. *n.*

cudg el (kuj′əl), a short, thick stick used as a weapon; club. *n.*

cun ning (kun′ing), **1.** clever in deceiving; sly: *a cunning villain.* **2.** slyness in getting what one wants; cleverness in deceiving one's enemies: *A fox has a great deal of cunning.* 1 *adj.,* 2 *n.*

cur rach (kur′əH or kur′ə), *Irish.* a boat made of wicker, formerly used in Ireland, Wales, and West Scotland. *n.*

czar (zär), emperor. It was the title of the rulers of Russia (until 1918). *n.* Also, **tsar, tzar.**

Czech (chek), of or having to do with Czechoslovakia, its language, or its people. *adj.*

da ho ri (dä hô′rē), *Papuan.* tomorrow; some time. *n., adv.*

de fect (dē′fekt or di fekt′), fault; blemish; imperfection. *n.*

de lir i um (di lir′ē əm), a temporary disorder of the mind that sometimes occurs during fevers. *n.*

de mean or (di mēn′ər), way a person looks and acts; behavior; conduct; manner: *She has a quiet, modest demeanor. n.*

de ploy (di ploi′), spread out: *The troops deployed on the battlefield. v.*

de pot (dep′ō), storehouse; warehouse. *n.*

des ti ny (des′tə nē), **1.** what becomes of a person or thing in the end; one's lot or fortune: *It was his destiny to die in battle.* **2.** what will happen in spite of all efforts to change or prevent it. *n., pl.* **des ti nies.**

Did rik son (did′rik sn), **Mildred Ella ("Babe"),** 1914-1956, famous American woman athlete. She married George Zaharias (zə har′ē əs) in 1938. *n.*

hat, āge, cãre, fär; let, bē, tėrm; it, īce; hot, gō, ôrder; oil, out; cup, pút, rüle, ūse; ch, child; ng, long; th, thin; ŦH, then; zh, measure; ə represents *a* in about, *e* in taken, *i* in April, *o* in lemon, *u* in circus.

dire (dĭr), causing great fear or suffering; dreadful. *adj.,* **dir er, dir est.**

dirge (dèrj), a funeral song or tune. *n.*

← DISCUS

Man throwing a discus

dis crim i na tion (dis krim′ə- nā′shən), making a difference in favor of or against: *There was discrim- ination against Jews in Germany.n.*

dis cus (dis′kəs), a heavy, circular plate of stone or metal, used in athletic games as a test of skill and strength in throwing. *n.*

dolt (dōlt), a dull, stupid person. *n.*

do nor (dō′nər), person who contributes; giver. *n.*

do ry (dô′rē or dō′rē), rowboat with a flat bottom and high sides, often used by fisher- men. *n., pl.* **do ries.**

draughts (drafts), *British.* game of checkers. *n. pl.*

Drew (drü), **Charles Richard,** 1904-1950, American Negro doctor who developed the blood bank. *n.*

Driss (dris), *Berber. n.*

Driv er (drĭv′ər), **William,** 1810-1886, American Negro sea captain from Salem, Massachusetts, who named the American flag "Old Glory." *n.*

drogue chute (drōg), a small parachute that slows down a space craft as it returns to earth.

dry run, a practice test or session.

du bu (dü′bü), *Papuan.* 1. men's club- house in Papua. 2. a man or boy of the dubu house. 3. of or having to do with a dubu. 1, 2 *n.,* 3 *adj.*

du gong (dü′gong), a large fish-shaped mammal of tropical seas with flipperlike forelimbs and paddle- like tail. *n.*

Dugong (10 ft. long)

Dun kirk (dun′kèrk), seaport in northern France where British forces escaped from the German army in 1940. *n.*

Dutch Gui a na (gi ä′nə or gi an′ə), a Dutch territory in northern South America.

dy na mo (dĭ′nə mō), machine that changes mechanical energy into electric energy and produces electric current. *n., pl.* **dy na mos.**

-ee, suffix used to form nouns:
1. person who is ＿＿: *Absentee = person who is absent.*
2. person who is ＿＿ed: *Appointee = person who is appointed.*

3. person to whom something is ＿＿ed: *Mortgagee = person to whom something is mortgaged.*

ef fect (ə fekt′), 1. result: *The effect of the gale was to overturn several boats.* 2. get done; bring about: *The war effected changes all over the world.* 3. force; power; in- fluence: *The medi- cine had an immedi- ate effect.* 4. impres- sion produced. 1, 3, 4 *n.,* 2 *v.*

egret (ē′gret or eg′ret), any of various herons with tufts of beautiful, long plumes. *n.*

Great white egret of America

Eid fjord (āt′fyôrd), a village in south- western Norway. *n.*

Eif fel (ā fel′), **Gus tave** (gʏs täv′), 1832- 1923, French engineer. *n.*

Eif fel Tower (ī′fl), a lofty tower in Paris. 984 ft.

el e ment (el′ə mənt), 1. one of the sim- ple substances, such as gold, iron, carbon, sulfur, oxygen, and hydrogen, that cannot as yet be separated into simpler parts by ordi- nary means; substance composed of atoms that are chemically alike. 2. one of the parts of which anything is made up. *n.*

younger element, younger generation.

el e men tal (el′ə men′tl), 1. of the forces of nature. Primitive peoples usually worship elemental gods, such as the sun, earth, thunder, etc. 2. as found in nature; simple but powerful: *Hunger is an elemental feeling. adj.*

Ele na (ā lā′nä), *Spanish. n.*

El e va la (el′e vä′lä), *Papuan. n.*

el o quent (el′ə kwənt), very expressive: *an eloquent look. adj.*

el ti bu rón (el tē bü rōn′), *Spanish.* the shark.

El ve da len (el′və dä′lən), *Norwegian. n.*

ema ci at ed (i mā′shē āt′id), unnaturally thin or wasted away: *The invalid was pale and emaciated. adj.*

emerge (i mèrj′), come out; come up; come into view. *v.,* **emerged, emerg ing.**

em i grate (em′ə grāt), leave one's own country or region to settle in another. *v.,* **em i grat ed, em i grat ing.**

Eng strand (eng′stränd), *Norwegian. n.*

en sign (en′sīn or en′sn), flag; banner: *The ensign of the United States is the Stars and Stripes. n.*

en sue (en sü′), come after; follow: *The ensuing year means the next year. v.,* **en- sued, en su ing.**

Ep i me theus (ep′ə mē′thüs or ep′ə mē′-

thē əs), in Greek mythology, the brother of Prometheus and the husband of Pandora. *n.*

eq uer ry (ek′wər ē), **1.** officer of a royal or noble household who has charge of the horses or who accompanies his master's carriage. **2.** attendant on a royal or noble person. *n., pl.* **eq uer ries.**

-ery, suffix added to another noun, a verb, or an adjective to form a noun:
1. place for ____ing, as in *cannery, hatchery.*
2. place for ____s, as in *nunnery.*
3. occupation or business of a ____, as in *cookery.*
4. state or condition of a ____, as in *slavery.*
5. qualities, actions, etc., of a ____, as in *knavery.*
6. ____s as a group, as in *machinery.*

Ev an (ev′ən), *Welsh. n.*

evolve (i volv′), **1.** develop gradually; work out. **2.** develop by a process of growth and change to a more highly organized condition. *v.,* **evolved, evolv ing.**

ex ca vate (eks′kə vāt), dig out; scoop out: *Power shovels excavated the dirt. v.,* **ex ca vat ed, ex ca vat ing.**

ex e cute (ek′sə kūt), **1.** carry out; do; perform: *The nurse executed the doctor's orders.* **2.** make according to a plan or design: *An artist executes a painting. v.,* **ex e cut ed, ex e cut ing.**

ex hil a rate (eg zil′ə rāt), make merry or lively; put into high spirits; stimulate. *v.,* **ex hil a rat ed, ex hil a rat ing.**

ex ile (eg′zīl or ek′sīl), **1.** force (a person) to leave his country or home; banish: *Many people were exiled from the country.* **2.** an exiled person: *He had been an exile for ten years.* 1 *v.,* **ex iled, ex il ing;** 2 *n.*

ex tol or **ex toll** (eks tōl′), praise highly; commend: *The newspapers extolled the winning team. v.,* **ex tolled, ex tol ling.**

ex ult ant (eg zult′nt), rejoicing greatly; triumphant: *He gave an exultant shout. adj.*
—**ex ult′ant ly,** *adv.*

fast ness (fast′nis), a strong, safe place; stronghold: *a mountain fastness. n.*

fath om (faŦH′əm), a unit of measure equal to 6 feet, used mostly in measuring the depth of water and the length of ships' ropes, cables, etc. *n., pl.* **fath oms** or (*esp. collectively*) **fath om.**

Fat ma (fät′mə), *Berber. n.*

feat (fēt), a great or unusual deed; act showing great skill, strength, etc. *n.*

Fer ra ro (fer rä′rō), *Italian. n.*

Fer ri er (fer rē ā′), *French. n.*

fi di (fē′dē), *Papuan. n.*

field hand, 1. originally, a slave who worked in the fields. **2.** now, any hired farm laborer.

fiord (fyôrd or fyōrd), a long, narrow bay of the sea between high banks or cliffs. Norway has many fiords. *n.* Also, **fjord.**

Fiord

flag stone (flag′-stōn′), a large, flat stone, used for paving walks, etc. *n.*

flail (flāl), beat; thrash. *v.*

Flam bor ough Head (flam′bər ə), a chalk cliff in Yorkshire, England, on the east coast.

for age (fôr′ij or for′ij), **1.** hunt or search for food: *Rabbits forage in our garden.* **2.** hunt; search about: *The boys foraged for old metal.* **3.** plunder. *v.,* **for aged, for ag ing.**

fore bitt (fôr′bit′), a strong post on a ship's foredeck to which ropes, cables, etc., are fastened. *n.*

fore bod ing (fôr bōd′ing or fōr bōd′ing), a feeling that something bad is going to happen. *n.*

fore cas tle (fōk′sl or fôr′kas′l), the sailors' rooms in a merchant ship, formerly in the forward part of the ship. *n.*

for feit (fôr′fit), lose or have to give up as a penalty for some act, neglect, fault, etc. *v.*

forge[1] (fôrj or fōrj), **1.** place with fire where metal is heated very hot and then hammered into shape. **2.** make; shape; form. 1 *n.,* 2 *v.,* **forged, forg ing.**

forge[2] (fôrj or fōrj), move forward slowly but steadily: *One runner forged ahead of the others and won the race. v.,* **forged, forg ing.**

funk (fungk), *Informal.* fear; panic. *n.*

furl (fèrl), roll up; fold up: *furl a sail, furl a flag. v.*

fu ror (fyúr′ôr), outburst of wild enthusiasm or excitement. *n.*

fu su ma (fü′sə mä), a sliding paper door, framed in wood, used in Japanese homes. *n.*

G. (jē), a unit of force equal to the force of gravity on a body at the surface of the earth. An astronaut experiences a force of several G's on his body during lift-off and reëntry. A force of 2 G's means the body weight is doubled.

---

hat, āge, cãre, fär; let, bē, tèrm; it, īce; hot, gō, ôrder; oil, out; cup, pùt, rüle; ūse; ch, child; ng, long; th, thin; ŦH, then; zh, measure; ə represents *a* in about, *e* in taken, *i* in April, *o* in lemon, *u* in circus.

gall (gôl), a bitter liquid produced in the liver. *n.*

gal ley (gal´ē), 1. a long, narrow ship of former times having oars and sails. 2. a large rowboat. 3. kitchen of a ship. *n., pl.* **gal leys.**

Galley (def. 1)

gal lows (gal´ōz), 1. a wooden frame made of a crossbar on two upright posts, used for hanging criminals. 2. hanging as a punishment. *n., pl.* **gal lows es** or **gal lows.**

gal va nize (gal´və nīz), cover (iron or steel) with a thin coating of zinc to prevent rust. *v.,* **gal va nized, gal va niz ing.**

Gan ges (gan´jēz), a famous and sacred river in northern India. *n.*

gang plank (gang´plangk´), a movable bridge used by persons or animals in getting on and off a ship, etc. *n.*

gang way (gang´wā´), gangplank. *n.*

gan try (gan´trē), a tall frame structure used for servicing large rockets. *n.*

ga ru pa (gä rü´pä), *Spanish.* grouper. *n.*

gaunt let (gônt´lit or gänt´lit). **Run the gauntlet** means pass between two rows of men each of whom strikes the victim as he passes. *n.* Also, **gantlet.**

gear (gir), 1. arrangement of fixed and moving parts for transmitting or changing motion; mechanism; machinery: *The car ran off the road when the steering gear broke.* 2. equipment needed for some purpose. Harness, clothes, household goods, tools, tackle, and rigging are various kinds of gear. *n.*

gen er a tor (jen´ər ā´tər), machine that changes mechanical energy into electrical energy; dynamo. *n.*

Gen ta ro Sa to (gen tä´rō sä´tō), *Japanese.*

ge o log i cal (jē´ə loj´ə kl), of geology; having to do with geology. *adj.*

ge ol o gy (jē ol´ə jē), 1. science that deals with the earth's crust, the layers of which it is composed, and their history. 2. features of the earth's crust in a place or region; rocks, rock formation, etc., of a particular area. *n., pl.* **ge ol o gies.**

ges tic u late (jes tik´yə lāt), make motions to show ideas or feelings: *The speaker gesticulated by raising his arms, pounding the desk, and stamping his foot. v.,* **ges tic u lat ed, ges tic u lat ing.**

gib ber ish (jib´ər ish or gib´ər ish), senseless chatter; rapid, indistinct talk. *n.*

gib bet (jib´it), 1. an upright post with a projecting arm at the top, from which the bodies of criminals were hung after execution. 2. gallows. *n.*

Gio van ni (jō vän´nē), *Italian. n.*

gir dle (gėr´dl), belt, sash, cord, etc., worn around the waist. *n.*

gnu (nü or nū), a large, African antelope with an oxlike head, curved horns, and a long tail; wildebeest. *n., pl.* **gnus** or (*esp.* collectively) **gnu.**

Gnu (about 4 ft. high at the shoulder)

go bail (bāl), *British slang.* to be sure.

Gold Coast, a region in West Africa, former British colony, now largely included in Ghana.

Gor get (gôr´jit).

Go vind (gō´vind), *Hindu. n.*

Grac es (grās´iz), three Greek sister goddesses controlling beauty and charm in people and in nature. *n. pl.*

Gra na da (grə nä´də), a city in southern Spain, the stronghold of the Moors till they were driven out of Spain. *n.*

Grant (grant), **Ulysses Simpson,** 1822-1885, American general, 18th president of the United States, from 1869 to 1877. *n.*

grav i ta tion (grav´ə tā´shən), the fact that the earth pulls any object toward it and that the sun, moon, stars, and other such bodies in the universe do the same; the force or pull that makes bodies in the universe tend to move toward one another. *n.*

grav i ta tion al field (grav´ə tā´shən l), space in which gravitation operates.

gre nade (grə nād´), a small bomb, usually thrown by hand: *The soldiers threw grenades into the enemy's trenches. n.*

gri mace (grə mās´ or grim´is), 1. a twisting of the face; ugly or funny smile: *a grimace caused by pain.* 2. make grimaces. 1 *n.,* 2 *v.,* **gri maced, gri mac ing.**

gris ly (griz´lē), frightful; horrible; ghastly. *adj.,* **gris li er, gris li est.**

Gross mut ter (grōs´mút´ər), *German.* grandmother. *n.*

gro tesque (grō tesk´), 1. odd or unnatural in shape, appearance, manner, etc.; fantastic; queer. 2. ridiculous; absurd. *adj.* —**gro tesque´ly,** *adv.*

group er (grüp´ər), a large food fish of warm seas. *n., pl.* **group ers** or (*esp.* collectively) **group er.**

guile (gīl), crafty deceit; sly tricks. *n.*

hai ku (hī´kü), an unrhymed Japanese poem in three lines of five, then seven, then five syllables. A haiku often refers in some way to one of the seasons of the year. *n., pl.* **hai ku.**

Ha le a ka la (hä′lā ä′kä lä′), an extinct volcano on the island of Maui, Hawaii, that has the largest crater in the world. *n.*

hal yard (hal′yərd), rope or tackle used on a ship to raise or lower a sail, yard, flag, etc. *n.* Also, **halliard.**

Hans (häns), *German. n.*

hard tack (härd′tak′), a very hard, dry biscuit, eaten by sailors. *n.*

Ha ri Singh (hä′rē sing), *Hindu.*

har row (har′ō), arouse uncomfortable feelings in; distress; torment: *The man was harrowed by grief. v.*

hatch (hach), **1.** a small door or opening. **2.** a door or opening leading into a lower compartment, especially of a ship. *n.*

hatch way (hach′wā′), an opening in the deck of a ship to the lower part. *n.*

Hat ter as (hat′ər əs), **Cape,** end of an island off eastern North Carolina. *n.*

haw ser (hô′zər or hô′sər), a large rope or small cable. Hawsers are used for mooring or towing ships. *n.*

head land (hed′lənd), point of land jutting out into water; cape. *n.*

hea then (hē′ᴛʜən), **1.** person who does not believe in the God of the Bible; person who is not a Christian, Jew, or Moslem. **2.** of or having to do with the heathen; not Christian, Jewish, or Moslem. 1 *n., pl.* **hea thens** or **hea then;** 2 *adj.*

herb (ėrb or hėrb), plant whose leaves or stems are used for medicine, seasoning, food, or perfume. Sage, mint, and lavender are herbs. *n.*

Her re ro (e rer′ō), *Spanish. n.*

Him a la yas (him′ə lā′əz or hə mäl′yəz), a mountain range extending for 1600 miles along the northern borders of India and Pakistan. Their highest peak, Mt. Everest, 29,028 feet, is the highest mountain in the world. *n. pl.*

Hip Wo (hip′ wō′), *Chinese.*

hogs head (hogz′hed or hôgz′hed), a large barrel that contains from 100 to 140 gallons. *n.*

ho la (ō′lä), *Spanish.* hello; ahoy. *interj.*

hone (hōn), **1.** a fine-grained whetstone on which to sharpen cutting tools, especially razors. **2.** sharpen on a hone. 1 *n.,* 2 *v.,* **honed, hon ing.**

Hong Kong or **Hong kong** (hong′ kong′ or hông′kông′), a British colony adjoining southeastern China. *n.*

-hood, suffix meaning:
1. state or condition of being, as in *boyhood,* *likelihood.*

2. character or nature of, as in *manhood,* *sainthood.*
3. group, body of, as in *priesthood.*

Ho pi (hō′pē), member of a tribe of Pueblo Indians living largely in stone-built towns in northern Arizona. *n., pl.* **Ho pis.**

horn bill (hôrn′bil′), a large bird having a very large bill with a horn or horny lump on it. *n.*

Hours (ourz), in Greek mythology, the three sister goddesses of the seasons, orderliness, justice, and peace. *n. pl.*

How ard University (hou′ərd), a university in Washington, D.C.

Indian hornbill
(about 4 ft. long)

il lu sion (i lü′zhən), **1.** appearance which is not real; misleading appearance. **2.** a false idea, notion, or belief. *n.*

im mi grant (im′ə grənt), person who comes into a foreign country or region to live: *Canada has many immigrants from Europe. California has many immigrants from other States. n.*

Optical illusion. The verticals appear to converge and diverge under the influence of the crosspieces.

im pact (im′pakt), a striking (of one thing against another); collision: *The impact of the two swords broke both of them. n.*

im pair (im pãr′), make worse; damage; weaken: *Poor food impaired his health. v.*

im per cep ti ble (im′pər sep′tə bl), very slight; gradual. *adj.* —**im′per cep′ti bly,** *adv.*

im pos tor (im pos′tər), person who assumes a false name or character. *n.*

im pro vise (im′prə vīz), make (something) by using whatever is at hand. *v.,* **im pro vised, im pro vis ing.**

in al ien a ble (in āl′yən ə bl), that cannot be given away or taken away: *Life, liberty, and the pursuit of happiness have been called the inalienable rights of man. adj.*

in co her ent (in′kō hir′ənt), disconnected; confused. *adj.* —**in′co her′ent ly,** *adv.*

in com pre hen si ble (in′kom pri hen′-

hat, āge, cãre, fär; let, bē, tėrm; it, īce; hot, gō, ôrder; oil, out; cup, pùt, rüle, ūse; ch, child; ng, long; th, thin; ᴛʜ, then; zh, measure; ə represents *a* in about, *e* in taken, *i* in April, *o* in lemon, *u* in circus.

501

sə bl), impossible to understand. *adj.*

in dom i ta ble (in dom′ə tə bl), unconquerable; unyielding. *adj.*

in dul gence (in dul′jəns), 1. kindness. 2. favor; privilege. *n.*

in grained (in grānd′), deeply and firmly fixed: *ingrained honesty. adj.*

in im i ta ble (in im′ə bl), that cannot be imitated or copied; matchless. *adj.*

ink ling (ingk′ling), a slight suggestion; vague notion; hint. *n.*

in sig nia (in sig′nē ə), medals, badges, or other distinguishing marks of a position or of some honor. *n. pl. of* **in sig ne** (in sig′nē).

in stinct (in′stingkt), natural feeling, knowledge, or power, such as guides animals; unlearned tendency: *An instinct leads birds to fly. n.*

in tel li gent life (in tel′ə jənt), a form of life that has a high degree of intelligence and mental capacity.

in te ri or (in tir′ē ər), 1. inside; inner surface or part. 2. part of a region or country away from the coast or border. *n.*

in ter mi na ble (in tèr′mə nə bl), endless; so long as to seem endless. *adj.*

in ter ro ga tion (in ter′ə gā′shən), a questioning. *n.*

in trep id (in trep′id), fearless; dauntless; courageous; very brave: *A policeman or soldier must be intrepid. adj.*

in trigue (in trēg′), excite the curiosity and interest of: *The book's unusual title intrigued me. v.,* **in trigued, in tri guing.**

in vet er ate (in vet′ər it), doing a certain thing by habit: *an inveterate smoker. adj.*

io (ē′ō), *Papuan.* yes.

ir res o lute (i rez′ə lüt), not resolute; unable to make up one's mind; not sure of what one wants; hesitating: *Irresolute persons make poor leaders. adj.*

-ism, suffix meaning:
1. action; practice, as in *criticism.*
2. doctrine; system; principle, as in *socialism.*
3. quality; characteristic; state; condition, as in *heroism, Americanism.*
4. illustration; case; instance, as in *witticism.*
5. unhealthy condition caused by, as in *alcoholism.*

-ist, suffix meaning:
1. a person who does or makes, as in *tourist.*
2. one who knows about or has skill with, as in *pianist.*
3. one engaged in or busy with, as in *machinist.*
4. one who believes in, as in *idealist.*

Ivan (i vän′), *Russian. n.*

-ive, suffix meaning:
1. of or having to do with, as in *instinctive, defensive.*

2. tending to; likely to, as in *active, appreciative.*

ja (yä), *Norwegian.* yes.

jack al (jak′ôl or jak′l), a wild dog of Asia and Africa. It was supposed to hunt prey for the lion and eat what the lion left. *n.*

Ja mai ca (jə mā′kə), an island in the West Indies, south of Cuba, formerly a British colony. *n.*

Jas sy (jäs′ē), *Hindu. n.*

Jetty

jaun ty (jôn′tē or jän′tē), 1. easy and lively; carefree: *The happy boy walked with jaunty steps.* 2. smart; stylish: *She wore a jaunty little hat. adj.,* **jaun ti er, jaun ti est.** —**jaun′ti ly,** *adv.*

jave lin (jav′lən), a light spear thrown by hand. *n.*

Jean (zhäN), *French. n.*

jel la ba (jə lä′bə), a man's loose woolen cloak with a hood, worn in North Africa. *n.*

jet ty (jet′ē), 1. structure built out into the water to protect a harbor or influence the current; breakwater. 2. a landing place; pier. *n., pl.* **jet ties.**

jib boom (jib), spar extending out from a ship's bowsprit. On a large sailing ship the jib is fastened to it.

JIB BOOM
BOWSPRIT
FORWARD PART OF SHIP

Ji go ri (jē gô′rē), *Papuan. n.*

Jo han nes (yō hän′əs), *German. n.*

Jo ku ri (jō kü′rē), *Papuan. n.*

Jones (jōnz), **John Paul,** 1747-1792, American naval commander in the American Revolution. *n.*

Jove (jōv), the Roman god Jupiter, king of gods and men. *n.*

Juan (hwän), *Spanish. n.*

ju bi lant (jü′bl ənt), rejoicing; exulting: *a jubilant shout. adj.*

ju jube (jü′jüb), a tree or shrub bearing an edible, datelike fruit. *n.*

Ka ang (kä′äng), *African. n.*

Kai va (kī′vä), *Papuan. n.*

Ka la ha ri (kä′lä hä′rē), a large desert in South Africa. *n.*

Ken ya (ken′yə or kēn′yə), a country in eastern Africa, formerly a British colony and protectorate. *n.*

Ke re ma (kə rē′mə), a town in Papua, 140 miles northwest of Port Moresby. *n.*

ker o sene (ker′ə sēn), a thin oil made from petroleum, used in lamps and stoves. *n.*

ketch (kech), a fore-and-aft-rigged sailing ship with a large mainmast toward the bow and a smaller mast toward the stern. *n.*

Ki a poo (kē ä′pü), a tribe of pygmies, living in Papua. *n.*

Klon dike (klon′dĭk), region in north-western Canada, along the Yukon River, famous for its gold fields. *n.*

Kö nig (kœ′nĭg), *German. n.*

Kös ter (kœs′tər), *German. n.*

Ko vacs (kō′väch), *Hungarian. n.*

Ko wal czyk (kō väl′chik), *Polish. n.*

Ko yo (kō′yō′), Japanese poet. *n.*

kraal (kräl), 1. village of South African natives, protected by a fence. 2. pen for cattle or sheep in South Africa. *n.*

kro ne (krō′nə), a Danish or Norwegian silver coin worth about 14 cents in 1964. *n., pl.* **kro ner** (-nər).

Ku ku-ku ku (kü′kə kü′kü), 1. a group of people inhabiting parts of Papua in eastern New Guinea. 2. one of these people. 3. of or having to do with the Kuku-kuku. 1, 2 *n.,* 3 *adj.*

Ku ku pi (kü′kü pē), a village in Papua, 30 miles east of Kerema. *n.*

ku nai (kü′nī), a kind of coarse, tall grass. *n.*

Kyo to (kyō′tō), city in central Japan. It was formerly the capital. *n.*

Lae (lī), a harbor town in Papua, 180 miles north of Port Moresby. *n.*

lag gard (lag′ərd), person who moves too slowly or falls behind. *n.*

La ke ma nu (lä′kə mä′nü), river in Papua, the mouth of which is 30 miles east of Kerema. *n.*

La nai (lə nī′), one of the Hawaiian Islands. *n.*

Land Rover, a jeeplike vehicle specifically designed to be used in rough country.

Lang ley (lang′lē), Field, Air Force training center at Hampton, Virginia. *n.*

lash[1] (lash), wave or beat back and forth: *The lion lashed his tail. The wind lashes the sails. v.*

lash[2] (lash), tie or fasten with a rope, cord, etc.: *The boys lashed logs together to make a raft. v.*

leg a cy (leg′ə sē), money or other property left to a person, usually by a will. *n., pl.* **leg a cies.**

L'En fant (län fäN′), **Pierre** (pyăr) **Charles** (shärl), 1754-1825, French engineer who drew the plans for the city of Washington, D.C. *n.*

li chen (lī′kən), a dry-looking, flowerless plant that grows like a patch of skin on rocks, trees, and other surfaces. *n.*

Li Lai-tong (lē′ lī′tong′), *Chinese.*

lin go (ling′gō), *Used humorously or in contempt.* 1. language. 2. any speech regarded as outlandish or queer. *n., pl.* **lin goes.**

lith o graph (lith′ə graf), 1. picture, print, etc., made from a flat, specially prepared stone or a metal plate. 2. print from a stone or plate. 1 *n.,* 2 *v.*

li thog ra pher (li thog′rə fər), person who lithographs. *n.*

lit ter (lit′ər), 1. young animals produced at one time: *a litter of puppies.* 2. stretcher for carrying a sick or wounded person. *n.*

lock jaw (lok′jô′), blood poisoning in which the jaws become firmly closed. Tetanus is another name for lockjaw. *n.*

lo co (lō′kō), *Spanish.* crazy. *adj.*

loin cloth (loin′klôth′ or loin′kloth′), piece of cloth worn around the hips and between the thighs by natives of warm countries. *n.*

lo ry (lô′rē or lō′rē), a small, bright-colored parrot of Australia and nearby islands. *n., pl.* **lo ries.**

lum ba go (lum bā′gō), pain in the muscles in the lower part of the back. *n.*

lusty (lus′tē), strong and healthy. *adj.,* lust i er, lust i est.

Lyng en (lyng′ən), *Norwegian. n.*

Ma Chu (mä′ chü′), *Chinese.*

mag is trate (maj′is trāt), officer of the government who has power to apply the law and put it in force. *n.*

mag ní fi co (mäg nē′fē kō), *Spanish.* magnificent. *adj.*

Mai pa (mī′pä), *Papuan. n.*

ma lar ia (mə lãr′ē ə), a disease that causes chills, fever, and sweating. *n.*

ma ña na (mä nyä′nä), *Spanish.* tomorrow; some time. *n., adv.*

man grove (mang′grōv), a tropical tree that sends down many branches that take root and form new trunks. Mangroves grow in swamps along the banks of rivers. *n.*

Mangrove (10 to 20 ft. high)

Ma nuel (mä nwel′), *Spanish. n.*

---

hat, āge, cãre, fär; let, bē, tèrm; it, īce; hot, gō, ôrder; oil, out; cup, pùt, rüle, ūse; ch, child; ng, long; th, thin; ₮H, then; zh, measure; ə represents *a* in about, *e* in taken, *i* in April, *o* in lemon, *u* in circus.

mar i o nette (mar′ē ə net′), a small doll or puppet moved by strings or by the hands. *n.*

Mar tian (mär′shən),   **1.** of the planet Mars. **2.** a supposed inhabitant of the planet Mars. 1 *adj.*, 2 *n.*

Ma sa hi de (mä′sä hē′dā),   Japanese poet. *n.*

mea ger or **mea gre** (mē′gər),   poor; scanty: *a meager meal. adj.*

me men to (mə men′tō),   thing serving as a reminder or remembrance: *These post cards are mementos of our trip abroad. n., pl.* **me men tos** or **me men toes.**

mer chan dise (mėr′chən dīz   or   mėr′chən dīs),   goods for sale; wares; articles bought and sold. *n.*

mere[1] (mir),   nothing else than; only; simple: *The cut was the merest scratch. adj., superl.* **mer est.**

mere[2] (mir),   *Poetic.* lake; pond. *n.*

Middle Passage,   the trip across the Atlantic Ocean from West Africa to the West Indies or America, which was the route of the former slave trade.

mil let (mil′it),   **1.** a very small grain used for food in Asia and Africa. **2.** the plant that it grows on. *n.*

mi ra (mē′rä),   *Spanish.* look!

mis-,   prefix meaning:
1. bad, as in *misgovernment.*
2. badly, as in *misbehave, mismanage.*
3. wrong, as in *mispronunciation.*
4. wrongly, as in *misapply, misunderstand.*

miz zen mast (miz′n mast′; *Nautical* miz′n məst),   mast nearest the stern in a two-masted or three-masted ship. *n.*

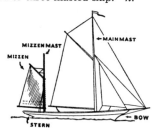

mo bile unit (mō′bl or mō′bēl),   an establishment on wheels (as an automobile or trailer) equipped for some special service.

mod i fi ca tion (mod′ə fə kā′shən),   partial alteration or change: *The teacher recommended six modifications in my essay. n.*

mon i tor (mon′ə tər),   check (a radio or television transmission) by listening in with a receiver. *v.*

moor (mur),   **1.** put or keep (a ship, etc.) in place by means of ropes or chains fastened

to the shore or to anchors. **2.** moor a ship. **3.** be made secure by ropes, anchors, etc. *v.*

Moor (mur),   member of a race related to the Arabs, living in northwestern Africa. In the eighth century A.D. the Moors invaded and conquered Spain. They were finally driven out in 1492. *n.*

mo sa ic (mō zā′ik),
1. small pieces of stone, glass, wood, etc., of different colors inlaid to form a picture or design. **2.** anything like a mosaic. *n.*

Mosaic design

Mos lem (moz′ləm),   follower of Mohammed; believer in the religion founded by him. *n., pl.* **Mos lems** or **Mos lem.** Also, **Muslem, Muslim.**

moth er-of-pearl (muŦH′ər əv pėrl′),   the hard, rainbow-colored lining of certain shells. It is used to make buttons and ornaments. *n.*

Mo tu (mō′tü),   a group of dark-skinned people in Papua. *n.*

Mo tu an (mō′tü ən),   **1.** of or having to do with the Motu. **2.** the language or dialect of the Motu. 1 *adj.*, 2 *n.*

Mo vi a vi (mō′vē ä′vē),   **1.** a region in Papua. **2.** person living in Moviavi. **3.** of or having to do with Moviavi. 1, 2 *n.*, 3 *adj.*

mu cho (mü′chō),   *Spanish.* much.

musk (musk),   **1.** substance with a strong and lasting odor, used in making perfumes. Musk is found in a special gland in the male musk deer. **2.** odor of musk. *n.*

mu tu al (mü′chü əl),   done, said, felt, etc. by each toward the other. *adj.*

NASA (nas′ə),   National Aeronautics and Space Administration. *n.*

na tive (nā′tiv),   **1.** person born in a certain place or country. The natives are the people living in a place, not visitors or foreigners. **2.** born in a certain place or country: *People born in New York are native sons and daughters of New York.* **3.** belonging to one because of his birth: *one's native land.* **4.** belonging to one because of his country or the nation to which he belongs: *one's native language.* **5.** born in a person; natural: *native ability, native courtesy.* **6.** one of the original inhabitants of a place, as contrasted with conquerors, settlers, visitors, etc.; especially, a member of a less civilized race. **7.** of or having to do with the original inhabitants, especially those not white: *native customs, native huts.* **8.** originating, grown, or produced in a certain place: *Tobacco is native to America.* 1, 6 *n.*, 2-5, 7, 8 *adj.*

Na tua (nä′twä),   *Papuan. n.*

net tle (net′l),   irritate; provoke. *v.* **net tled, net tling.**

New Guin ea (gin′ē), **1.** a large island north of Australia. Part of New Guinea belongs to the Netherlands and part to Aus-

tralia. Also, **Papua. 2. Territory of,** an Australian trust territory including northeastern New Guinea and nearby islands.

niche (nich), a recess or hollow in a wall, cliff, etc. *n.*

nigh (nī), **1.** near. **2.** nearly. 1, 2 *adv.*, 1 *adj.*, **nigh er, nigh est** or **next;** 1 *prep.*

Nils Thor son (nils tôr′sôn), *Norwegian.*

ni pa (nē′pə), a kind of palm tree whose long strong leaves are used for thatching roofs and making baskets. *n.*

no es ver dad (nō es ver däd′), *Spanish.* It is not true. Also used as a question meaning "Is it not so?"

No mu sa (nō mü′sä), *Zulu. n.*

Nor dal (nôr′däl), a village in western Norway. *n.*

Norse man (nôrs′mən), member of a tall, blond race that lived in ancient Scandinavia; Northman. The Vikings were Norsemen. *n., pl.* **Norse men.**

ob serv a to ry (əb zėr′və tô′rē or əb-zėr′və tō′rē), place or building with a telescope for observing the stars and other heavenly bodies. *n., pl.* **ob serv a to ries.**

ocher or **ochre** (ō′kər), any of various earths ranging in coloring from pale yellow to orange, brown, and red, used as pigments. *n.*

of fal (ôf′l or of′l), **1.** the waste parts of an animal killed for food. **2.** garbage; refuse. *n.*

O-hayo go zai ma su (ō hä′yō gō′zī-mä′sü), *Japanese.*

Olen (œ′lən), village in southwestern Norway. *n.*

Oli pai River (ō′li pī).

Olym pus (ō lim′pəs), **Mount,** mountain in northeastern Greece, where the greater Greek gods were supposed to live. *n.*

om i nous (om′ə nəs), of bad omen; un-favorable; threatening: *Those clouds look ominous for our picnic. adj.*

Orai (ō′rī), *Papuan. n.*

or gan ism (ôr′gən iz əm), a living body having organs or an organized structure; individual animal or plant. *n.*

Ori no co (ô′rə nō′kō or ō′rə nō′kō), a large river in South America, flowing through Venezuela into the Atlantic Ocean. *n.*

or ni thol o gist (ôr′nə thol′ə jist), person who studies birds or who knows much about birds. *n.*

out rig ger (out′-rig′ər), frame-work ending in a float, extending outward from the side of a canoe to prevent upsetting. *n.*

Outrigger

Pal o mar (pal′ō mär), **Mount,** peak in southern California. An observatory is on top of Mount Palomar. *n.*

pal try (pôl′trē), almost worthless. *adj.*, **pal tri er, pal tri est.**

pan de mo ni um (pan′də mō′nē əm), wild uproar or lawlessness. *n.*

Pan do ra (pan dô′rə), in Greek mythology, the first woman created by the gods to punish mankind for having learned the use of fire. Curiosity led her to open a box and thus let out all sorts of ills into the world. Only Hope remained at the bottom. *n.*

Pap ua (pap′yü ə or pä′pú ä), **1.** New Guinea. **2. Territory of,** the southeastern part of New Guinea, with nearby islands. It is a territory of Australia. *Capital:* Port Moresby. See **New Guinea** for map. *n.*

Pap u an (pap′yü ən or pä′pú ən), **1.** of or having to do with Papua or with the native negroid race living in Papua. **2.** native or inhabitant of Papua. **3.** any of the Papuan languages or dialects. 1 *adj.*, 2, 3 *n.*

par a dise (par′ə dīs), **1.** heaven. **2.** place or condition of great happiness. **3.** place of great beauty. *n.*

par ish (par′ish), **1.** district that has its own church and clergyman. **2.** a civil district in Great Britain. *n.*

pate (pāt), the head; the top of the head: *a bald pate. n.*

pat ro nym ic (pat′rə nim′ik), name derived from the name of a father or ancestor:

---

hat, āge, cãre, fär; let, bē, tèrm; it, īce; hot, gō, ôrder; oil, out; cup, pùt, rüle, ūse; ch, child; ng, long; th, thin; ₮H, then; zh, measure; ə represents *a* in about, *e* in taken, *i* in April, *o* in lemon, *u* in circus.

505

pauper

Williamson meaning "son of William" is a patronymic. n.

pau per (pô′pər),   a very poor person. *n.*

ped es tal (ped′is tl),   1. base on which a column or a statue stands. 2. base of a tall vase, lamp, etc. 3. base; support; foundation. *n.*

Pe dri llo (pā drē′yō), *Spanish. n.*

Peg a sus (peg′ə səs),   1. in Greek mythology, a horse with wings, the steed of the Muses. 2. group of stars in the northern sky. *n.*

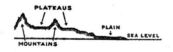
Pedestal supporting a bust

Pei ping (pā′ping′ or bā′ping′),   a city in northeastern China. *n.*

Pe re gil (per′e hēl′), *Spanish. n.*

per man ga nate   (pər mang′gə nāt),   crystals used in a solution to disinfect. *n.*

per me ate (pėr′mē āt),   1. spread through the whole of; pass through; soak through: *Smoke permeated the house.* 2. penetrate: *Water will easily permeate a cotton dress. v.,* **per me at ed, per me at ing.**

per se cute (pėr′sə kūt),   1. treat badly; do harm to again and again; oppress. 2. punish for religious reasons. *v.,* **per se-cut ed, per se cut ing.**

per se vere (pėr′sə vir′),   continue steadily in doing something hard; persist. *v.,* **per se vered, per se ver ing.**

Phoe bus Apol lo (fē′bəs ə pol′ō),   the Greek god of the sun. *n.*

Phul pur (pül′pur),   a village in northern India. *n.*

pied (pīd),   having patches of two or more colors. *adj.*

pil lage (pil′ij),   rob with violence; plunder: *Pirates pillaged the towns along the coast. v.,* **pil laged, pil lag ing.**

pin ion (pin′yən),   bind securely. *v.*

pique (pēk),   arouse; stir up: *The curiosity of the boys was piqued by the locked trunk. v.,* **piqued, pi quing.**

plas ma (plaz′mə),   the liquid part of blood, as distinguished from the red and white blood cells. *n.*

pla teau (pla tō′),   plain in the mountains or at a height above the sea; large, high plain. *n., pl.* **pla teaus** or **pla teaux** (-tōz′).

PLATEAUS / PLAIN / SEA LEVEL / MOUNTAINS

pneu mat ic (nü mat′ik   or   nū mat′ik),   1. filled with air. 2. worked by air. *adj.*

pomp (pomp),   splendid show or display; magnificence: *The king was crowned with great pomp. n.*

psychological

por ce lain (pôr′sl in),   very fine earthenware; china. *n.*

port[1] (pôrt or pōrt),   1. place where ships and boats can be sheltered from storms; harbor. 2. place where ships and boats can load and unload; city or town with a harbor. *n.*

port[2] (pôrt or pōrt),   1. opening in the side of a ship to let in light and air. 2. opening in a ship through which to shoot. *n.*

port[3] (pôrt or pōrt),   the left side of a ship, when facing the bow. *n.*

po ten tial (pə ten′shəl),   possible as opposed to actual. *adj.*

pound ster ling (stėr′ling),   unit of money of Great Britain. 1 pound = 20 shillings. The gold in one pound sterling was worth about five dollars in 1900, and about $2.80 in 1964.

prac ti ca ble (prak′tə kə bl),   1. that can be done; capable of being put into practice: *a practicable idea.* 2. that can be used: *a practicable road. adj.*

pre dic a ment (pri dik′ə mənt),   1. an unpleasant, difficult, or dangerous situation: *Mary was in a predicament when she missed the last train home.* 2. any condition, state, or situation. *n.*

prej u dice (prej′ə dis),   opinion formed without taking time and care to judge fairly: *a prejudice against doctors. n.*

pres tige (pres tēzh′),   reputation, influence, or distinction based on what is known of one's abilities, achievements, opportunities, associations, etc. *n.*

pride of lions,   a group of lions.

pri va tion (prī vā′shən),   lack of the comforts or of the necessities of life: *Many people died because of privation during the war. n.*

probe (prōb),   1. search; penetrate: *probe into the causes of crime.* 2. an exploratory advance or survey to collect information on outer space. 1 *v.,* **probed, prob ing;** 2 *n.*

prod (prod),   1. poke or jab: *prod an animal with a stick.* 2. stir up; urge on. *v.,* **prod ded, prod ding.**

Pro me the us (prə mē′thē əs   or   prə-mē′thüs),   in Greek mythology, one of the Titans. He stole fire from heaven and taught men its use. Zeus punished him by chaining him to a rock. *n.*

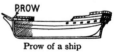
Prow of a ship

prone (prōn),   lying face down. *adj.*

prow (prou),   the pointed front part of a ship or boat; bow. *n.*

Prus sia (prush′ə),   a former state in northern Germany. *n.*

psy cho log i cal (sī′kə loj′ə kl),   of the mind. *adj.* —**psy′cho log′i cal ly,** *adv.*

506

puf·fin (puf′ən), a sea bird of the northern Atlantic that has a high, narrow, furrowed bill of several colors. *n.*

pu-gai (pü′gī′), *Chinese. n.*

puk-puk (půk′půk), *Papuan. n.*

Pu ra ri (pü rä′rē), a river in Papua, flowing south to the Gulf of Papua. *n.*

pu ri-pu ri (pü′rē pü′rē), *Papuan. n.*

Pu sa (pü′sä), a village in northeastern India. *n.*

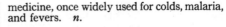

Puffin (about 13 in. from bill to tip of tail)

put the shot, send a heavy metal ball as far as one can with one push.

pyg my (pig′mē), a very small person; dwarf. The pygmies living in Africa and Asia are less than five feet high. *n., pl.* **pyg mies.** Also, **pigmy.**

py thon (pī′thon), any of several large snakes that kill their prey by crushing. Pythons usually live in trees near water. *n.*

qual i ty (kwol′ə tē), 1. something special about a person or object that makes it what it is: *One quality of iron is hardness; one quality of sugar is sweetness. She had many good qualities.* 2. the kind that anything is: *That is a poor quality of cloth.* 3. merit; excellence: *Look for quality rather than quantity. n., pl.* **qual i ties.**

qualm (kwäm or kwälm), 1. a sudden disturbing feeling in the mind; uneasiness; misgiving; doubt: *I tried the test with some qualms.* 2. disturbance or scruple of conscience: *She felt some qualms at staying away from church. n.*

quar ry (kwôr′ē or kwor′ē), animal chased in a hunt; game; prey. *n., pl.* **quar ries.**

quar ter (kwôr′tər), 1. certain part of a community, group, etc. 2. mercy shown a defeated enemy in sparing his life. *n.*

quarters, place to live or stay: *The baseball team has winter quarters in the South.*

quar ter deck (kwôr′tər dek′), part of the upper deck between the mainmast and the stern, used especially by the officers of a ship. *n.*

queue (kū), braid of hair hanging down from the back of the head. *n.*

qui nine (kwī′nīn), a bitter

Chinese queue

medicine, once widely used for colds, malaria, and fevers. *n.*

Rab ka (räb′kä), *Berber. n.*

ra di ate (rā′dē āt), spread out from a center: *Roads radiate from the city in every direction. v.,* **ra di at ed, ra di at ing.**

Ra gi ana (rä′jē än′ə).

rain forest, a tropical forest with an annual rainfall of at least 100 inches.

ra mi (rä′mē), strong, shiny fabric made from the fibers of a plant called rami. *n.*

rapt (rapt), 1. lost in delight. 2. so busy thinking of or enjoying one thing that one does not know what else is happening: *The girls listened with rapt attention. adj.*

ra·tion (rash′ən or rā′shən), a fixed allowance of food; daily allowance of food for a person or animal. *n.*

rat tan (ra tan′), 1. kind of palm with a very long stem. 2. stems of such palm trees, used for wickerwork, etc. *n.* Also, **ratan.**

re as sure (rē′ə shůr′), restore to confidence: *The captain's confidence during the storm reassured the passengers. v.,* **re as sured, re as sur ing.**

Red stone (red′stōn′), a type of rocket that is used to launch a space capsule. *n.*

re fract (ri frakt′), bend (a ray of light, etc.) from a straight course. Water refracts light. *v.*

re fuse[1] (ri fūz′), 1. decline to accept; reject: *refuse an offer.* 2. deny (a request, demand, invitation); decline to give or grant: *refuse admittance.* 3. decline (to do something): *refuse to discuss the question.* 4. decline to accept or consent: *She is free to refuse. v.,* **re fused, re fus ing.**

ref use[2] (ref′ūs), useless stuff; waste; rubbish: *The street-cleaning department took away all refuse from the streets. n.*

re join der (ri join′dər), an answer to a reply; response. *n.*

re lin quish (ri ling′kwish), give up; let go: *The small dog relinquished his bone to the big dog. She has relinquished all hope of going to Europe this year. v.*

re ple tion (ri plē′shən), fullness; excessive fullness. *n.*

rep li ca (rep′lə kə), copy; reproduction: *The artist made a replica of his picture. n.*

ret ro-rock et (ret′rō rok′it), rocket fired to produce a thrust against the forward motion of a space craft, thereby decreasing its speed. Sometimes called a **retro.** *n.*

rev er ence (rev′ər əns), 1. a feeling of deep respect, mixed with wonder, awe, and

hat, āge, cãre, fär; let, bē, tėrm; it, īce; hot, gō, ôrder; oil, out; cup, pút, rüle, ūse; ch, child; ng, long; th, thin; ᴛʜ, then; zh, measure; ə represents *a* in about, *e* in taken, *i* in April, *o* in lemon, *u* in circus.

507

love. 2. a deep bow. *n.*

rev er ent (rev′ər ənt), feeling reverence; showing reverence. *adj.* —**rev′er ent ly,** *adv.*

Roe bling (rō′bling), **John Augustus,** 1806-1869, German-American engineer. *n.*

Roe bling (rō′bling), **Washington Augustus,** 1837-1926, American engineer, son of John Augustus Roebling. *n.*

Roms dal (rôms′däl′), a province in western Norway. *n.*

rou tine (rü tēn′), 1. a fixed, regular method of doing things; habitual doing of the same things in the same way: *Getting up and going to bed are parts of your daily routine.* 2. using routine: *routine methods, routine workers.* 1 *n.,* 2 *adj.*

ru ma mo mo (rü′mä mō′mō), *Papuan.*

ru pee (rü pē′), a unit of money of India, worth about 21 cents in 1964. *n.*

rust (rust), 1. the reddish-brown or orange coating that forms on iron or steel when exposed to air or moisture. 2. a plant disease that spots leaves and stems. *n.*

sage (sāj), a very wise man. *n.*

sa go (sā′gō), 1. a starchy food used in making puddings, etc. 2. a palm tree (**sago palm**) from whose pith this starchy food is made. *n., pl.* **sa gos.**

Sa ma rai (sä′mä rī′), *Papuan. n.*

sam bio (säm′byō), *Papuan.*

sam pan (sam′pan), any of various small boats of China, etc. A sampan is sculled by one or more oars at the stern; it usually has a single sail and a cabin made of mats. *n.*

Sampan

scab bard (skab′ərd), sheath or case for the blade of a sword, dagger, etc. *n.*

Schi a pa rel li (skyä′pä rel′lē), **Giovanni,** 1835-1910, Italian astronomer. *n.*

Schmidt (shmit), *German. n.*

sconce (skons), bracket projecting from a wall, used to hold a candle or other light. *n.*

scourge (skėrj), beat; whip. *v.,* **scourged, scourg ing.**

scru pu lous (skrü′pyə ləs), 1. having or showing a strict regard for what is right. 2. attending thoroughly to details; very careful: *A soldier must pay scrupulous attention to orders. adj.* —**scru′pu lous ly,** *adv.*

scu ba (skü′bə or skū′bə), an apparatus used for breathing under water. *n.*

seam (sēm), line left by a cut or wound; scar. *n.*

Sean (shôn), *Irish. n.*

se cede (si sēd′), withdraw formally from an organization. *v.,* **se ced ed, se ced ing.**

sec ond ary (sek′ən der′ē), not main or chief; having less importance: *Reading fast is secondary to reading well. adj.*

se rum (sir′əm), a clear, pale-yellow, watery part of the blood that is left after blood has clotted. *n.*

shack le (shak′l), a metal band fastened around the ankle or wrist of a prisoner, slave, etc. Shackles are usually fastened to each other, the wall, floor, etc., by chains. *n.*

Shackles

shil le lagh or **shil la lah** (shə lā′lē or shə lā′lə), *Irish.* a stick to hit with; cudgel. *n.*

ship (ship), 1. a large seagoing vessel with masts and sails. 2. any large vessel for use on water or in air, such as a steamship, a battleship, etc. 3. send or carry from one place to another by a ship, train, truck, etc. 4. fix in a ship or boat in its proper place for use: *ship a rudder.* 1, 2 *n.,* 3, 4 *v.,* **shipped, ship ping.**

ship ping (ship′ing), the ships of a nation, city, or business. *n.*

Shklov sky (shklôf′skē), **I.S.,** born 1916, Russian astronomer. *n.*

Sho ba (shō′bä), *Hindu. n.*

shroud (shroud), cloth or garment in which a dead person is wrapped for burial. *n.*

si (sē), *Spanish.* yes.

Si di Ah med (sē′dē ä′məd), *Berber.*

sin glet (sing′glit), kind of undershirt or jersey worn by men. *n.*

sin u ous (sin′yü əs), having many curves or turns; winding: *The motion of a snake is sinuous. adj.*

sis ter (sis′tər), 1. daughter of the same parents or parent. A girl is a sister to the other children of her parents or parent. 2. *Chiefly British.* a nurse. *n.*

skin diver, a swimmer equipped to go skin diving.

skin diving, swimming about easily under water for long periods of time equipped with oxygen tanks and other gear. *n.*

skip per (skip′ər), captain of a ship, especially of a small trading or fishing boat. *n.*

slat (slat), flap, as a loose sail, against a mast. *v.,* **slat ted, slat ting.**

slav er (slāv′ər), dealer in slaves. *n.*

sloop of war (slüp), a small warship having guns on the upper deck only.

slough (slou or slü), a soft, deep, muddy place; a swampy place. *n.*

slug gard (slug′ərd), a lazy, idle person. *n.*

smelling salts, a form of ammonia

inhaled to relieve faintness, headaches, etc.

Smit (smit), *Dutch. n.*

snare (snãr), noose for catching small animals and birds. *n.*

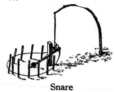
Snare

so cial ize (sō'shəl-īz), take part in social activities. *v.*, **so cial ized, so cial iz ing.**

sod (sod), **1.** ground covered with grass. **2.** piece or layer of this containing the grass and its roots. *n.*

Sol o mon (sol'ə mən), a king of Israel who was a son of David. Solomon built a great temple in Jerusalem. He was famous for his wisdom. *n.*

son ic (son'ik), **1.** of, having to do with, or using sound waves. **2.** having to do with the rate at which sound travels in air (1087 feet per second). *adj.*

spe cies (spē'shēz or spē'sēz), group of animals or plants that have certain permanent characteristics in common: *Wheat is a species of grass. n., pl.* **spe cies.**

spec i men (spes'ə mən), **1.** one of a group or class taken to show what the others are like; single part, thing, etc., regarded as an example of its kind: *The statue was a fine specimen of Greek sculpture.* **2.** *Informal.* a human being; person: *The tramp was a queer specimen. n.*

spec u late (spek'yə lāt), reflect; meditate; consider; guess. *v.*, **spec u lat ed, spec u lat ing.**

spec u la tive (spek'yə lā'tiv), thoughtful; reflective. *adj.* —**spec'u la'tive ly,** *adv.*

spir it less (spir'it lis), without spirit or courage; depressed. *adj.*

spoils (spoilz), things taken by force: *the spoils of war. n.*

Sprech en sie Deutsch? (shpre'Hən zē doich'), *German.* Do you speak German?

squad ron (skwod'rən), part of a naval fleet used for special service. *n.*

squire (skwīr), a young man of noble family who attended a knight till he himself was made a knight. *n.*

stal wart (stôl'wərt), **1.** strongly built. **2.** strong and brave: *a stalwart soldier.* **3.** firm; steadfast. *adj.*

star board (stär'bərd or stär'bôrd), **1.** the right side of a ship, when facing forward. **2.** on the right side of a ship. **1** *n.*, **2** *adj.*

stark (stärk), **1.** downright; complete: *That fool is talking stark nonsense.* **2.** entirely; completely: *The boys went swimming stark naked.* **1** *adj.*, **2** *adv.* —**stark'ly,** *adv.*

Sta van ger (stä väng'ər), a town on the southwestern coast of Norway. *n.*

steer age (stir'ij), part of a passenger ship occupied by passengers traveling at the cheapest rate. *n.*

Stein metz (stīn'mets), **Charles P.,** 1865-1923, American scientist and engineer, born in Germany. *n.*

ste ve dore (stē'və dôr or stē'və dōr), man who loads and unloads ships. *n.*

sub stan ti ate (səb stan'shē āt), establish by evidence; prove: *substantiate a rumor. v.*, **sub stan ti at ed, sub stan ti at ing.**

sub ter fuge (sub'tər fūj), trick, excuse, or expedient used to escape something unpleasant: *The girl's headache was only a subterfuge to avoid taking the examination. n.*

Su mi ko (sü'mē kō), *Japanese. n.*

super-, prefix meaning:
1. over; above, as in *superimpose, superstructure.*
2. besides, as in *supertax.*
3. in high proportion; to excess; exceedingly, as in *superabundant, supersensitive.*
4. surpassing, as in *superman, supernatural.*

su per son ic (sü'pər son'ik), greater than the speed of sound in air (761 miles per hour at sea level). *adj.*

sus pen sion bridge (səs pen'shən), bridge hung on cables or chains between towers.

Syd ney (sid'nē), the largest city and most important seaport in Australia. *n.*

tail gate, a board at the back end of a wagon that can be let down or removed when loading or unloading.

tal is man (tal'is mən or tal'iz mən), **1.** a stone, ring, etc., engraved with figures or characters supposed to have magic power; charm. **2.** anything that acts as a charm. *n., pl.* **tal is mans.**

Tan gier or **Tan giers** (tan jir' or tan-jirz'), seaport in northwestern Africa, on the Strait of Gibraltar. *n.*

ta ro (tä'rō), a starchy root grown for food in the Pacific islands and other tropical regions. *n., pl.* **ta ros.**

ta ta mi (tə tä'mē), straw matting used as a floor covering in a Japanese home. *n.*

tat too (ta tü'), series of raps, taps, etc. *n., pl.* **tat toos.**

tau ba da (tou bä'dä), *Papuan. n.*

---

hat, āge, cãre, fär; let, bē, tèrm; it, īce; hot, gō, ôrder; oil, out; cup, pút, rüle, ūse; ch, child; ng, long; th, thin; ŦH, then; zh, measure; ə represents *a* in about, *e* in taken, *i* in April, *o* in lemon, *u* in circus.

Tau ri (tou′rē), a river in Papua, the mouth of which is 30 miles east of Kerema. *n.*

taw ny (tô′nē), brownish yellow. *adj.*, **taw ni er, taw ni est.**

tech nique (tek nēk′), a special method or system used to accomplish something. *n.*

tent fly, piece of canvas forming an extra, outer top for a tent.

Thames (temz), river flowing from southwestern England into the North Sea. London is on the Thames. *n.*

the sis (thē′sis), essay; essay presented by a candidate for a diploma or degree. *n., pl.* **the ses** (-sēz).

Thom son's ga zelle (tom′snz gə zel′), an East African gazelle that is the smallest of the gazelles. *n.*

ti ki (tē′kē), *Papuan. n.*

tis sue (tish′ü), mass of cells forming some part of an animal or plant: *The teacher showed pictures of muscle tissues. n.*

to ko no ma (tō′kō nō′mä), *Japanese. n.*

tongue (tung), 1. the movable piece of flesh in the mouth. The tongue is used in tasting and, by people, for talking. 2. way of speaking; speech; talk: *a flattering tongue.* 3. the language of a people: *the English tongue.* 4. modify tones of (a flute, cornet, etc.) with the tongue. 1-3 *n.*, 4 *v.*, **tongu ing.**

tongue-and-groove joint, a kind of joint in which a tongue (a projecting strip) on one board fits exactly into a groove in another board.

tor rent (tôr′ənt or tor′ənt), 1. a violent, rushing stream of water. 2. a heavy downpour. 3. any violent, rushing stream; flood: *a torrent of abuse. n.*

tor ren tial (tô ren′shəl or to ren′shəl), of, caused by, or like a torrent: *torrential rains. adj.*

to tem (tō′təm), 1. among American Indians, a natural object, often an animal, taken as the emblem of a tribe, clan, family, etc. 2. image of a totem. Totems are often carved and painted on poles. *n.*

tour na ment (tėr′nə mənt or tùr′nə mənt), contest between two groups of knights on horseback who fought for a prize. *n.*

Tower (tou′ər), an ancient palace-fortress of London. It has been used as a palace, prison, mint, and arsenal. It is often called the Tower of London. *n.*

Indian totem pole

trans fu sion (trans fū′zhən), transferring blood from one person or animal to another. *n.*

trap pings (trap′ingz), ornamental coverings for a horse. *n. pl.*

tread water (tred), keep oneself from sinking by moving the feet up and down.

truc u lent (truk′yə lənt), savagely threatening or bullying; fierce and cruel. *adj.*

tryst (trist), appointment to meet at a certain time and place. *n.*

Tua reg (twä′reg), one of the main nomad tribes of the central and western Sahara Desert. *n.*

Tun gom (tùng′gôm), *Papuan. n.*

turf (tėrf), 1. grass with its matted roots; sod. 2. piece of this. *n., pl.* **turfs.**

Um ta ka ti (ùm′tä kä′tē), *Zulu. n.* **um ten te** (ùm ten′tē).

un can ny (un kan′ē), strange and mysterious; weird. *adj.*

Union Jack, the British national flag.

un re mit ting (un′ri mit′ing), never stopping; not slackening; maintained steadily. *adj.*

un scathed (un skāᵮHd′), not harmed; uninjured. *adj.*

ur chin (ėr′chən), 1. a small boy. 2. a mischievous boy. 3. a poor, ragged child. *n.*

Vad heim (väd′hām), a village in western Norway. *n.*

vag a bond (vag′ə bond), a good-for-nothing person; rascal. *n.*

Val hal la (val hal′ə), in Norse mythology, the hall where the souls of heroes slain in battle feast with the god Odin. *n.*

vault[1] (vôlt), 1. an arched roof or ceiling; series of 'arches. 2. something like an arched roof. 3. make in the form of a vault. 4. an underground cellar or storehouse. 1, 2, 4 *n.*, 3 *v.*

vault[2] (vôlt), jump or leap over by using a pole or the hands. *v.*

Vault of a roof

ven dor (ven′dər), seller; peddler. *n.*

vig i lant (vij′ə lənt), watchful; alert. *adj.*

Vi king or **vi king** (vī′king), one of the daring Scandinavian pirates who raided the coasts of Europe from the eighth to tenth centuries A.D. *n.*

vi sor (vī′zər), 1. the movable front part of a helmet, covering the face. 2. mask. *n.* Also, **vizor.**

viz ard (viz′ərd), visor. *n.*

Vlk

Vlk (vlk), *Czech.* *n.*

vo li tion (vō lish′ən), act of willing: *The man went away of his own volition.* *n.*

vo ra cious (və rā′shəs), eating much; greedy in eating; ravenous. *adj.*

Vul can (vul′kən), the Roman god of fire and metalworking. *n.*

vul ture (vul′chər), a large bird of prey related to eagles, hawks, etc., that eats the flesh of dead animals. *n.*

Vulture (about 2½ ft. long)

wake¹ (wāk), 1. stop sleeping. 2. cause to stop sleeping. *v.*, **waked** or **woke, waked, wak ing.**

wake² (wāk), 1. track left behind a moving ship. 2. track left behind any moving thing. *n.*

Wales (wālz), the division of Great Britain west of England; the land of the Welsh. *n.*

wal la by (wol′ə bē), a kangaroo of the smaller sorts. Some wallabies are no larger than rabbits. *n., pl.* **wal la bies** or (*esp. collectively*) **wal la by.**

weld (weld), 1. join together (metal, plastic, etc.) by hammering or pressing while soft and hot. 2. a welded joint. 1 *v.*, 2 *n.*

Welsh (welsh or welch), 1. of or having to do with Wales, its people, or their Celtic language. 2. the people of Wales. 3. their language. 1 *adj.*, 2, 3 *n.*

west er (wes′tər), move, turn, or shift toward the west: *As the sun westered, dark storm clouds appeared.* *v.*

wharf (hwôrf or wôrf), platform built on the shore or out from the shore, beside which ships can load and unload. *n., pl.* **wharves** or **wharfs.**

whet (hwet), sharpen by rubbing: *whet a knife.* *v.*, **whet ted, whet ting.**

White ha ven (hwīt′hā′vən), a seaport in northwestern England on the Irish Sea. *n.*

wil de beest (wil′də bēst′), the gnu, an African antelope. *n.*

Zululand

witch doctor, medicine man, especially among African tribes.

withe (wiᴛʜ or with), any tough, easily bent twig suitable for binding things together. *n.*

wiz ened (wiz′nd), dried up; withered; shriveled: *a wizened face.* *adj.*

word element, a form of a word (English or other) used for combining with other words or word elements, as *counter-* in *counteract.*

World War II, war in Europe, Asia, Africa, and elsewhere, from September 1, 1939, to August 14, 1945. It began as a war between Great Britain, France, and Poland on one side and Germany on the other, and ultimately involved most of the world. The chief conflict was between Great Britain, the United States, and the Soviet Union on one side and Germany, Italy, and Japan on the other.

wrack (rak), wreckage. *n.*

wran gle (rang′gl), argue or dispute in a noisy or angry way; quarrel. *v.*, **wran gled, wran gling.**

writhe (rīᴛʜ), twist and turn; twist. *v.*, **writhed, writh ing.**

wrought iron (rôt), a tough form of iron that does not break easily.

yam (yam), the starchy root of a vine grown for food in warm countries. *n.*

yard arm (yärd′ärm′), either end of a long, slender beam or pole used to support a square sail. *n.*

You-Seff (ū′səf), *Berber.* *n.*

Yule (ūl), **Mount,** mountain in Papua. *n.*

Zeus (züs), the chief god of the ancient Greeks, the ruler of gods and men, identified by the Romans with Jupiter. *n.*

Zi tu (zē′tü), *Zulu.* *n.*

Zu lu (zü′lü), 1. member of a warlike tribe in southeastern Africa. 2. of the Zulus. 1 *n., pl.* **Zulus** or **Zulu**; 2 *adj.*

Zu lu land (zü′lü land′), a part of Natal, an eastern province of the Union of South Africa. *n.*

hat, āge, cāre, fär; let, bē, tėrm; it, īce; hot, gō, ôrder; oil, out; cup, put, rüle, ūse; ch, child; ng, long; th, thin; ᴛʜ, then; zh, measure; ə represents *a* in about, *e* in taken, *i* in April, *o* in lemon, *u* in circus.

Illustrations

The illustrations in this book are by:

Phoebe Moore (cover, 270-271, 275); John Massey (pp. 7, 95, 175, 245, 311); Dick Wiley (pp. 8-33, 35-46, 48-71); Jan Wills (pp. 34, 189-190); Hiro Mizushima (p. 47); Orville Hurt (pp. 84-93, 96-107, 278-287); Charles McBarron (pp. 108-138, 141-144, 146-164, 246-254); Carl Martin (pp. 139, 256-261, 265-266); Tom Strobel (pp. 140, 145, 165, 230); Wendell Kling (pp. 176-188); Ed Broussard (pp. 202-211, 324-339); Chesley Bonestell (pp. 231-243); Chuck Kessler (pp. 288-297); Al Stine (pp. 298-309); Fernando Dias Da Silva (pp. 312-322, 355, 358-385); Hope Taylor (pp. 323, 349-352); Rod Ruth (pp. 340-348, 386-397).

1 2 3 4 5 6 7 8 9 10 11 12 13 14 15 16 17 18 19 20 21 22 23 24 25 NR 75 74 73 72 71 70 69 68 67 66 65 64